OTHER BOOKS BY NOEL B. GERSON

FICTION

The Golden Ghetto
Sam Houston
Jefferson Square
I'll Storm Hell
The Anthem
The Swamp Fox
Give Me Liberty
Yankee Doodle Dandy
The Slender Reed
Old Hickory
The Golden Lyre
The Trojan
The Land Is Bright
The Hittite

The Yankee from Tennessee
The Emperor's Ladies
Daughter of Eve
The Silver Lion
The Conqueror's Wife
That Egyptian Woman
The Highwayman
The Forest Lord
The Impostor
The Golden Eagle
The Cumberland Rifles
The Mohawk Ladder
Savage Gentleman

NONFICTION

P.J., My Friend
Franklin: America's Lost State
Passage to the West
Survival Jamestown
Light-horse Harry
Mr. Madison's War
Kit Carson
Sex and the Adult Woman
   (with Ellen F. Birchall, M.D.)

Belgium: Future, Present, Past
Rock of Freedom
Sex and the Mature Man
   (with Louis P. Saxe, M.D.)
Food
Valley Forge
The Legend of Pocahontas
Nathan Hale

TR

TR

NOEL B. GERSON

DOUBLEDAY & COMPANY, INC.

GARDEN CITY, NEW YORK

1970

Library of Congress Catalog Card Number 69–17863
Copyright ©1970 by Noel B. Gerson
Printed in the United States of America
First Edition

For

ELSA LICHTENSTEIN

PREFACE

MY FATHER, a Chicago daily newspaper city editor, was the toughest, most awe-inspiring man whom I, as a small boy, had ever known. So it is small wonder that my child's world fell apart on that day in January 1919 when he came home from work, laden as usual with the final editions of the metropolitan newspapers, all of which carried huge headlines.

"Theodore Roosevelt is dead," my father said, and burst into tears.

That was the beginning of my own interest, later to become absorbing, in the greatest American of his age. When I grew somewhat older I learned more of my father's "proprietary" interest in TR. A newspaper reporter in September 1901, he attended the Pan-American Exposition in Buffalo, New York, while on vacation, and through sheer chance saw President William McKinley shot by Leon Czolgosz. It was that scoop that created his reputation as a newsman; thereafter he joined the press "death watch," while McKinley slowly sank, and he was on hand when, on September 14, Theodore Roosevelt was sworn in as the 26th President of the United States.

My fourth-grade teacher was another worshiper of TR, and that clinched matters. Then I read *Hunting the Grisly*, one of Roosevelt's minor adventure books, and was hooked. In the years that followed I read all of his books, and to this day own the complete set I was given on my sixteenth birthday.

I long wanted to write about TR, but forced myself to wait until I could attain a plateau of sufficient objectivity to treat the subject with justice. He was far too complex a man to be treated by an idolator.

Here, then, a half-century after I first heard his name under what to me were dramatic circumstances, is my portrait of Theodore Roosevelt. I deliberately chose the biographical novel form, in part because I believed I could best show him in depth in this medium, in part because it would have been presumptuous to "compete" with the superb William Henry Harbaugh biography or the Pulitzer Prize biography by Henry F. Pringle.

The biographical novel is a sometimes misunderstood medium. In the biographical novel, the author invents dialogue and, to an extent, enters the minds of his characters. But, in dealing with Theodore Roosevelt, I have followed several strict, self-imposed rules. I have tried to let his actions speak for themselves. And, particularly in all matters relating to his public life, I have tried to fashion the dialogue in accordance with his actual views, as expressed in public or private statements, correspondence and other sources.

For example, I have told the Panama Canal story only in terms of what the record can substantiate. The scene between President Roosevelt and the two young Intelligence officers just returned from a mission to South and Central America must be classified as fiction, in that there is no record of what was said. But the officers were real people, the meeting actually took place, and my invented dialogue conforms to the facts known about their mission and Roosevelt's known reactions after he had seen them.

I have applied this principle throughout the book.

It should be added that virtually no character in these pages is the product of the author's imagination. They are, almost without exception, real persons who, in one way or another, were associated with TR.

I regret that limitations of space make it impossible to deal more fully with many aspects of Theodore Roosevelt's life. It has been necessary to sketch in only the broad outlines of his life as a Dakota rancher, for instance; and I have not been able to dwell, in detail, on his family life and friendships, much less the intricacies of the Progressive party movement or his friendship-feud with William Howard Taft.

I am grateful to editors Lee Barker and Sam Vaughan of Doubleday for their encouragement and help, to my own editor Matthew Harris, for zealous guidance and assistance beyond the call of duty, and to the generosity of the Library of Congress in opening so many files to me.

N.B.G.

Clinton, Conn.

TR

I

1858–1881

*My father, Theodore Roosevelt, was the best man I ever knew . . .
he was the only man of whom I was ever really afraid.*

B Y THE STANDARDS of New York's wealthiest citizens the substantial house at 28 East 20th Street was modestly furnished, but
in taste that was as aristocratic as it was orthodox. The parlor, with
antimacassars carefully covering the backs of the overstuffed sofas
and chairs, was closed; it was opened only on Sundays, for family use,
and on infrequent occasions for other social activities. The dining
room, with its table of polished oak and matching chairs, covered in
black haircloth, was the most cheerful and spacious room on the first
floor, and Martha Roosevelt, accustomed to the comfortable home of
her Southern childhood, would have been content to spend her evenings there, or, perhaps, in her second-floor sewing room. But Theodore preferred the library, and it did not cross his mind that his wife
might not appreciate the aesthetic qualities of a room filled with heavy
chairs of dark leather, ponderous tables, and bookcases of deep walnut
filled with books from floor to ceiling.

At best, there were a few hundred citizens of New York City who
enjoyed the advantages that were evident to anyone invited to the
Roosevelt house, and Theodore had ample reason to be pleased with
himself. He had made his mark in business and, as a contributor to
charities, virtually every door in New York was open to him, and to
Martha, of course. And his children would never suffer from the difficulties and privations that plagued ordinary people. His house, as he
so often told himself, was a symbol of his standing, and everyone—of
his own class, at least—knew it.

Occasionally he entertained a slight suspicion that Martha considered her existence less than perfect, but even the sweetest and most
charming of women needed guidance, direction, and authority, and
he knew what was best for her. Like most upper middle-class New

Yorkers descended from the early Dutch settlers, he could be stubborn beyond belief when there was even a hint of interference or conflict with his likes and desires. The employees in his glass merchant's office knew it, his fellow directors on the boards of several charitable institutions knew it, the children in his Sunday school mission class knew it and, above all, his wife knew it.

There was no sound in the library but the hissing of the occasionally flickering gas jets that provided light, and Martha, sewing a new sampler, sighed quietly. Her husband, a heavy-shouldered man of medium height with a thick mustache that made his face seem even broader than it was, was too immersed in his reading of Aristotle's *Politics* to look up. When he read in Greek, which he did at least two evenings each week to discipline his mind, he had the ability to shut out the world.

The new servingmaid, a girl from Glasgow only recently arrived in the United States, appeared in the open doorway, hesitated for a moment and tentatively made a sound that was a cross between clucking and clearing her throat. Theodore was unaware of her existence, but Martha raised her head.

"Excuse me, ma'am, but the baby is whimperin' again."

Martha thanked her, and, although deeply worried, hesitated a moment before interrupting her husband's reading. "Theodore."

He continued to read.

Her voice became a little strident. "Theodore!"

"Mmm." He did not raise his head.

"The baby is crying again."

"It seems to me that baby is always wailing. I refuse to spoil him."

"He's whimpering, and I'm afraid he might be sick again."

Deliberately, making no attempt to conceal his annoyance, he placed his book on the table beside him. "A husband and wife should be permitted to spend their evenings as they please."

What really outraged him, she knew, was the thought that a child born to them could be frail; Roosevelts had been healthy, vigorous men and women for centuries. "I think," she said, "we'd better go upstairs."

He knew that if there was a problem she would be incapable of handling it alone. And, much as he hated to admit it, he felt a niggling worry about the health of his first-born son. Having reached a decision, he left his chair, crossed the room quickly and bounded up the stairs to his son.

Martha followed as rapidly as she could, gathering her rustling skirts of bombazine around her. She found him in the nursery, an expression of pity and alarm on his face as he gazed down at the eight-week-old infant in the crib.

The baby was gasping for breath, his face scarlet.

"It's the asthma again," Theodore said.

His wife had already crossed the chamber to a shelf for a container of foul-smeller elixir, and taking the bottle, began to shake it vigorously.

"Don't bother," Theodore said. "He nearly choked to death on it night before last."

"But the doctor—"

"Doctors don't know everything. If they did, they'd have cured him by now."

Martha, pushing her wavy hair from her forehead, felt that disloyalty to anyone, physicians included, was a sin, and therefore had to protest. "You're so impatient, Theodore. If we can just get the baby to keep down a few drops—"

"Impatience be damned!" The man bent low and picked up his son, for whom every breath was a torment. Wrapping the infant carefully in his sheet and blankets, Theodore straightened and, holding his bundle in the crook of one arm, wrenched open the nursery window with his free hand.

A raw, mid-December wind blew into the room, and Martha tried to intervene. "He'll catch the ague, Theodore."

Her husband silenced her with the wave of a heavy, strong hand, then drew up a rocking chair directly in front of the window. "What he needs is fresh air," he declared in the positive tone that every member of the Roosevelt family would have recognized as the final, authoritative word on the subject.

Martha stood, shivering slightly, unable to decide what to do next. She watched as Theodore began to rock very slowly and gently, just enough to lull the baby, and marveled at the delicacy of the powerfully built man.

Gradually the infant's spasm subsided, his breathing became normal and the excess color drained from his face.

"Fresh air," Theodore said quietly, a hint of satisfaction in his voice. "Don't stay here," he added, aware of his wife's discomfort. "You'll freeze."

"So will you."

The baby had dropped off to sleep, and not even his father's hearty laugh disturbed him.

"How long do you intend to stay here, sir?" Martha's soft Georgian drawl always became more pronounced when she was upset.

"If he has enough clean air in his lungs, he'll be all right for the rest of the night." He continued to rock, his rhythm steady and unchanging.

Martha silently left the chamber, returning a few moments later with a thick shawl of her own. Hearing her husband's voice, she stopped short.

"Never you fear, Teedee," he said softly. "Maybe, some day, you'll be as strong as any other boy. If not, you'll be smarter. Papa will help you in every way I can. I promise."

Draping the shawl around her unheeding husband's shoulders, Martha blinked back tears as she crept out into the corridor and closed the nursery door behind her. Perhaps she had been spoiled: their first child, Anna, was four, and had enjoyed the usual Roosevelt and Bulloch good health since the day she had been born, and it terrified Martha that her tiny son should be in the grip of such a debilitating ailment.

She knew superstitious friends were murmuring that she and Theodore were being punished by the Almighty, but she was too enlightened to accept such nonsense. She and her husband had committed no sin, and, even if they had, God was both just and merciful, and would not allow an innocent child to suffer for someone else's wrongdoing.

She wept for her son, her heart heavy at the thought of the crushing burden he would carry with him through life. Only the strong survived, as she had discovered in the years since she had married Theodore, left her beloved Georgia and moved to his home in New York.

Frightened as she was for her baby, her tears were for herself, too. She had no legitimate complaint against Theodore, who was the most generous and considerate of husbands, but he alone made every decision affecting their lives, even supervising the cook's food purchases and hiring new domestic servants. It was probably true that he knew, far better than she herself, what was right or wrong for her, but she sometimes felt helpless, unable to express her own desires. It would be melodramatic to say she occasionally suffered the uncomfortable sensation of being a prisoner in his house.

That was nonsense, and he'd be hurt if he ever knew she harbored such absurdly disloyal sentiments. Yet she couldn't help wishing he would give her a freer hand in rearing their children and managing their household.

The real trouble, she knew, was the difference between living in the largest and most prosperous northern city and the easy, gentle existence she had always taken for granted in the South. With relations between the two sections of the country rapidly deteriorating and everyone predicting civil war would break out at any time, it was small wonder she felt lonely and bewildered. The prospect of such a conflict filled her with dread, and made her feel more than ever as if she were an alien in New York, even though she admired and respected her husband more than any other person on earth.

If a war should come, she knew, her brothers would remain loyal to Georgia, just as the Roosevelts would work with their awe-inspiring, furious zeal for a northern victory. She had made her own choice, of course, and her love would sustain her.

But where would Teedee gain the courage, stamina, and strength to see him through the crises that, inevitably, would envelop him in the course of his own life? Someone who grew to manhood with a puny, pain-racked body would be suffering from a handicap too great to overcome, yet she and Theodore would have to exercise great care in dealing with the child. If they favored him too much, deferring to him because of his ailment, his character and mind would become warped, too.

Theodore would know how to treat him, of course, and she took comfort in the realization. As she had told her father-in-law recently, Theodore's understanding of others, particularly children, was remarkable. James had merely smiled, without condescension, and had replied, "He's a Roosevelt." Once she would have laughed, but it was true that the Roosevelts were unique, successes in business, politics, banking, whatever interested them.

Perhaps that, above all, was what gave her hope. In spite of his crushing burden, Teedee was a Roosevelt, too.

Anna felt she was being cheated, just a little, of the privileges due her as the eldest child. Elliott and Corinne were still babies, of course, and scarcely mattered. But she was eight, and it didn't seem right to her that Teedee should be allowed to stay up past her own bedtime several evenings every week. She didn't really want to go along when Papa took him on carriage rides after dark, principally because the weather was so cold, but there was a principle at stake. It was wrong to deny a girl of her age the privileges granted a boy of only four.

If she complained again, Mama and Papa would repeat what they always told her, that Teedee was sick, and that a carriage ride at night wasn't one of the many games Papa played with the children. Nevertheless she wished that, just once, Papa would say, "Bamie, come with us." Then she could refuse, and her dignity as a Roosevelt would be restored. She would lose nothing by trying, so she gathered her hat, coat, mittens, and scarf, and hurried downstairs.

She happened to be loitering in the entrance hall when Papa and Teedee appeared, her brother's stocking cap tucked inside the upturned collar of his greatcoat.

Papa had an uncanny ability to read the mind of a little girl. "Bamie," he said, "I'll take you for a ride of your own on Sunday afternoon. Will that satisfy you?"

She nodded, partly mollified, but still convinced she was the victim of injustice.

"Do you know why I can't take you now?"

Anna glanced at Teedee, and had to admit he didn't look healthy. His face was ashen, he was breathing with difficulty, and the rasping, wheezing noises he made reminded her of the ancient pump organ in the old Dutch Reformed Church. "Because he's sick," she said dutifully.

Teedee was feeling too miserable to gloat.

"We drive so fast to help him breathe," Papa said, "that I need a free hand to hold him on the buckboard when we hit bumps. So I can't look after more than one child. But I promise you I'll drive just as fast on Sunday."

She was enveloped in his smothering hug, and happily returned his kiss.

Then Papa picked up Teedee, carrying him under one arm, and went out to the curb, where the groom was waiting beside the phaeton. Lifting the boy to the seat of the open-sided carriage, Papa made certain the oiled canvas roof was securely fastened, joined his son on the seat and took the reins from the groom.

Honest Abe, a two-year-old gelding, was the most spirited horse in the Roosevelt stable, and seemed to know what was expected of him. He was docile enough until they reached Fifth Avenue, but began to prance as they headed uptown. The weather was so cold there were few horsemen and fewer carriages abroad, even though the street was dry, and Honest Abe increased his pace to a rapid trot as his master guided him with a light hand.

New York was expanding at a remarkable rate, her proud citizens certain that she was the fastest-growing metropolis on earth. From the carriage buckboard it was possible to look downtown, in the direction of lower Broadway, and see the impressive spire of the recently completed Niblo's Garden and the Academy of Music, the most modern center of culture on earth. Everyone had considered it a tragedy when the old music center, Tripler's Hall, had burned down in 1854, but the industrious people of the city had erected a larger, infinitely more sumptuous theatre on the same site. Even those who had traveled extensively in Europe claimed there was no symphonic hall as grand in London or Paris, Vienna or St. Petersburg.

Far uptown, at Fiftieth Street, was the even higher Gothic pile of St. Patrick's Cathedral; construction had been started on the huge church in 1858, and had been completed only a year and a half later, which was something of a miracle. Even non-Catholics were proud of the Cathedral, and couldn't resist mentioning to European visitors that centuries had been required for the construction of the more important churches in the Old World.

Driving up Fifth Avenue, the proud New Yorker saw what every well-bred American considered one of the wonders of America, the Crystal Palace built on Murray's Hill to house the World's Fair of 1853, and used since that time as a permanent museum and art gallery. The Crystal Palace, with its huge windows, vaulted entrances, and magnificent chandeliers proved that those who called Americans barbarians simply didn't know what they were saying.

New York simply refused to stand still. In 1856 the city had purchased a huge tract of land between Fifth and Sixth Avenues, north of 59th Street, and, tentatively naming it Central Park, had become engrossed in plans for landscaping it and putting roads through it.

Theodore Roosevelt had been a member of a vocal minority group of prominent citizens who had wanted to keep the new park as a forest preserve, but he had been persuaded that the thinking of the planning commission charged with the task of preparing the park for public use was sound. George Bancroft, the distinguished historian, former Cabinet member and diplomat, contended that New York was growing too rapidly to permit such a luxury; the entire population of New York would want to use the park, so some trees would have to be sacrificed for playgrounds, a restaurant or two and, perhaps, a zoo. William Cullen Bryant, the editor of the *Post,* who was hard-headed even though he dabbled in poetry, pointed out that gangs of robbers might make their headquarters in a forest, and that the park would be safe only if its woods were thinned. Author Washington Irving, the nation's most successful man of letters, whose financial solvency proved he was sensible, claimed that a network of roads would make the park as safe as the city's streets.

So Theodore Roosevelt, like his friends, agreed that, for the sake of progress, safety, and the needs of the citizenry, much of the forest would have to go. For the present, however, the pines were still thick, and although no roads had as yet been cut through the park itself, Fifth Avenue above 59th Street had just been cobbled, making it possible for carriage owners to drive along the outer edge of the woods.

"The smell of pines always seems to help you, Teedee," Papa said. "So we'll drive into the open country above 59th Street. How does that sound to you, boy?"

Teedee, mittened hands tightly grasping the seat on both sides, was suffering from such labored breathing that he could not reply, and bobbed his head. For Papa's sake, knowing his father was so concerned, he tried to smile, but the effort was in vain, and all he could manage was a feeble grimace that looked like an expression of pain.

The phaeton joggled and bounced as it swept up Fifth Avenue, past the huge, four-story drygoods stores, the new brownstone houses that were becoming fashionable and the older, stately homes of the wealthy, each with its picket fence and elm-studded lawn. A few soldiers in the blue uniform and peaked forage cap of the Union Army were wandering aimlessly, and, unfamiliar with the city, were searching for saloons before returning to active combat duty with the Army of the Potomac. No one had told them that Fifth Avenue was too elegant and proper to permit the establishment of drinking places so close to the dwellings of New York's first citizens.

Above 34th Street the last vestiges of commercialism disappeared, and at 42nd Street the grounds surrounding each house became more spacious. But there were no longer any vacant lots for sale, and it was true that the city was rapidly expanding northward. Many men were growing wealthy supplying food, clothing, and munitions to the Army, and Theodore Roosevelt, Senior, did not hide his disgust as he looked at some of the new mansions being erected. There weren't many who shared his conviction that everyone who could afford to serve his country without receiving more than token wages in return should do everything within his power for the Union cause, and still fewer followed his example.

"We'll soon be in the open country, Teedee," he said, "and then you'll begin to feel better." He jiggled the reins, and Honest Abe broke into a rhythmic, loping canter.

The biting wind became sharper, the child's eyes began to smart and his nose started to run. But his wheezes became less intense, and, as his discomfort eased, he was able to smile naturally for the first time.

His father nodded, communicated with the horse through some form of magic performed with the reins, and the phaeton rolled even more rapidly, both of its springs squeaking in futile protest. The cobblestones on the newly paved section of the street were still rough, the light carriage swayed and jolted its passengers, and the man reached out a protective hand to insure that the boy was not thrown.

"This is bully, Papa!" Excitement as well as the cold air brought color to the small boy's cheeks, and his breathing was sufficiently normal for him to shout above the singing of the wind.

The evening's therapeutic treatment was not yet completed, however, Theodore Roosevelt, Senior, having convinced himself, against medical advice, that his elder son would enjoy relatively normal breathing for the next few days only if he forced more fresh air into his lungs. So the phaeton's pace did not slacken until they reached the dirt road north of the paved street, and even after they plunged into the woods of upper Manhattan Island the gelding continued to move at a slow, steady canter.

Teedee felt well enough to push his father's hand away.

The man grinned and withdrew a few inches, ready to intervene again if it should become necessary.

At last they drew to a halt, deep in the woods of pine, elm and oak, to give the horse a brief respite. Teedee, as vigorous now as any healthy four-year-old boy in spite of the late hour, squirmed on the buckboard and opened his mouth to speak.

But there was a rustling sound in the dead leaves of the underbrush a short distance to their left, and his father silenced him with a sharp gesture, then pointed as a large, almost pure white rabbit hopped into the middle of the road and sat complacently, only a few feet from the phaeton.

Teedee stood and stared, squinting hard, finally turning to his father with an unasked question.

Again the man pointed, jabbing his forefinger in the direction of the animal.

The child's eyes became narrow slits as he peered down the road. "I don't see anything, Papa," he complained in a high treble.

At the sound of the human voice the rabbit vanished into the underbrush from which he had materialized.

"You didn't see the rabbit?" It was difficult for the man to hide his irritation. The light of a three-quarter moon had filtered through the bare branches of the trees, and the animal had been plainly visible.

Teedee gulped to prevent himself from weeping, and shook his head.

His father looked at him intently, then spoke in a gentler tone. "Can you see the dead leaves on that big branch over there?"

The boy made a supreme effort. "No, Papa," he said miserably.

Theodore Roosevelt, Senior, sighed, and knew his wife had been right when she had told him only a day or two ago that Teedee's eyesight was poor. Apparently he needed glasses, and his father, pitying him, wondered how any boy handicapped by asthma, a delicate body and impaired vision would be able to make his way in the world.

Bamie—Anna—had acquired the adolescent's disdain for the younger children, but Teedee, Conie, and Ellie—that is, Theodore, Corinne, and Elliott—were inseparable, particularly during the winter months, when they studied together. They attended no school, and their teachers were their mother, her sister, Anna Bulloch, who had come to live with them, and a young French governess, who helped them acquire a reasonably good working knowledge of her native tongue but was almost as deficient as they in the fundamentals of arithmetic.

Summer was the children's favorite time of year, in part because they weren't required to study, and partly because they loved the huge Aspinwall estate, near Barrytown, in Dutchess County, that Theodore Roosevelt, Senior, was renting every year. There were orchards, barns, and woods to explore, a pond and two creeks, and, at the far end of the property, rolling hills strewn with huge boulders. Teedee often retired there, several books under his arm, when he grew tired of Ellie's dictatorial manner and the incessant giggling of Conie and her friend, Edith Carow, who was a frequent visitor.

The others found him there one warm afternoon, and stared down reproachfully at the hollow behind a boulder, where he had made himself comfortable. Their expressions were identical, and he was so amused he laughed aloud. That made them furious, which surprised him slightly, as he hadn't intended to hurt their feelings, so he busied himself cleaning his spectacles.

"We've been looking and looking for you," Conie said.

Small sisters could be a nuisance. "I've had things to do," Teedee replied vaguely.

"Well, you've done enough by now." Elliott, who loved to emulate Papa, sounded very firm. "We're going to run a relay race."

"Go ahead," Teedee said reasonably.

"You know very well we can't race unless we have two teams," Elliott told him as the trio descended into the hollow. "I'm faster than you and Edith is faster than Conie, so you and Edith will race Conie and me."

"I don't feel like racing just now." Teedee made an elaborate show of opening his book.

Edith Carow broke the uncomfortable silence that followed. "What are you reading?"

"*Swiss Family Robinson,* and it's silly."

"Then stop reading and come with us!" Ellie directed.

Teedee appeared absorbed in his reading.

"Why is it silly?" Edith asked.

"The author doesn't know anything about animals," Teedee declared promptly. "Or sea creatures, or birds. For instance, the Robinsons found a lobster. Now, I'll wager that Wyss, who wrote the book, never saw a real lobster. Anybody who ever spent two minutes studying one knows that lobsters have one big claw and one little claw. What's more, there aren't any lobsters in that part of the South Pacific Ocean where they were supposed to be shipwrecked."

Elliott was afraid they would be subjected to another of his brother's endless lectures on wild life, and decided a challenge might halt the flow of words. "How do you know there aren't any lobsters there? You've never been there. You've never even been out of the United States!"

"I've read all there is to know about the South Pacific," Teedee said loftily. "That's how. But you wouldn't understand about things like that, because you never read anything!"

The girls exchanged apprehensive glances, afraid there would be blows, and Edith deftly intervened. "What animals in the book are silly?"

When Theodore's jaw jutted forward authoritatively, he managed, in spite of his frail constitution, to look more like his father than did the robust Elliott. "Well, the Robinson boys caught a monkey and tamed it. I'll wager that Wyss never saw a monkey, either."

"Neither have you," Ellie muttered.

Teedee's eyes, behind his spectacles, were as cold as his voice was withering. "I've read five books on monkeys. No, six, including the one from Grandpa's library. No monkey ever looked like the one the Robinson boys caught. I'll show you some drawings when we go back up to the house, Edith. You'll want to see them, too, Conie. And the way they tamed that monkey was the silliest of all. Monkeys are very easy to train, if you know how to do it. First, you get them to like you by giving them food, but on the Robinson island there was all the food that monkey could eat. Now, it's plain that—"

"Are you coming to race with us or aren't you?" Ellie cut in.

Theodore hesitated, knowing his brother's patience had worn thin. Although younger, Elliott was far stronger, and Teedee, although not afraid of him, didn't relish the spectacle of being beaten in a wrestling match, especially in front of girls. Before making up his mind, however, he had to make certain he wouldn't be giving in because of fear. Cowardice, as Papa so often said, was one of the very worst of man's sins, and a boy who was craven wouldn't be able to live with himself.

Unable to reach an honest conclusion within himself, he realized he had to risk taking the beating, which was the lesser humiliation. He plucked a blade of thick rye grass to mark his place in the book, then stood slowly and brushed himself off. "Elliott," he said, "I don't tell you what to do. So don't tell me, either. I'll race when I'm good and ready, and when I do, Edith and I will win. Right now, though, I'm going to finish my chapter."

A threat of physical force could not intimidate the younger boy, but he was incapable of overcoming a display of reasonable and firm common sense. "Well . . ."

Theodore was quick to capitalize on victory. "When I'm ready, I'll meet you behind the apple orchard." He sat again, and flicked through the remaining pages of the chapter.

"It'll take you all afternoon," Ellie wailed.

"Not Teedee," Conie said. "He reads faster than anybody. If that's as far as he's going to read, he'll meet us in a few minutes."

"They'll be fewer if you'll leave me in peace." Teedee watched them retreat, unaware that he was gloating after winning the battle of wills. A victory for its own sake always made a boy feel good, and this particular triumph was especially sweet. It wasn't often that he could force a strong-minded younger sister and a younger brother whose physical prowess was far superior to his own to obey him. This was an incident to be remembered, to be savored at night, in bed, when sudden attacks of asthma made it impossible for him to sleep.

But, he discovered, he could take no real pleasure in his victory. The knowledge that he had compelled them to obey him was small compensation for the fact that they wouldn't want to play with him again for the rest of the day. He liked his own company, of course—more than that of others, he told himself fiercely—but very often he couldn't help feeling abysmally lonely.

Theodore enjoyed the sea voyage across the Atlantic Ocean on the paddle-wheel steamer, *Scotia,* even though he, like Mama and the girls, spent two miserable days in bed when a storm hit the ship. Papa and Elliott remained healthy, seemingly immune to seasickness, but the older boy had reconciled himself to the fact of life that they were as indestructible as he was weak. The whole family enjoyed its visit in Liverpool with Martha Roosevelt's two brothers, Confederate officers who had been forced to resettle abroad after the defeat of the South by the Union.

London was a huge, bewildering city that bored Teedee, as it did his younger brother and sister, and they were unable to share the enthusiasm of Bamie, who was fifteen, for Shakespearean plays and art galleries. The moors and hills of Scotland were far more interesting to a boy whose asthma still forced him to spend much of his time outdoors, but he found Holland and Belgium dull, and tolerated the family's visit to Germany only because his eleventh birthday, on October 27, 1869, was celebrated in Cologne.

One day he overheard his parents agreeing that he, Corinne, and Elliott were too young to enjoy the cultural advantages of the Old World, and although he wasn't certain what they meant, he knew he would have preferred home to an endless succession of hotel rooms. Vienna, capital of the Austro-Hungarian Empire, was the most sophisticated of cities, but Theodore spent hours catching up on entries in the diary he had decided to keep, and not until he saw the Alps of Austria and Switzerland did his spirits revive.

At Interlaken, in the shadow of the Jungfrau, he spent a day alone, wandering through fields and woods in the foothills, and shortly before sundown returned to the hotel room he shared with Elliott, a suspicious bulge beneath his sweater. Carefully locking the door behind him, he turned up the wick on the oil lamp that stood on a table beside his bed, and emptied the contents of his sweater onto the table.

Elliott, who had been watching him in silence, drew closer.

"Stay away!" Theodore said sharply. "These things are mine, and I forbid you to touch them!" He hunched over the table, extending an arm to keep his brother at a distance.

Elliott tried to peer over his shoulder. "I don't want your old rubbish."

"Rubbish?" Teedee's voice rose a half-octave. "I've killed two mice, a snake, and a frog that doesn't look like any we have at home."

The younger boy groaned. "You're going to make our room smell again."

"I plan to mount these fine specimens," Theodore replied, a trace of pomposity in his manner. "They'll be very valuable additions to my collection."

"You've already filled a whole valise with your stupid animal and bird skins."

"I'm sorry for you, Ellie, because you're so ignorant. The Roosevelt Museum of Natural History will be famous all over the world."

Elliott's whoop of laughter filled the room.

Theodore's temper flared. "You're the one who is stupid!" he shouted.

They charged at each other, collided and fell to the floor with a crash, arms and legs flailing.

Someone tried the door, found it bolted and knocked authoritatively.

The boys leaped to their feet, made a hasty effort to straighten their attire and, as Elliott backed away, Theodore unlocked the door and opened it.

Their father stalked into the bedchamber, glaring first at one boy, then the other. "You've been warned about roughhousing in the room," he said.

"We were just having a—a friendly little argument, Papa," Teedee said.

"So I see." Theodore Roosevelt, Senior, picked up a chair that had toppled over and glared at his elder son. "I suppose you started this, as usual."

Experience had taught Teedee it would be useless to defend himself. Any explanation he might offer would be regarded as a self-justifying excuse by a father who demanded perfection from him, so it was wiser to accept the blame in silence. The more he said, the more he would compound his difficulty. Papa's punishments were heavy, and he passed judgment swiftly, rarely reversing a decision.

"Your mother has been inclined to favor you in these ungentlemanly brawls because of your delicate health." The man rocked back and forth, hands clasped behind him, and glowered. "It's my opinion, as I've told her many times, that you take advantage of her compassion."

Teedee knew, of course, that Mama often took his side when he quarreled with his brother, and in all fairness he had to admit that her partiality sometimes made him a trifle bolder than he otherwise would have been. On the other hand, Papa's insistence that he walk the narrowest of straight paths more than made up for her mild inclination to give him the benefit of the doubt.

"What have you to say for yourself, boy?" Theodore, Senior, demanded.

Teedee swallowed hard, and made the one reply that would save him from severe punishment. "I accept the full blame, Papa."

Elliott, who had remained silent, felt compelled to follow his example and share the guilt. A boy tried to avoid a reprimand if he could, but would have to live with his brother after Papa left them alone again. "It was my fault, too," he muttered.

"What was the cause of your—ah—friendly little argument?"

For a moment neither boy spoke, then Theodore took a deep breath. "Ellie doesn't like my specimens."

"That's because they smell," his brother said defensively. "It started with the grouse that Uncle James shot in Scotland and gave him, and every hotel room we've had since then has smelled something awful."

The man sniffed appreciatively, his nose wrinkling, and then went to the table to study the day's collection made by the curator and sole proprietor of the Roosevelt Museum of Natural History. "I can appreciate Ellie's point of view," he said, "but it would be wrong to discourage Teedee's interest in wild life. Have you done any more work on your notebook, Theodore?"

"Yes, sir!" The boy went to a dresser and, with great care, removed a leather-covered book, which he had carefully hidden beneath a pile of shirts.

His father leafed through it. "Remarkable. I have no inclination in this direction myself, but I can appreciate someone else's hobby."

"It isn't a hobby, Papa," Theodore told him. "I'm going to be a natural scientist when I grow up."

"Then I hope you'll be a good one. How many specimens have you classified in this book?" The man continued to stare at the closely written pages.

"Two hundred and seventy-six, not including the frog. I've got to study the snake to see if he's bigger than the one I caught in Lucerne."

Theodore Roosevelt, Senior, was silent for a moment. "I assume your task would be easier if I bought you some reference books."

"That would be wonderful, Papa!"

Elliott looked stricken.

His father smiled at him reassuringly, then turned back to the older boy. "I also assume there would be fewer offensive odors—or, at least, they'd vanish sooner, if you have a professional mounting kit."

Theodore's ecstasy rendered him speechless.

"I'll send to Zurich for the supplies in the morning."

Theodore tried to thank him.

But his father cut him short. "No two people in the world are exactly alike, or have the same tastes. Ellie, I want to hear no more complaints about Teedee's collections. And Theodore, you'll have to tolerate what you call the clutter of Elliott's ice skates and mountain-climbing equipment. Every man must live in peace with his neighbor —and treat him with respect, even though he has different interests. Do what pleases you, provided it's healthy and moral, and makes you stronger both mentally and physically, but always grant the other fellow the same right."

Teedee's feeling of joy gradually dissipated as he forced himself to listen to his father's sermon. This, the boy knew from experience, was just the first in what would be a series of moralizing lectures, the price he would have to pay for the professional mounting kit. The pomposity of Papa's speeches bored him, and the realization made him feel guilty, which contributed nothing to his peace of mind.

Worst of all, he knew, was the fact that Papa was right, which made it no easier, however, to listen respectfully, not daring to fidget, constantly on guard against a sudden request to repeat a sentence or paragraph verbatim. Roosevelts, Papa insisted, lived according to

a higher, more strict code of morality than other people, but Teedee
had never been able to summon the courage to ask him why.

By the time the Roosevelt family returned from Europe in 1870
Theodore was growing taller so rapidly that he needed new clothes
every few months. But his body remained puny, and his father installed a gymnasium in the house on 20th Street, ordering him to
exercise there at least an hour each day. The boy, who had no choice,
obeyed without enthusiasm, went through the necessary motions,
and then returned to the two great passions of his life, reading and
the collection of specimens.

Developing an interest in fish, he went downtown several times
each week to the Fulton Market for any odd creatures he might see
when the nets of the fishermen were emptied. It did not occur to him
that he was an exceptionally lonely boy, or that the ever-present odor
of fish that clung to him did nothing to increase his popularity with
the sons of the family's friends. He had grown so accustomed to loneliness that he took his way of life for granted.

He exercised faithfully for the next two years, but only because he
was obeying his father's orders, and made no attempt to conceal his
boredom. By the spring of 1872, when he was thirteen, he remained
scrawny, with a complexion that was still sallow, even though he
spent at least an hour or two in the open air every day, no matter what the weather.

The most violent asthma attack he had suffered in years sent him
to bed for a week in May, and his suffering thereafter remained so
intense that his parents decided a stay in the pine forests at Moose-
head Lake, Maine, would be necessary to give him relief and restore
his health. Neither his mother nor his father was able to accompany
him, Anna was busy, and it was finally decided that, for the first time
in his life, he would make the journey alone.

Carrying two valises, one of them filled with books and taxidermy
equipment, Theodore traveled by train from New York to Boston,
changed to another train that took him as far as Portsmouth, New
Hampshire, and there transferred to an old-fashioned stagecoach,
pulled by a pair of geldings sturdy enough to be plow horses. There
were only a few passengers in the stage, but directly opposite Theodore, on the dusty seats of faded, plum-colored plush, were two boys
of about his own age. One was tall, husky and blond, and his stocky
companion was very dark.

Although they ignored him, Theodore studied them with interest, pleased that he might be able to pass the time with his peers. Both boys seemed fairly well dressed, although their scuffed boots needed shining, and after concluding they were gentlemen, he cleared his throat.

"I wonder if you lads know," he said genially, a touch of condescension in his voice, "that some of the finest specimens of snow owls to be found anywhere in all of North America live in the woods less than fifty miles from here."

The two boys exchanged startled glances, but did not speak, and there was no sound but the creak of the stage's wheels and the steady pounding of the horses' hoofs on the hard-packed dirt road.

"Only a few years ago—no more than ten, actually—ornithologists were afraid the snow owl might become extinct." Theodore was enjoying himself, and it was plain that the boys were impressed by the scope of his knowledge. "But those fears proved groundless. The breed is hardier than anyone supposed, and thrives in the wooded sections of northern New England. Obviously," he added with an artificial, high-pitched laugh, "the better part of the country hereabouts is wooded, so the future of the snow owl seems assured."

"He's crazy," the tall boy said.

His companion nodded vigorously, and inspected the handsomely attired but spindly New Yorker.

It seemed they were jealous of his learning, and Theodore felt sorry for them. His endowments were unique, as a friend of Papa's who was a professor at Harvard College had remarked recently; he had not only become an expert on wild life, but repeatedly demonstrated that his memory was phenomenal. "As you'd be led to expect by his name, the snow owl is a pure white in the winter months, but in summer his plumage—"

"Shut your mouth," the shorter boy growled.

Theodore was stunned by his rudeness. Never had anyone addressed him so insultingly, and without cause. "I beg your pardon, sir!" His voice rose to a high, indignant squeak.

The boys laughed until tears came into their eyes. "He sounds like an owl that got its wings clipped," the stocky one said, "and he looks like an owl, too. His eyes do, anyway. I never saw an owl with great big teeth that stick out, though."

"I think," the tall boy said, "that he looks like one of those horses up front. The ugly one."

Theodore was irritated, but reminded himself that a gentleman was expected to pay no attention to the coarseness of his inferiors.

"You're pretty near right," the stocky boy said. "He's like a horse, all right, but the other end."

His friend gazed intently at Theodore, then said with mock solemnity, "By crickety, the only difference between his face and the rear end of a horse is that there's no tail hanging down from his forehead."

Theodore could feel the color burning in his cheeks, and tried in vain to curb his soaring temper. But he knew it was against the law to create a disturbance on a moving stagecoach, so he clenched his fists, digging his nails into the palms of his hands, and forced himself to remain silent.

His tormentors realized their shafts were striking home, and for the next two hours they teased him mercilessly, pretending for short periods that he did not exist, then trying to outdo each other in their insults.

The torture was unbearable, and when the stage pulled to a halt Theodore was in a seething rage, angrier than he had ever been in all his thirteen years.

The boys unleashed a final barrage of crude remarks, took carpetbags from the wooden rack above the window and left the coach.

Theodore followed them, so anxious to even the score that he jumped to the ground instead of climbing down the four steps passengers were requested to use. "You, there!" he called, his voice strident. "Wait!"

The pair turned to him, grinning.

He removed his spectacles, placing them in the embroidered case his mother had made for him. "I took enough of your abuse," he said. "Put up your hands!"

The stocky boy dropped his carpetbag onto the ground. "What do you know?" he asked, speaking in a voice loud enough so that passengers waiting to board the stage could hear. "I never knew the rear end of a horse could fight."

Theodore lunged at him, swinging both arms wildly.

The dark-haired boy stepped aside.

His assailant staggered and almost fell.

"By crickety," the tall boy said, "he fights like a girl. Come on, girl. See if you can hit me."

Theodore turned and struck at him, but a long arm was extended, a hand pushed against his chest and although he struck repeatedly, he pawed thin air, unable to touch his foe, much less hurt him.

The smaller boy had no intention of missing the fun. "Your arms are too long," he said. "Now it's my turn." He moved closer to the New Yorker, his friend relinquishing the victim to him.

Theodore charged again and again, his arms flailing, but not once was he able to strike his opponent. The short boy mocked him by tapping him on the nose, chin and chest with playful punches, yet avoided every blow aimed at him, and more furious the energy that Theodore expended, the more easily his tormentor handled him.

The passengers and several loiterers had formed a circle around the trio, and most of the men were laughing. The farce might have lasted until Theodore fell to the ground in exhaustion, but the stagecoach driver finally intervened.

"Leave him be, boys," he said. "We're on our way, and seeing his ticket has been paid for, I don't think his folks would take kindly to his being left behind."

The pair retreated, laughing.

Theodore would have followed them, but the driver caught hold of his arm. "You've had enough of the ring for one day, youngster." He dragged the reluctant boy back to the coach.

Groping his way toward his seat, Theodore tried to shut out the humiliating, jocular roar of the crowd gathered outside the stage. Unable to force himself to look out of the window, he took his spectacles from their case, hoping they would conceal the hot tears that almost blinded him.

His pride was shattered, and for a long time he sat motionless, hunched in his seat. At last he took his writing kit from a valise and, unmindful of the swaying, bouncing stagecoach, started an urgent letter. *Dear Papa*, he wrote, *I want to take boxing lessons as soon as I come home. It is urgent that I begin at once. I will gladly earn the money to pay for them myself* . . .

Theodore Roosevelt, Senior, had been a founder of the Young Men's Christian Association in New York City, and knew that the institution's athletic director, John Long, was a former prize fighter who, some years earlier, had been a contender for the middleweight championship of the world. Long agreed to accept a pupil, and became a daily visitor to the Roosevelt house.

By the autumn of 1872, when Theodore turned fourteen, his father always knew where to find him when he wasn't in his own bedchamber, and one cool evening, about two hours after dinner, he went there in search of the boy. There was no sound from the gymnasium, and when the elder Roosevelt opened the door, he stopped short.

His son, attired in a boxer's trunks and sleeveless undershirt, was working on the horizontal bars, raising and lowering himself with the rhythmic, monotonous regularity of a clock's pendulum. The muscles in his upper arms were bulging, a vein stood out at one side of his forehead and perspiration was pouring unheeded down his face as he raised, lowered, and raised himself, his feet never touching the floor.

"Theodore," the man said, taking care not to use the intimate family name which his son no longer liked.

"Good evening, Papa." In spite of his exertions the boy was breathing easily.

"Don't you think you've done enough for one day? Mama tells me you spent half the morning here, and that you boxed with Mr. Long for an hour and a half this afternoon."

"What time is it, Papa?"

"Almost nine o'clock. Don't you think—"

"I'll need another half hour if I'm to keep to my schedule of four hours per day." Theodore grinned broadly, showing his teeth. "I measured myself today, Papa. My chest has expanded five-eighths of an inch in the past five months."

"Splendid."

"I intend to do better."

"I hope you'll go to bed when you're finished for the night here, Theodore."

"Well, not right off, Papa. I've started reading some of the novels of Charles Dickens ever since the newspapers began calling him a great literary artist, and I need to do some work on my natural history notebooks." The boy neither faltered nor paused as he continued his exercises.

The elder Roosevent wanted to warn him that too much exertion might cause an asthma attack, but decided not to mention the subject. Theodore's health had been improving steadily ever since he had launched his campaign to make himself strong. "What do you think of Mr. Dickens' work?"

"Oh, he writes ably enough, I suppose, but he's too sentimental for my taste. And he exaggerates terribly. His poor people are always the victims of greedy property owners and lords. Dickens doesn't seem to realize that any man can improve his lot if he works hard enough."

"It isn't necessary to do all of one's work in a day, Theodore, or even in a single year."

The boy laughed, relishing his increasing physical prowess. "Papa, you have friends who were in the Grand Army of the Republic."

"Many of them. Why?"

"I'd like to spend an hour at their armory on 14th Street every Saturday morning, on my way to inspect the Fulton Street fish catch."

"It might be arranged." Theodore Roosevelt, Senior, was cautious, scarcely able to cope with the energies his elder son was displaying.

"I was ashamed of myself when I went duck hunting with you on Long Island last month, and I can improve my aim at the armory. I've made inquiries, and they have a fine rifle range there. What's more, it's right on my way to Fulton Street, so I won't waste any time."

The man hesitated, afraid his son's ambitions were so widespread that he could not fulfill more than a fraction of them. "Let me think about it."

"Do you remember my record that day?" Theodore's mood changed, and his self-disgust was so great that he dropped from the horizontal bars to the floor and stood in front of his father. "I fired seventeen rounds, and didn't make a single strike. That's disgraceful, Papa, and I can't live with myself unless I do better, a great deal better!" As much of a perfectionist now as his father, it did not occur to the boy that the problem did not warrant his state of near hysteria.

In the winter of 1872 the family went abroad again, this time for an extended stay of a year. Theodore Roosevelt, Senior, took his family up the Nile on a houseboat he bought for the purpose, accompanied them on a horseback tour of Palestine, and, after visiting Greece and Turkey, deposited Theodore and Elliott with one family in Dresden, and Corinne with another. There the youngsters would stay for several months in order to become as proficient in speaking, reading, and writing German as they were in French.

Theodore, maintaining his program of rigorous daily exercises and suffering no more than an occasional, mild attack of asthma, was old enough now to appreciate the benefits of foreign travel, and loved every moment of the long trip. He steeped himself in ancient Egyptian history and spent hours in the marshes along the banks of the Nile searching for specimens he could add to his natural history collection. In the latter he exhausted his hearty father, who frequently accompanied him.

I walked for hours with him through the bogs, Theodore Roosevelt, Senior, wrote one of his brothers, *at the risk of sinking hopelessly and helplessly. I felt I had to keep up with Teedee, but could not.*

The visits to Athens and Rhodes inspired the boy to teach himself Greek, and he began an intensive study of Aristotle's philosophy. Constantinople fascinated him, arousing his interest in the history of the Sultanate, Byzantine art, and ancient Hittite mythology. But it was in Dresden, where he celebrated his fifteenth birthday, that he really came into his own.

He mastered the German language so he could read, in the original, the literature in that tongue. He continued to collect specimens, and his host, a professor, blandly assured him the odors were inoffensive. He swam in the Elbe River above the city, and either boxed or wrestled regularly with several German boys, all of them a year or two his senior. He was also the founder of the Dresden Literary American Club, whose members included his reluctant younger sister and brother; to remain in good standing one was forced to write an essay or story, poem or play. The principal contributor was the club's president, who was finding it as easy and pleasant to put words on paper as it was to talk.

Above all, he relished his newest pastime. He had been given a breech-loading, double-barreled shotgun as a Christmas present by his father, and the weapon invariably accompanied him into the open countryside. His aim improved steadily, and most of the small animals and birds he shot were added to the collection of the Roosevelt Museum of Natural History, which now numbered more than three hundred specimens and, of necessity, reposed in an outbuilding behind the professor's house.

The gun was slung over his shoulder, as usual, one afternoon in the late autumn of 1873 when, after persuading Corinne and Elliott to accompany him, he set out on a hike through the valley that stretched out on both sides of the Elbe. He wanted to see both the battlefield where King Charles XII, Sweden's ascetic military genius, had defeated an army of Poles and Saxons, and the campsite, still preserved, where the French legions of Napoleon I had made a bivouac.

Theodore walked purposefully, with long, nervous strides, until Conie protested.

"I can't keep up with you," she complained.

He slowed his pace. "You're such a good fellow," he said apologetically, "that I keep forgetting you're a girl."

She realized he intended the remark as a compliment, but felt compelled to retaliate. "And I don't see why you have to carry that horrid rifle."

Elliott, whose nightly repose was disturbed by the rank odors emanating from an old owl that had not yet been stuffed, smiled broadly.

"It's a shotgun, not a rifle," Theodore said in a tone that indicated he was long-suffering but infinitely patient. "Why is it horrid?"

"Because you kill harmless, sweet little creatures with it!"

The boy was puzzled. "The purpose of hunting," he declared, a ring of authority in his voice, "is to bring down one's quarry. One doesn't merely shoot at targets, you know!"

His sister refused to accept the explanation. An adolescent herself now, she was rapidly developing a mind of her own. "What I don't understand, Teedee," she said, deliberately using his childhood nickname because it would annoy him, "is how you can pretend you love animals."

Theodore's eyes gleamed behind his glasses, and he clicked his teeth, grinding them for a moment as he tried to curb his indignation. "Pretend? Who takes care of the dogs at home, and both the cats? I do! What's more, when Papa buys us our own horses after we go out to the summer place he's going to rent on Long Island, you'll see who takes the best care of his horse! I'll groom him myself, I'll—"

"If you love animals so much," Conie persisted, "how can you kill them?"

"I don't kill pets!"

"Any animals," she said stubbornly.

Theodore thought carefully before replying. Conie didn't appreciate pets as he did, failed to share his enthusiasm for collecting specimens and, like every girl he had ever known, Edith Carow excepted, could not understand why males enjoyed hunting. He wanted to be fair to her, however, and made an effort. "There's no connection," he said, "between liking natural history and liking hunting. They give me different kinds of pleasure, and different feelings of accomplishment."

Conie couldn't or wouldn't believe him. "That's nonsense. Either you want to save animals and birds—like your precious white owls—or you want to murder them."

Theodore managed to strike a theatrical pose without breaking his stride, his right hand sawing the air in a manner reminiscent of a Dresden lecturer he admired. "You'll have to take my word for it, that's all. You think my tastes are contradictory, but you're wrong." He spoke so rapidly that only a close relative could have distinguished his words. "I agree with the old saying that oil and water don't mix. It was Benjamin Franklin who said that, I think. I must look it up. But natural history and hunting aren't related, as oil and water are, both being liquids. They're completely separate. When you're older," he concluded patronizingly, "you'll see what I mean."

Conie needed help, and Elliott, who had remained silent, came to her rescue. He knew he wasn't capable of matching wits with his brother, however, and therefore decided to attack on a different front. "The Oracle of Delphi has spoken. Three cheers for the philosopher-poet."

"Very amusing." Theodore did not sound amused. "I'm not yet a philosopher, and I'm not sure I'll ever become a poet. My talents are limited."

"You try to look like a poet," Ellie said.

The older boy sniffed, his dignity affronted.

"When Mama and Papa see how long you've let your hair grow," Ellie continued, "they'll be disgusted."

"Historically and in every other sense," Theodore replied vigorously, "long hair doesn't mean one lacks manly virtues. Goethe had long hair. Schiller had long hair, and so did Münster. Hegel's hair wasn't short, what there was of it, and Schopenhauer's was long. The only portrait of Heinrich Heine I ever saw showed him with long hair, and Max von Regensberg said that when he was in Frankfurt-am-Main last year and went to a reading of poetry by August Hoffmann, the old man's hair was hanging down below his shoulders."

Elliott had no idea whether his brother's ammunition was accurate or fancied, but realized he shouldn't have become involved in a debate with someone who neither could nor would tolerate defeat. "You aren't any of those people," he said.

Theodore's gaze was pitying. "I find that a surface resemblance to the great German poets and philosophers puts one more in tune with their moods. It's a question of sensitivity that only a student of their work would understand." Suddenly he stiffened, peered off toward a patch of woods and motioned the others to stand back. "Be very quiet and don't move," he whispered. "See that bird up there in the beech tree? It's a Saxon grosbeak, and for a long time I've been wanting one for my collection." Smiling confidently, he raised his shotgun to his shoulder.

The Roosevelts returned to New York in time to spend Christmas, 1873, in a new, spacious brownstone house that had just been built for them at 6 West 57th Street, just off the corner of Fifth Avenue. There Theodore had his own library adjoining his bedchamber, and was delighted by the gymnasium on the third floor, which boasted an open-air annex. Still reading hungrily in each of the many subjects that interested him, he cut his hair short again and resumed his boxing lessons with John Long.

Although he was in his sixteenth year he had never enjoyed the benefits of formal schooling, and his parents, in consultation with their many relatives, made long-range plans for his future education. They decided to send him to Harvard in the autumn of 1876, provided he qualified, and a private tutor was engaged to help him prepare for college.

The boy worked with a zeal that pleased his father and alarmed his mother, even during the summers the family now spent at a rented estate on Oyster Bay, Long Island, where Theodore also swam, rode, hunted, hiked, collected specimens and went boating. His asthma rarely bothered him now and, although still slender, he had developed broad shoulders and a thick chest.

Although he no longer resembled the sickly child who had been in such delicate health, Martha Roosevelt was ill at ease, afraid that anyone who worked and played so hard would be forced to pay the physical consequences for his reckless expenditure of energy. Her husband laughed gently at her fears, assuring her Theodore had become "as perfect a specimen as any in his collection," so she kept her thoughts to herself, but watched her son discreetly.

One afternoon, in the summer of 1875, while entertaining several women and girls of the large Roosevelt clan at tea, she heard Theodore's voice in the distance, beyond the rented property. Although she could not make out what he was saying, or shouting, she felt certain she heard a note of urgent distress in his voice, which alternately soared higher and then faded to an indistinct rumble.

Martha excused herself, headed across the lawn and walked toward the twin hills that stood beyond the stable, overlooking Oyster Bay Cove. A lady never permitted anyone to think she was in undue haste, but she found it difficult to restrain herself, and increased her pace as soon as she thought it improbable that her guests were watching her.

Breathless as she drew near the crest of the smaller hill, she halted when she saw Theodore at the top of the larger. He was wearing the old boots, trousers and shirt that were his habitual summer attire, and stood with his back to her, waving his arms. He seemed to be lamenting something, but she was still unable to hear him, and in her anxiety called out to him.

"Theodore! Are you all right?"

The boy turned, saw her and grinned, his spectacles glinting and his teeth looking very white in the bright sunshine. He immediately sprinted down the slope and, not slacking his pace, raced up the smaller hill to his mother's side. "I thought you had company this afternoon, Mama." Respect for his parents made it impossible for him to add that he had never known her to indulge in hiking or other strenuous physical activities.

"I heard you from the veranda," Martha said, afraid she had made a fool of herself and therefore stiffening. "You sounded as though you were in pain."

Theodore's stridently high-pitched laugh echoed across the harbor, where two small sloops were sailing out toward the open waters of Long Island Sound. Then, seeing his mother's reproachful gaze he stifled his mirth.

She had to admit he was tanned, clear-eyed and robust. Although he studied seven or eight hours every day and played equally long, he was acquiring a stamina and resilience greater than that of anyone else in the hearty family. All the same, she had heard anguish in his voice. "I thought you had suffered an asthma attack and needed help."

"I was behind in my work because I stopped to put a sail on the skiff for Edith and Conie after I finished my tennis match. So I was making up for lost time."

Martha was bewildered and increasingly annoyed.

"Cicero's works were written for delivery as speeches, Mama, and weren't meant to be read in silence. Listen." The boy flung his arms wide, declaiming, "*Aptissima omnino sunt arma senectutis, artes, exercitationesque virtutum, quae in omni aetate cultae cum multum, diuque vixeris, mirificos efferunt fructus, non solum quia nunquam deserunt, ne in extremo quidem tempore aetatis, verum etiam quia conscientia bene actae vitae, mulorumque benefactorum recordatio jucundissima est.*"

His mother was surprised by the sonorous depth and timbre of his voice, which in no way resembled his normally high-pitched speaking voice. And, although his gestures were awkward, he suddenly had seemed dignified and mature.

"I'm sorry, Mama," he said abruptly. "I forgot you don't understand Latin. Let me give you a translation—my own, as it happens. 'The best armor of old age is an early life well spent in the practice and exercise of virtuous deeds. For when one is advanced in years, his previous good deeds bring a great reward, since his habits of virtue still abide with him—'"

"I must go back to my company, Theodore."

"Let me finish!"

"It would be rude to keep my guests waiting for me."

Theodore started down the hill with her. "If you insist, but I'll translate the whole thing for you later, if you'd like."

Martha forced a smile, wincing inwardly. "That would be nice." Some of his enthusiasms were difficult to digest.

"Have you ever heard such noble sentiments?" His teeth made a clicking sound when he became excited, a habit his mother attributed to his inability to breathe easily when he had been younger. "I intend to take Cicero's advice, Mama. It's as valid today as it was when he wrote those words about two thousand years ago!"

Again she smiled, but with greater effort.

Suddenly the boy turned, bolted back up the slope and, before he reached the summit, began declaiming again, his voice reminiscent of the patriotic orators who had damned Martha's beloved South during the War between the States.

Aware that no one could hear her, she allowed herself the luxury of a long, tremulous sigh. She had always known Theodore had a brilliant mind, he was developing a remarkably strong body, and his interests were so many and varied that she could no longer remember more than a fraction of them. But she was afraid, when he spoke of noble sentiments and practicing virtuous deeds, that he might grow up to be a prig. She could only hope that his ever-increasing vitality, almost animal-like in its intensity, would prove a compensating, saving grace.

Socially complacent, secure in the knowledge that she was the leading institute of higher learning in the United States as well as the oldest, Harvard University surveyed the world with tranquillity from her spreading brick buildings on the banks of the Charles River in Cambridge, Massachusetts. Since the earliest of American colonial days her faculty and graduates had been the most distinguished of men, beginning with Cotton Mather and Samuel Sewall. John Adams, the 2nd President of the United States, had been a graduate, as had John Hancock, and since their time Harvard alumni always had been prominent in the nation's affairs of state.

Philosophers, theologians, and educators studded the roster of her alumni, among them Henry Ware, Emerson and Thoreau. Historians Sparks and Bancroft were two of the many members of their profession who had received degrees there, Longfellow had been a member of the faculty, and had been succeeded by James Russell Lowell, himself a Harvard graduate, who was still a professor. In medicine no one had a more distinguished name than Dr. Oliver Wendell Holmes, who taught physiology and anatomy, and memories of Louis Agassiz still echoed across the Yard.

No one who had known him would forget Harvard's president from 1846–49, Edward Everett, the greatest of American orators, who had taught Greek literature before becoming the chief executive of the school. And both friends and foes agreed that young Charles W. Eliot, now in the seventh year of his administration, would leave his mark on the university, be it for better or worse as he made strenuous efforts to modernize the curriculum.

Tradition ruled the college, the undergraduate realm, with a firm hand. Eccentrics and rebels sometimes ruffled the serenity of Harvard life, to be sure, but the majority of the eight hundred young men seeking bachelors' degrees tolerated them with faintly amused scorn. Harvard men were expected to accept time-tested standards, wear their sophistication lightly, coupling it with a faint air of boredom, and, if serious about their studies, were to pretend they had no genuine interest in the development of their intellects. The Harvard student remained calm, at least on the surface, no matter what the provocation, and always remembered he belonged to a select breed of gentlemen.

From the day of Theodore Roosevelt's arrival in Cambridge in the early autumn of 1876, he failed to fit into the Harvard mold. The only quarters available in the Yard for a freshman were damp, ground-floor cells, so he rented private rooms at 16 Winthrop Street, located a short distance between the Yard and the Charles River. This, as his new friends and classmates subsequently remarked, was fortunate—

for them. He was still collecting natural history specimens, and the odors would have forced the residents of any undergraduate dormitory to eject him.

Handsomely attired in a new wardrobe of the latest fashion, including peg-top trousers and suit jackets with a cutaway effect, he was considered too flashy by the conservatives, who also disapproved of his recently grown, long sideburns. He was not a complete iconoclast, however, and when Bamie came to Cambridge from New York to help him put his quarters in order, she found a large banner in his bedroom that read FREE TRADE, FREE PRESS, AND FREE BEER.

His aristocratic background and his family's comfortable financial circumstances were at least partly responsible for his election to the exclusive Porcellian Club, where he ate most of his meals. Quick to pursue his extracurricular interests, he joined the staff of a student newspaper, the *Advocate*, joined the Natural History Club, and became a member of the intramural boxing squad. *I hope to become the lightweight champion of the College,* he wrote his father a few months after his arrival at Harvard, *but I must confess that, until now, I have been taking drubbings three afternoons each week.*

Faculty members who taught young Roosevelt soon learned to treat him warily. Unlike his peers, who listened to lectures in somnolent silence, he frequently jumped to his feet, challenging any assertion with which he disagreed. This was the pattern he had formed with his tutor, he found debate stimulating, and he saw no reason to change his habits simply because Harvard students were not expected to contradict their professors. His instructors in literature and American history were particularly unfortunate, since he knew his subjects and could present reasoned, logical refutations of their claims, delivering miniature lectures of his own with forceful gusto.

Theodore discovered girls for the first time, and shattered Porcellian Club precedence by taking one there for lunch. The young lady was treated with the utmost politeness by the members, who had no desire to embarrass her, but later that day a committee of seniors called on Theodore at his Winthrop Street rooms and upbraided him. "If she were homely," he said, ushering them to the door, "I wouldn't blame you. But you'll have to grant she's the prettiest girl in Boston, so tradition becomes meaningless."

Although he became friendly with classmates who were members of Boston's oldest aristocracy, among them a Saltonstall, a Bacon, and a Minot, he gradually acquired a reputation as an eccentric. His devotion to natural history and boxing defied the Harvard code of indifference, and he was so engrossed in his studies that he often read in the midst of social conversations, thus displaying one of the worst of Harvard's offenses, bad form.

In the autumn of 1877, at the beginning of his sophomore year, Theodore received a note requesting him to visit the office of Henry Cabot Lodge, a young instructor in American history. Lodge, still in his twenties, had the most impressive of credentials and knew it. A wealthy scion of two patrician families, himself a Harvard graduate and, eighteen months earlier, of her Law School, he served as co-editor with Henry Adams, grandson of an American President and great-grandson of another, of the *North American Review,* which was rapidly acquiring a reputation as one of the nation's most erudite and polished journals. Everyone who knew Lodge believed it inevitable that he would become a great man, and he shared the opinion; self-confidence was one of his natural assets, but modesty was not.

The conservatively dressed instructor with the thin, ascetic face and the broad-jawed, flamboyant undergraduate stared at each other, neither concealing his hostility, and Lodge broke the silence. "I happened to glance out of my window just now, and saw you running, Mr. Roosevelt."

Theodore thought he knew what was coming, but merely nodded.

"Since you're in your second year here, surely you know by now that Harvard men always walk."

"I always run, sir." Theodore's words were proper, but his manner was openly belligerent.

"May I ask why?"

"I save time, and I keep in good physical condition."

"You enjoy breaking unwritten rules, Mr. Roosevelt."

"As an attorney, Mr. Lodge, you undoubtedly know that under the American system of jurisprudence laws are written. We don't follow the English."

Lodge couldn't help smiling. The boy might be impertinent, but he was right. "I called you here because I've been given to understand that you hope to write a book on the War of 1812."

"It's more than a hope, sir. I shall definitely write my book. Nothing adequate has ever been done on the naval history of the war, so I'm going to concentrate on that phase."

Lodge raised an eyebrow. "Do you have a naval background, Mr. Roosevelt?"

Theodore suspected he was being baited. "I sail," he said curtly.

"How old are you?"

"Nineteen, sir."

Lodge recognized his own quality of overabundant self-confidence when he saw it in someone else. "You have courage. But I can't help wondering why you aren't taking my course on the period."

Theodore tried to reply discreetly. "My schedule is filled, Mr. Lodge."

"President Eliot has introduced the principle of elective courses to fit situations like yours."

"If you must know, sir, I've been told that you not only give very low grades but insist that your students accept your points of view if they hope to pass your courses."

Lodge had never heard such candor from an undergraduate, but recovered quickly. "I'm no naval expert, but my course on the period from 1783 to 1824 might give you background material that you'd find useful."

Theodore had no intention of enrolling in the course, and in his impatience became reckless. "I dare say I can read the same sources that you use, Mr. Lodge."

The instructor was annoyed. "You may be very bright, young man, although your grades last year weren't particularly outstanding. Are you familiar with the Bible?"

"Of course!"

"Then it would do you no harm to reflect on a passage from the Book of Proverbs. *'Pride goeth before destruction, and a haughty spirit before a fall.'*"

The blow fell in February 1878. Theodore Roosevelt, Senior, had fallen ill the previous autumn after trying his hand at mountain climbing, and his health had declined steadily. At his insistence the news had been kept from his elder son for fear the boy would worry to the detriment of his studies, so the shock was intense when Theodore was informed, by telegram, that his father had died.

Theodore's world collapsed. He was so grief-stricken that he could not read the newspaper articles extolling the elder Roosevelt's philanthropic virtues, and after returning to Harvard from the funeral, expressed a view that had not appeared anywhere in print. "My father," he told his friend and classmate, Robert Bacon, "enjoyed life more than any other man I ever knew."

Early in his freshman year he had written to his parents, *Not another boy in college has a family who loves him as well as you all do me, and I am* sure *there is no one who has a father who is also his best and most intimate friend.* He had lost that best friend, who had also been his protector and guide, goad and guardian.

For a week he remained alone in his rooms on Winthrop Street, emerging only to buy bread and meat which he used to make an occasional sandwich. Friends were unable to console him, and he told his good friend, Richard Saltonstall, "Part of me—the best part—is gone forever."

Incapable of dwelling indefinitely on the past, he wrote to his mother, *With the help of my God I will try to lead such a life as he would have wished.*

A heavy blanket of snow carpeted the Yard, and Henry Cabot Lodge saw that young Roosevelt was walking toward his office at a sedate pace. The boy's eyes were bloodshot behind his spectacles, but he made no attempt to conceal the burden of his sorrow. It was evident that he had been weeping, and he didn't care who knew it.

There was a new, unexpected dignity in his manner as he greeted the instructor, and when he refrained from mentioning his tragedy, Lodge also took care to avoid the subject, knowing that the intrusion of outsiders would not be welcome.

Theodore didn't know what to do with a bulky folder when the instructor extended his hand, and finally placed it on the edge of the desk. "I should have sent advance word that I was coming, sir, so you could have been elsewhere."

"I'm paid to see students," Lodge replied.

Theodore stopped feeling sorry for himself and straightened. "It's too late in the year to start taking your class," he said.

The instructor turned away for a moment to hide a smile, and decided that irony was a far better antidote for grief than sympathy. "Why would you want to waste your time? You wouldn't learn anything new."

"Probably not," Theodore said, a gleam appearing in his tired eyes, "but it might not do me any harm. Mr. Lodge, if you have nothing better to do, I wonder if you'd be interested in looking over the first chapters of my manuscript and my notes. They're fairly well organized." Suddenly unsure of himself, he gestured in the direction of the folder.

"Sit down." Lodge made himself comfortable behind his desk and leafed through the pages, then returned to the first chapter. "Well. *The view professed by Great Britain in 1812 respecting the rights of belligerents and neutrals was diametrically opposite to that held by the United States.'* You surprise me, Mr. Roosevelt. That's an orthodox beginning."

Theodore didn't realize he had developed the habit of expressing intellectual indignation by baring his teeth. "I'm not a radical or an anarchist, sir! It's the duty of the historian to report the facts of history accurately and interpret them impartially."

In spite of his sharp tongue and occasional pomposity, Lodge thought, the youth's approach was sound. "I'll take great pleasure in reading what you've written."

The imperious scholar's façade faded, and a grateful boy smiled broadly for the first time since his father had died. "I'm in your debt, sir."

"Not if you write a good book. There's a need for a naval history of the War of 1812. For that matter, there's no good account of military operations, either."

"I hope to write a companion book on that phase of the war, including the Battle of New Orleans."

Lodge looked at him curiously. "You're ambitious, Mr. Roosevelt."

"When I first came to Harvard I had hoped to become a museum curator, but I find the laboratory science courses too dull and technical." Theodore found it odd to be confiding in someone he had considered cold and impersonal. "I prefer human history, particularly that of my own country. The field is unlimited."

"What makes you think so?"

"Most historians don't understand people. Or politics. Or power. The reason George Bancroft's histories are so good is because he served as Secretary of the Navy in President Polk's cabinet and was Minister to Great Britain for the State Department."

"I've held the same theory myself," Lodge said, almost forgetting he was conversing with an undergraduate eight years his junior. "And there's no reason history can't be written with the same smoothness of style we demand in the *Review*."

Theodore's friends would have been astonished by his sudden modesty. "Please don't judge my chapters by your *Review* standards, sir!"

"Why not?"

"I'm no author, Mr. Lodge."

"If you intend to write a book you want people to buy and read, you'd better become one." Something occurred to the instructor that he should have seen all along: young Roosevelt's self-confidence was a pose that enabled him to hide feelings of insecurity and discomfort. "I'm told you're a boxer. How long did it take you to learn how to fight?"

Theodore rubbed a tender ear and sore jaw. "I'm still learning, Mr. Lodge."

"Don't expect to become another George Bancroft overnight, either. After I've read your material, let's have dinner together some evening, soon, and perhaps I can make a few suggestions that might help you."

"That would be bully, sir!" Theodore was pleased, but his mood suddenly changed. "I'll accept criticism of my style, but I won't change the content of the book. I have my own ideas about the War of 1812, and I won't stand for tampering."

Lodge suspected he had many fixed opinions, which was unusual in one so young. The very qualities that made him irritating, his sudden enthusiasms and belligerence, his refusal to compromise and his insistence on maintaining his individuality were also strengths that made him unlike other members of his generation. He was unique, fascinating, and therefore worth cultivating, provided it was possible to tolerate his mercurial temperament. There was no way of knowing whether he would accept or reject advice, but an association with him would help relieve the tedium of a teaching career.

Hard work at Harvard and a summer devoted to vigorous physical activity dulled the edge of Theodore's grief for his father. At Oyster Bay he sailed, swam, and rode, and then he went to Maine for six weeks of camping in the open, hiking and hunting with Bill Sewall. The even-tempered guide did not mind listening by the hour to a young man's opinions of literature, history and the shortcomings of President Rutherford B. Hayes, who, Theodore believed, was making a shambles of the Republican party and undermining the integrity of the United States.

Now the nominal head of the family, Theodore heartily agreed with his mother's decision to make no reductions in his father's annual contributions to charity. *My uncles,* he wrote to Henry Cabot Lodge, with whom he was corresponding, *tell me the plight of the poor in New York is almost beyond description. So I am pleased our financial situation is such that Mother and I can continue Father's good work.*

*Although we are far less wealthy than the families of many chaps I
know at school, we can, all the same, make contributions worthy of
Father's memory.*

Theodore appeared to be more of a conformist when he returned
to Harvard for his junior year. In rapid succession he was elected to
the editorial board of the *Advocate*, became an officer of Hasty Pud-
ding, the drama society, and was made president of the Harvard
chapter of Alpha Delta Phi fraternity.

"It's strange and paradoxical," Robert Bacon said. "Theodore insists he isn't a leader, but he's being forced, in spite of himself, to
lead."

Harry Shaw, another friend, had a somewhat different point of view.
"Everyone knows Theodore, and he's invited to every party, of
course. In fact, he and I gave a party together at the opera a short
time ago. But it's surprising how few of us really like him. He'd be far
more popular if he'd talk less and wouldn't insist that everyone share
his enthusiasms and his confounded opinions."

Theodore blithely continued to walk his own path, indifferent to
what anyone thought of him. Then, on October 18, 1878, everything
changed. Richard Saltonstall's parents gave a small dinner party at
their Boston home for some of his friends, and one of the guests was
Richard's cousin, Alice Hathaway Lee of Chestnut Hill.

She was seventeen, with golden hair, blue eyes and a slender figure,
and was so sweet, pleasant and unruffled that her relatives and friends
called her "Sunshine." From the moment Theodore saw her he was
fascinated, and neither knowing nor caring why he found her unlike
any other girl he had ever met, gaped at her all through the dinner,
ignoring the young ladies who sat on either side of him.

No matter who his companions might be, he always felt compelled
to dominate any conversation in which he participated, and in his
urgent desire to impress Alice he gave his friends little chance to say
more than a few words. Although he wasn't heavy enough to play football, he discussed the Harvard team at length, indifferent to the presence of three members of the squad at the table. He had taken no
courses from William James, a young professor of psychology whose
ideas were creating a stir, yet he criticized James's theories with such
forceful logic that two physicians, who were among the chaperons,
were impressed by his arguments. Finally, in a long monologue no
one was capable of interrupting, he compared and contrasted the
poets of England, Russia, France, Germany, and the United States.

Only his fellow students who had become accustomed to his di-
atribes, lectures, and harangues accepted his performance with equanimity. The other guests were stunned, and Alice looked apprehensive
when Theodore sought her out after the guests had adjourned to the
parlor of the Saltonstall house.

He bowed to her in the European manner, and although another
young man might have looked a trifle ludicrous, his intensity enabled
him to carry off the gesture. "Miss Lee," he said earnestly, "I'd consider
it a great honor if you'd allow me to escort you home at the end of
the evening."

Apparently he didn't know she lived in a suburb southwest of the
city, a considerable distance from Cambridge. But she was curious
about someone who had been so frank in his admiration. "Do you
have a carriage?" She was slightly embarrassed when she realized she
couldn't remember his name.

"No, but I'll gladly rent one."

His interest was overwhelming, and Alice was relieved that she had
an honest excuse to avoid the invitation. "I'm sorry, but I'm staying
here overnight."

Theodore was undaunted, showing only a flicker of disappointment. "You're going home tomorrow?"

The girl nodded, and unconsciously began plucking at a lace cuff
of her blouse.

"Then I'd be very happy to hire a carriage tomorrow afternoon,
and we could drive out into the country to see the autumn foliage.
Naturally," he added when she hesitated, "we'd take Dick along as a
chaperon, and any friends you'd care to invite."

"I'm afraid I have a piano lesson. And tomorrow is the day my
French tutor comes to the house."

Refusing to be discouraged, he tried again. "Our weather is so
balmy for this time of year that I'm sure you'd enjoy a picnic on Sunday. I'll order some hampers made up for a whole crowd of us, if
you'd like."

Never had any boy subjected her to such pressure, and she became alarmed. "Oh, dear. I have another engagement on Sunday."

For the first time in his life Theodore felt a pang of jealousy, and
did not like the sensation.

Alice smiled fleetingly and escaped to the far side of the crowded
parlor.

Theodore bowed again, clenching his teeth so hard that his jawline turned white.

Alice unobtrusively signaled her cousin, and Richard, who was chatting with several others, immediately joined her in a far corner.

"Your friend, whatever his name is, is very persistent."

Richard chuckled. "Theodore Roosevelt. And he certainly is. You should have heard him argue about the value of elective courses when we had President Eliot for lunch at the Porcellian last week. Dr. Eliot called him dynamic, which was a polite understatement."

Alice brushed back a lock of her long, blond hair. "Well, you can tell Teddy—"

"Never call him that. He hates it. Theodore."

"All right, Theodore. Tell him perseverance may be a virtue, but he ought to learn to accept a lady's refusal. Do it nicely, Dick. I don't want to hurt his feelings."

Richard Saltonstall hooked his thumbs in the pockets of his velvet waistcoat. "It wouldn't do any good," he replied, chuckling. "He can be very obstinate."

"So can I!"

"Don't challenge him to a contest. Then he'll never give up."

Alice sighed. "Does he pound every girl over the head with a mallet?"

"Until tonight I've never known him to show any real interest in anyone."

She looked stricken.

"I advise you brace yourself, Alice. Whether you like it or not, you're going to see a great deal of Theodore."

"The grizzly bear," Theodore said, "was a huge, shaggy creature. He was the most powerful of all the beasts in the forest, but at the moment he happened to be in a good mood. He had eaten some honey and delicious berries for his supper, and he was enjoying his nap."

The two children sitting on hassocks a few inches from his knees in the parlor of the Lee house nodded. Rose, who was in early adolescence, tried not to show her excitement, but her five-year-old brother couldn't stop squirming.

"He ate some people for his supper, too," the little boy said. "Didn't he?"

"No, grizzlies are vegetarians," Theodore told him. "That means they don't eat any kind of meat. When they become angry or are threatened, they'll kill people. Or other animals. But this grizzly was very happy and sleepy. So he didn't even hear the wolves sneaking closer and closer through the forest. There were ten wolves in the pack, long, gray creatures with sharp fangs. They were the most treacherous animals in the whole forest."

Alice could hear his voice as she paused on the landing, and the total absorption she saw in the faces of her younger sister and brother dismayed her. Theodore seemed to be making a convert to his cause of every member of her family. The children worshiped him, partly because of the stories he told them and, in Rose's case, because he sometimes danced with her. To be more accurate, it was his own version of dancing, a furious hopping and prancing that left anyone over the age of fifteen utterly exhausted.

Even Alice's parents had succumbed. George Cabot Lee, showing the caution of a Boston banker, had warmed slowly to Theodore, but now called him a paragon. And, to the girl's distress, even her mother thought him charming.

Waiting on the landing while Theodore finished telling the children how the noble grizzly bear had scattered the wicked wolves, Alice couldn't help wishing she reciprocated his obvious affection for her, but at the same time hoped his infatuation would dissipate. Perhaps, when he finally accepted her word that she had no intention of being tied to one young man and wanted to enjoy the company of others, too, he would turn to someone else.

The story came to an end, and before he could respond to the clamor of the children for another, Alice descended the stairs.

Theodore jumped to his feet. "You look lovely!" he boomed. "I've never seen anyone prettier."

She had not been able to accustom herself to a courtship conducted in shouts and roars, but she couldn't help basking in his admiration.

"I've hired a phaeton for the evening," he said. "Are you sure you'll be warm enough in that light cloak?"

"Yes, it's a lovely spring evening." He was as fussy as her mother, she thought, allowing him to drape the cloak over her shoulders.

Theodore dashed to the door so he could hold it open for her, then carefully dusted off the seat of the phaeton before half-lifting her up to it. As always, she was surprised by such indications of his physical strength. He was so slim and such a dandy in his attire that she found it difficult to think of him as an athlete.

"We're meeting the others at the theatre," he said as they started toward Boston. "I understand the program has been changed, and we're going to hear *Aïda,* by that Italian chap, Verdi. Harry Shaw tells me it's very colorful and dramatic."

"My parents saw the first performance in New York, and said it was exciting."

His interest in music was limited, he had far more important matters on his mind and had no intention of discussing the opera on the long ride into Boston. "I drove out alone," he said, settling his silk top hat more firmly on his head, "because I wanted to have a private talk with you."

"My uncle," Alice declared, speaking rapidly, "knows a great deal about music, and he believes Signor Verdi's new opera is the best he's ever composed."

Theodore resisted the impulse to tell her that all opera bored him. "In fourteen months, I'll be graduated from Harvard."

Alice knew what was coming, but there was no way to stop him.

"I haven't decided what to do for a living, but I'll do something. Some of the fellows have no intention of working, but I believe that a man who has been educated has a moral obligation to society."

There was no need for her to reply, so she simply smiled, a trifle vaguely.

"My book on the War of 1812 will be finished by then, and if it should make money, I'll continue writing. I'm also thinking of studying law in my uncle's office. But whatever it may be, rest assured I won't be idle. I'd go mad."

Alice couldn't imagine him living a life of leisure; he was too energetic, far too restless.

"I won't starve, of course. I have enough for bread. But if one likes butter and jam—and I do—then I must earn it."

She made an attempt to turn the conversation toward less personal topics. "Listen to that bird! I wonder what it is."

"An oriole," he said absently. "It's surprising to hear one this far north so early in the year. Now, then. I told your father my situation when we had lunch together last week, and even though he's probably told you about it, I feel it only fair that you hear the details from me."

Alice had no idea he and her father had met, and was too shocked to protest. Apparently her father, knowing how she felt, had said nothing to her for fear she would become upset.

"I've inherited a tidy little sum from my father," Theodore said. "Depending on the current value of various securities and properties, I'm worth somewhere between two hundred thousand and two hundred and fifty thousand dollars. Hardly a great fortune."

She thought the sum impressive.

"I dislike dipping into capital, naturally."

As a banker's daughter she knew something about such matters, and approved. Aside from recklessly sending her flowers several days each week, he was surprisingly thrifty.

"Nevertheless," he continued, "I'll be well able to support a wife."

Alice's nails began to cut through her white gloves as she pressed her fingertips against her palms.

"Under these circumstances," Theodore concluded, "I have no reluctance in asking you to marry me." He did not dare look at her, but concentrated on the road.

There was a long, tense silence. Alice had no choice, and steeled herself. "I'm sorry, Theodore. I can't."

"If there's someone else," he flared, "I'll challenge him to a duel, and I'll win it. That's a fair warning."

"There's no one else," she said quietly.

He looked at her in stunned bewilderment. "Then what possible reason could you have?"

Again the girl was silent, but finally forced herself to speak. It was less cruel to tell him the truth, even though the immediate blow would be great. "I don't love you, Theodore."

He hunched his shoulders for a moment, then sat erect and exhaled slowly. For once in his life he was speechless, and only the white line around his mouth and his abnormally tight grip on the reins indicated that he was suffering.

Alice tried desperately but in vain to think of something to say. It would be insulting to tell him she thought of him as a good friend whom she liked, and rude to talk of frivolous matters.

Theodore continued to stare straight ahead.

The strain was becoming unbearable, and Alice hoped she wouldn't weep. She'd be the talk of Boston if she appeared at the opera with a red nose and bloodshot eyes.

"On Tuesday," Theodore said at last, speaking in an even higher-pitched voice than usual, "I'm fighting in my first intramural match for the lightweight championship. Although I wouldn't admit this to anyone else, I'm not certain I'm good enough to win and advance a notch.

So this may be the only chance to see me box. Would you care to come?"

"I—I think boxing is brutal."

"It's a manly sport!" he protested, but immediately backed down. "Naturally I wouldn't want you to do anything you find distasteful."

Alice inclined her head in thanks.

Again Theodore was silent for a long time, but there was a ring in his voice when he finally said, "Before the week ends I shall shoot and mount an oriole for you."

"Please don't. I'd much rather hear them sing, and I hate needless slaughter."

This was not the moment to convince her that the killing and mounting of a specimen was a scientific achievement, not slaughter.

"Perhaps," Alice said, "we should stop seeing each other."

Theodore's self-control vanished. "I refuse! I won't hear of it! I'll continue to call on you and take you out—if you'll go with me. If you won't, I'll pitch a tent on your father's lawn so I can catch glimpses of you. But one way or another I'm going to see you, and that's final!"

Robert Bacon, generally considered the most handsome member of the class of '80, looked bedraggled. His hair was mussed, there were deep smudges under his eyes and his usually immaculate suit was rumpled. He turned the oil lamp on the table in Theodore's Winthrop Street sitting room a little higher and made another effort to read his textbook on international tariffs, but it was impossible to concentrate, and he stuffed another load of tobacco into his pipe.

Then, suddenly, he heard approaching footsteps, and peered out of the open window into the dark street. Grimly composing himself, he returned to the room's one easy chair, and stared in the direction of the door.

Theodore let himself into the room, and was astonished to see his friend.

"I wonder if you know it's almost five o'clock in the morning," Bacon said.

"What are you doing here, Bob?"

"Waiting for you, obviously."

The weary Theodore dropped onto a straight-backed chair so heavily that it creaked.

"I came looking for you soon after dinner, around eight o'clock, and I came back at eleven. Dick Saltonstall tells me you've had a rough week, so I decided to wait for you. If you hadn't appeared by daybreak, I planned to notify the dean's office—and the police."

"I'm sorry I've inconvenienced you," Theodore murmured, and, removing his spectacles, searched without success for a clean handkerchief to wipe them off.

"You're soaked."

"It was raining tonight."

"That was around midnight, Theodore."

"It stayed wet in the woods."

"What woods?" Bacon asked irritably.

"On the far side of Cambridge."

"Look here. Do you mean to tell me you've spent the entire night wandering in the woods?"

"I like the out-of-doors, and I always feel at home where there are trees."

"I'll get you a drink," Bacon said. "Where do you keep your liquor?"

"I don't care for the stuff, and the way I'm feeling, even a sniff of brandy would make me ill." Theodore put his spectacles on the table and buried his face in his hands.

"Is it true you haven't slept for nights?"

Theodore raised his head, and, in an attempt to regain his dignity, reached for his spectacles. "Dick talks too much. What else did he tell you?" he demanded.

"There are no secrets when a good friend is in trouble." Bacon could be firm, too. "You've got to stop moping."

"She's driving me out of my senses," Theodore mumbled. "Most days I don't care if I live or die."

"The medical faculty can tell you that no one has ever died of a broken heart."

"I'm not so sure."

"Your work is suffering—"

"The devil you say. I've had two exams this past week, and got respectable grades in both of them."

"—and you have extracurricular obligations, don't forget."

"I'm not shirking any of them!"

Bacon realized another approach was necessary. Theodore seemed to possess an extraordinary ability to accomplish everything required of him, even when sleepless. "There must be hundreds of attractive girls, not only in Boston, but in New York and Philadelphia and other places, who would find your attention very flattering."

"I'm interested in Alice, nobody else."

"Be sensible, Theodore, and stop behaving like such a romantic. When a girl turns down a fellow, he forgets her and looks for someone else."

"I refuse!" Theodore shouted, pounding the table so hard that the oil lamp slid toward the edge.

Bacon rescued it before it toppled to the floor. "When *she* refuses to see *you*, take your defeat like a man!"

Theodore smiled crookedly. "Oh, but she doesn't. I still take her out one evening every week, and on either Saturday or Sunday I call on her as well. Unexpectedly. Her little sister and brother let me know when she's going to be home. Privately. She still hasn't found out how I learn so much."

"And she agrees to see you?"

"I give her no choice," Theodore said harshly. "If I as much as mention marriage she sends me away and goes off to her room. So I've got to be careful. But she hasn't completely cut me off, and as long as I can keep a foot in the door, I'm not beaten."

Bacon saw that his friend's mood was changing. His air of dejection vanished, and in its place appeared the stubborn Dutch determination that everyone found admirable but annoying.

"She won't have me," Theodore said. "But my mind is made up. *I'm* going to have *her!* So that's settled. Now, it's too late for bed, so let's go out for some breakfast." He bounded to his feet, his vitality restored.

Dr. Dudley Sargent, the Harvard physician, scribbled a few marks on the form he used for every routine undergraduate physical examination, and said, "You may finish dressing now, Roosevelt."

Theodore buttoned his shirt and stuffed the tail into his trousers. He glanced at the clock on the mantel in the doctor's office, anxious to take his leave.

Dr. Sargent saw the look, and gestured toward a chair. "Sit down for a moment, please."

Theodore hated to waste time, particularly when his health was so robust, but he obeyed.

"How long has it been since you've had an asthma attack?"

"Last year, Doctor, the beginning of my junior year." The young man put on his cravat without the aid of a mirror. "Strenuous exercise has cured me."

"I know about your boxing. What else do you do?"

"I went hiking and mountain climbing in Maine again this past summer. I swim and sail, of course. I ride and play tennis. And with winter coming, I'm looking forward to improving my ice-skating skills. I've only made a few short hunting trips lately—"

Dr. Sargent raised a hand. "Enough. It's no wonder you've abused your body."

Theodore raised an eyebrow.

"I'm sorry to tell you this, Roosevelt, but you're suffering from a heart murmur. It isn't serious, but it does serve as a warning. You shouldn't climb stairs, and you'll have to give up mountain climbing. Violent sports like tennis and boxing should be avoided. You can swim and ride, but in moderation. If you continue to put so many heavy strains on your body, you'll probably develop a serious heart condition."

"I cured my asthma and built up my strength by exercise, Doctor," Theodore protested.

"I can only urge you to take my advice. If you don't, I'm afraid you'll pay the consequences. Not immediately, perhaps, but within a few years at the most."

Theodore removed his spectacles and polished them. "Exercise cured me of one ailment, Doctor, so it seems to me I can strengthen my heart by increasing the pace."

The physician shook his head. "That would be the very worst thing you could do."

"I see." Careful not to commit himself, Theodore slipped into his waistcoat and suit jacket.

Dr. Sargent glanced at the coat rack on the far side of his office. "Surely you're wearing a greatcoat today! The temperature dropped below freezing this morning."

"I increase my stamina and resistance to disease by not wearing a coat or hat until the thermometer shows zero."

"Unless you change your habits, you'll be dead before your twenty-fifth birthday."

Theodore thanked him, but kept his own counsel. Had he followed the advice of family physicians, he'd still be crippled by asthma. Taking his leave, he waited until he rounded the corner and was out of sight of Dr. Sargent's office before breaking into a run. His day's schedule was a busy one, and he had no time to loiter.

Immediately after his next class he planned to box for an hour, and then would ride out to the Lee house in Chestnut Hill to take Alice on a long walk. Now that she and her mother had accepted Mama's invitation to visit the Roosevelts during the coming holidays, perhaps she was changing her mind about him, although nothing in her attitude had indicated that she was giving his suit serious consideration.

Reaching Massachusetts Hall, he bounded up the stairs two at a time to his fourth-floor classroom, ignoring tradition, other students who might be in his path, and Dr. Sargent's grave warning.

"I'm glad you were willing to come out to Long Island with me instead of spending the afternoon shopping with your mother and mine," Theodore said. "I've been—well, rather eager to show you Oyster Bay."

Alice found it difficult to keep a straight face, as, trying to maintain his swift, nervous pace, she walked beside him up the hill. "Rather eager" was an understatement; ever since she and her mother had arrived in New York he had been bombarding her with requests to accompany him to Oyster Bay.

"My uncles' summer houses are over there," he said, pointing, "and so is the place we've been renting. I'll show them to you later. I just had to bring you here first. My father knew how much I thought of this property, and bought it for me a short time before he died. It's called Sagamore Hill. Are we walking too fast?"

Alice struggled to gain her breath, but gallantly shook her head, knowing there was only one pace he found comfortable.

"You should have told me," Theodore said remorsefully. "We'll rest right here."

"No," she said, "it's only a few more steps to the top." She took his arm and continued the climb to the hilltop, where a stiff breeze forced her to tie a silk scarf around her head.

"To me," Theodore told her proudly, "this is the most beautiful view in all the world. Oyster Bay is off to our left, and you can see just about all of it from here. Cold Spring Harbor is on our right, and that narrow slip of water that lies between what are called Lloyd Neck and West Neck is Lloyd Harbor. The big body of water out there is the Sound, of course."

Alice stood silently, enjoying the view, her blond hair streaming behind her scarf.

"You sure look pretty in white," he blurted.

She indicated her appreciation with a smile, and, still admiring the view, thought it astonishing that someone with his incisive mind and sensitive spirit could be so blind. She always wore either white or pale blue, colors that flattered her, and he had made similar observations on scores of occasions, invariably with the same air of discovery.

"Almost four years ago," Theodore said, his voice suddenly becoming husky, "before I went off to Harvard, I decided I wanted to build a house of my own here. And ever since we met, I've dreamed of building it for you."

Alice turned toward him, her movements slow and deliberate.

Theodore saw the tenderness in her eyes, and although he was stunned, could not misinterpret her expression.

"I can't think of a place I'd rather live," she said, "although being together is all that matters."

He was still too startled to speak or move.

"A lady is entitled to change her mind," she told him, anticipating his question but struggling to overcome a wave of shyness. "I can't tell you when I started to fall in love with you. All I know is that it happened."

The miracle had occurred, and Theodore, coming to life, wanted to shout. Instead he stepped toward her, arms outstretched, to kiss and embrace her for the first time.

At last everything is settled; but it seems impossible to realize it, Theodore wrote in his diary. *I am so happy that I dare not trust in my own happiness . . . Oh, how bewitchingly pretty she looked. If loving her with my whole heart and soul can make her happy, she shall be happy . . . How she, so pure and sweet and beautiful, can think of marrying me I cannot understand, but I praise and thank God it is so.*

On June 30, 1880, Harvard awarded Theodore Roosevelt a Bachelor of Arts degree. Although neither his professors nor his fellow students had regarded him as a scholar, he ranked twenty-first in a class of one hundred and seventy-seven, was given his degree *cum laude,* and, to the surprise of everyone but himself, won membership in Phi Beta Kappa, the national scholastic honor society.

"I don't care one way or the other about the Phi Beta Kappa key itself," he told Alice, "but there was a principle at stake, and if I hadn't been good enough to be elected, I'd have felt that my college career had been a failure."

Alice decided they would be married in the autumn, and while her trousseau was being made, her future husband made his own strenuous preparations for a benedict's life. He swam, sailed, and rode at Oyster Bay, where ground was broken for the new house on Sagamore Hill. He went camping in Maine with Bill Sewall, and when Elliott fell ill his older brother prescribed his own type of remedy. They went off together on a six-week hunting trip in Illinois, Iowa, and the remote, sparsely settled Dakota Territory, a wilderness that had appealed to Theodore's imagination.

I got bitten by a snake, he wrote his bride-to-be, *but heated a knife and cut open the place on my leg where I was bitten, hence suffering no ill effects. Last week I was jolted out of our supply wagon, and twice have been thrown by my horse, but in spite of these minor mishaps I am having a grand time. Were you with me my happiness would be complete.*

In no hurry to launch a permanent career, Theodore enrolled at the Columbia University Law School, thinking that a legal background would be helpful, no matter what line of vocational endeavor he might choose. Then, followed a few days later by his mother, sisters, brother, and a host of other relatives, he went to Boston for his wedding.

Edith Carow accompanied Corinne, but the excited bridegroom failed to notice that his childhood friend was unusually silent and withdrawn.

Alice Hathaway Lee and Theodore Roosevelt were married in Brookline, Massachusetts, on October 27, 1880, the bridegroom's twenty-second birthday. His wife was nineteen.

After spending a few days alone at Oyster Bay, the young couple moved into quarters of their own in the family house on 57th Street in New York City. Alice and her mother-in-law were similar in many ways, quiet, gentle women, introspective and keenly aware of the sensitivities of others, and their relationship was harmonious and smooth.

Theodore immediately established a new routine as a husband, law student, and citizen. He walked to and from his classes each day, a six-mile jaunt in all, and when he felt the need for more exercise he trotted. He found his work easy and the law boring, so he was able to spend an hour each afternoon boxing with hired sparring partners. Alice kept her distance from the gymnasium on these occasions, and Theodore, aware of her acute distaste for violence, took pains to keep silent about his prowess.

Believing it his duty to serve his country, he joined the New York National Guard, and was given a commission as a second lieutenant. He spent every Thursday evening drilling at the old armory on 14th Street, and was so enthusiastic after these sessions that Alice became concerned.

"I hope you aren't thinking of joining the Regular Army," she said.

Theodore patted her hand. "If I'd wanted to be a professional soldier, I'd have gone to the Military Academy at West Point," he told her. "The Regulars have so little to keep them busy they're inclined to become lazy. I'm not suited for that life. But we have a tradition of citizen-soldiery that goes back to the militia of colonial days, and it makes me feel good to know I'm doing something useful. But I'll never become a Regular, so put the thought out of your mind. I can't tolerate idleness."

Alice was ever-conscious of his need for activity. The attractive newlyweds attended dinner parties and balls, went to concerts and theatrical performances regularly, and on weekends took Theodore's mother for long carriage drives.

Dissatisfaction with the prospects of the law turned the young man's mind back to his earlier plan to make a career for himself as an author. Unhappy with his *Naval War of 1812,* he returned to his unfinished manuscript with a vengeance, rewriting the better part of it.

In May, Theodore and Alice left for a belated honeymoon in Europe. While in England he conferred at length with one of his maternal uncles, who had been an officer in the Confederate Navy, and compiled badly needed information on a number of technical aspects of naval maneuvers in the War of 1812. He also persuaded the Royal Admiralty to permit him to inspect its archives so he could gain a perspective from the viewpoint of America's foe in that war.

Thereafter he spent several hours each day on his manuscript, which he completed during the summer. He and Alice went from England to France, Germany, Italy, and Austria, and he was surprised to find himself developing an interest in international affairs. Hoping to satisfy his growing curiosity, he immersed himself in the newspapers of every major city, reading omnivorously.

When the couple reached Switzerland, however, he put aside intellectual activities, and, ignoring the warning of Dr. Sargent, took up mountain climbing. He spent a week on practice slopes, then climbed the Jungfrau and Mount Pilatus. Both efforts were exhilarating, but neither challenged him, so he read several books on mountaineering, and then quietly proceeded with Alice to the little town of Zermatt, which many of the local inhabitants called Praborgne.

On the morning after their arrival he suggested they eat their breakfast on the terrace of their room, and there, as they sipped their hot chocolate, they looked across the grassy meadow at the cragged bulk of the Matterhorn. The snow was dazzling on its deeply blanketed heights, and although there was no breeze in Zermatt, swirls of powdered snow occasionally hid the crest.

"It's a grand sight," Theodore said.

Alice shuddered slightly, closing the collar of her quilted dressing gown. "I'm glad I'm down here," she murmured.

"It stands a little under fifteen thousand feet," he said, "although the obelisk shape makes it appear higher. There are several peaks in the Alps that are higher, and quite a few in our own Rockies and in the Canadian Rockies."

"It seems much more desolate than the other Alps."

"That's because it stands alone. It was first conquered only fifteen years ago, you know, by an Englishman named Edward Whymper."

Alice poured him another cup of chocolate. "Yes, and three members of his party were killed, and so was their guide, when they fell over a precipice of more than four thousand feet. My flesh crawls when I think of it."

"How did you know about Whymper's party?" Theodore was surprised.

"Some English people at the hotel in Interlaken told me about it the day you climbed the Jungfrau. It's a frightening story."

He avoided a direct reply. "There are strange quirks in history. Men had been trying to reach the top of the Matterhorn for centuries, and all of them failed. But three days after Whymper won his battle, a party led by a fellow named Carrel scaled the mountain from the Italian side. Neither party knew until later that the other had even made the attempt. Odd, isn't it?"

Alice started to reply, then saw him studying the Matterhorn intently. "Theodore!"

He turned back to her, smiling a trifle sheepishly.

"Surely you aren't thinking of climbing it!"

He couldn't meet her gaze. "To tell you the truth, my dear, I hired a guide yesterday, after we arrived. We're going to make a preliminary survey, so to speak, later this morning."

"You can't do it!"

He removed his spectacles and took his time polishing them. "Quite a few men have climbed it by now. There must be at least thirty in all, including the members of that Anglo-German club we met in Salzburg. Do you remember how they boasted? They seemed to think they were unique, that Americans couldn't do what they did. It made my blood boil!"

"Is that why you want to risk your life up there?"

He put on his spectacles and looked at her without flinching. "I don't really care about the opinion of an ignoramus or a bigot, Alice. I want to conquer the Matterhorn for my own sake."

She forced herself to speak calmly, hoping she wouldn't burst into tears. "But why, Theodore?"

"I've got to prove—to myself—that I can do it. The challenge is very simple. And very primitive, I suppose. A man's craving for adventure is a basic emotion. That's how William James would define it."

Alice was unable to accept his logic. "Do you see that little cloud, just above the place where the mountain starts to spread out? How far is it from there to the top?"

"About five or six thousand feet, I suspect."

"Five or six thousand feet of a sheer cliff! It isn't even straight up and down. It's concave, and no human being could climb up it!"

"But that's precisely what at least thirty men have done," Theodore said patiently. "It isn't really a sheer cliff. It just looks that way from here. That's why the guide and I are going to do a bit of preliminary exploring before we make the real climb tomorrow."

"How can I persuade you not to do it?" she cried.

"If I could find a valid reason not to go, I'd spare you, Alice. But I wouldn't be able to face myself in my shaving mirror."

"Then you're afraid, too."

Theodore retreated while he pondered her statement, although nothing in his expression or movement indicated a withdrawal. When there was something important to be weighed, the self-disciplined isolation of the sickly child had become habitual in the rugged young man. "Our society," he said at last, "encourages a woman to express her fears, and doesn't shame her when she shows them. But a man must overcome his if he's to be accepted as manly."

"Recklessness isn't manly, Theodore. If you should kill yourself—"

"I have every reason to stay alive." His introspection gave way to an unyielding aggressive attitude. "I'll be leaving at dawn tomorrow,

and I'll be back here by sundown the next night. You have my word
I'll be on time."

Heinrich Müller felt secretly contemptuous of the amateur moun-
taineers who hired him as a guide, but made an effort to conceal his
attitude, and usually was solicitous, taking care not to tax their stamina
or ask them to perform beyond their limited capabilities. But the
challenge of the Matterhorn forced him to concentrate his full attention on the task; his companion had been aware of the hazards from
the outset, and had no right to complain.

They had passed timberline early in the afternoon, shortly after
eating their noon meal of cold meat, bread, and cheese, which the
American had insisted on washing down with hot chocolate in a stone
jug his wife had given him. Never before had Müller known anyone to
refuse brandy or schnapps on the heights, and suspected the man
might be slightly mad. All the same, he had to admit that Roosevelt
displayed the strength and courage, if not the skill, of the professional
mountaineer.

They worked their way slowly, painfully, up the bleak ice field,
Müller cutting a step at a time in the glacier while his companion dug
his own ax into the ice and braced himself to steady them, the safety
line that extended from one to the other stretched taut. Layers of
fresh white snow that lay on the surface almost blinded them, and
the guide wondered how his companion could manage the climb
wearing spectacles, particularly when the wind whipped dry, powdered snow into their faces and eyes, causing them to weep.

In spite of the gusts of cold wind the sun overhead was hot, their
exertions caused them to perspire heavily, and sweat had soaked
their shirts of thick wool. They could not pause for more than a moment at a time to rest, however, since it was imperative that they
maintain their schedule. Those who had died trying to scale the Matterhorn had perished because they had not been able to maintain their
steady pace, and had weakened themselves by spending a night on
the open ice field. Müller had explained the situation to his client,
and the American surprised him by laboring unceasingly, even though
it was obvious that his arms and legs, like the guide's, were aching.

Making their own path, they inched their way up the steep slope,
avoiding deep snow that might conceal fissures and loose rock forma-
tions that might cause a landslide. Finally, a short time before sunset,
they arrived at their immediate destination, a grouping of heavy

boulders that gave them at least a semblance of cave-like protection.

"Congratulations," Theodore said. "You said you could find this spot without a map or compass, and you did."

"Help me spread the cloth on the ice," the guide said curtly, still surprised by the fluency of his client's German.

They stretched a double layer of canvas inside the "cave," then put another oiled cloth over the partial entrance, weighting it with stones.

"If it doesn't snow too hard, we'll be dry," the guide said, "and the canvas will help break the force of the wind."

Theodore lowered himself to the ground cloth, unbuckled the pack from his back and removed his crampons, spiked iron attachments strapped to his hobnailed boots that helped him maintain his footing on the glacier.

"Before you do anything else," the guide told him, "change your shirt and stockings."

Theodore obeyed, but was curious. "Why?"

"The clothing you wear now is wet, and will freeze in a quarter of an hour." Müller began to change his own attire, and when he was done he took a bundle of food from his pack.

Theodore was ravenously hungry, and ate all the meat, cheese, and chocolate that the guide gave him. He wanted more, but had read that a mountaineer might become ill if he ate too much in a rarefied atmosphere, so he deferred to the other man's professional judgment.

"Now," Müller commanded, "pull on both pairs of your gloves and wrap yourself in both your blankets."

Theodore did as he was directed, relishing the experience. In the opening between the canvas and the adjacent boulder he could see the stars in a sky of velvet-like black, and in his exhilaration wanted to learn all he could about his companion's experiences. "What would we have done if you hadn't found this cave? I mean, there must be ways we could have protected ourselves if—"

"Go to sleep," Müller interrupted. "If we want to reach the top by daybreak, we must be awake at three o'clock. And we will need all our strength tomorrow."

The instructions were sensible, but Theodore found it difficult to obey them. Good conversation was the essence of life, as essential as achievement, more important than food or rest, and it was torture to be deprived of stimulating talk. No matter how much the primitive urges of the civilized man compelled him to seek adventure, he needed to satisfy his mind, too, and, when the moon came out, casting a bright glow on the snowfield, the American was sorry he hadn't brought at least one book with him.

The pink light of the early morning sun spread slowly, burning off the haze below. Theodore, the guide beside him, stood triumphantly at the summit of the Matterhorn, indifferent to the stinging of the powdered snow that cut into his face. Far below the steep precipice on the Swiss side of the mountain the village of Zermatt snuggled in its green meadow, and he rejoiced when he thought how pleased Alice would be to share his victory.

On the other side, where the Matterhorn fell away gradually, stood the lesser heights of the Italian Alps, and Theodore studied the scene, trying to impress it on his memory. There were no maps of the area from this perspective, so he decided to draw his own after he returned to Zermatt. Not that he would have any specific use for such a map, but it would be a splendid exercise in memory training.

"We must start now," the guide shouted above the howling of the wind. "It is more difficult to climb down than up."

Theodore was not yet ready to leave, however. He reached into the pocket of his canvas-covered jacket of heavy wool, his gloved fingers fumbling, and finally brought out a small square of wood on which had been burned the legend; *T. Roosevelt, August 21, 1880.* He wedged it deep in between the rocks at the crest, driving it almost out of sight with the butt end of his ax. Then, but only then, was he ready to begin the descent. Taking one final, exultant look at the glorious view spread out below him, he was pleased he hadn't forgotten to make the token before leaving Zermatt. His triumph would not have been complete unless he had commemorated it in a fitting manner.

New York's literary and theatrical luminaries had been dining at Charley Pfaff's restaurant for more than thirty years, content because the hearty, simply prepared food was more important to them than the lack of décor. The walls were made of unadorned cedar, the floors and tables were scrubbed pine, and the chairs lacked arms. But customers ate huge platters of oysters, the largest and juiciest beefsteak on the Eastern seaboard, corn, potatoes and tomatoes that proprietor Pfaff grew in his own Staten Island vegetable garden, and fish that was served the same day it was caught.

Mark Twain and Walt Whitman were frequent guests at Pfaff's, as were the comedy team of Harrigan and Hart. Lew Wallace celebrated

the publication in 1880 of his historical novel *Ben-Hur* with a party
at Pfaff's, and even the fastidious Henry Adams, grandson of John
Quincy Adams, who was launched on a successful career as an author
in Washington, D.C., deigned to eat at Pfaff's when he visited New
York and told his friends that its food was not offensive to his palate.

Neither authors nor actors entered the doors of the restaurant on
lower Broadway at noon, however, when the atmosphere was more
subdued, almost solemn. The powerful private banker, John Pierpont
Morgan, senior partner of Drexel, Morgan & Company, had wandered
in one day, found the food good and the tables located far enough
apart to permit private conversations that could not be overheard. He
made it a habit to eat lunch at Pfaff's daily, and in his wake followed
other bankers, executives in the expanding coal mining, railroad,
and steel manufacturing industries, as well as stock brokers who were
trying to convince the magnates they belonged to a respectable
profession.

Inevitably, the neophytes in banking and industry who could afford
to pay Pfaff's steep prices adopted the habits of their superiors. Theodore, making his way through the main dining room to meet Robert
Bacon, who had joined the staff of Drexel, Morgan, was surprised to
see at least a score of Harvard classmates and men who had been
graduated a year or two ahead of him.

He stopped to shake hands with several, and then joined Bacon.
They had not seen each other since the recent return of Theodore and
Alice to the United States, and chatted about Europe over their
oysters; then, as they ate their pepperpot soup, Bacon described his
new life as a financier.

By the time the roast arrived at the table the apprentice investment
banker was growing weary of his friend's curious, searching questions,
and it was apparent that neither a college degree nor extended travel
had quenched his thirst for both useful and irrelevant information
on every subject under the sun. Bacon felt he had to counterattack.
"How are you enjoying law school this term?"

"I haven't gone back. I discovered that the law is a technical profession. It doesn't necessarily deal with right and wrong, but only with
the past decisions of justices whose judgment may have been
warped. It seemed to me that lawyers are taught how to evade the
laws rather than change them to fit the needs of society."

Lowering his head to hide a smile as he cut his meat, Bacon thought
it remarkable that an adult could remain as naïvely idealistic as a

Harvard freshman. Theodore hadn't yet learned that the world was imperfect and that even men of principle usually found it necessary to compromise if they wanted to accomplish anything.

"I've agreed to help organize an American Red Cross, Bob. I've seen what the Swiss have done to help the victims of natural catastrophes, and there's certainly a need for a similar organization in this country." Following his father's example, Theodore was devoting time, effort, and money to charitable causes.

"You're doing more than helping Clara Barton, I hope."

"Oh, yes. I'll start work on another book after the *Naval War of 1812* has been published, and in the meantime I'm writing some magazine articles on mountaineering for Cabot Lodge. He's a grand fellow, and I'm beginning to feel sorry I didn't take any of his courses when we were at Cambridge." Theodore paused, then added almost too casually, "I'm also developing something of an interest in politics."

Bacon was startled. "I beg your pardon?"

Theodore's diffidence vanished in a sudden wave of belligerence. "Don't bother to tell me what everyone else has said. I've heard a great many lectures lately, and I know that gentlemen don't become active in politics."

Bacon was relieved. "You mean you've signed as a party member. You've become a Democrat, I suppose."

"No, a Republican."

"Really? I know your father-in-law and most of your relatives are Democrats—"

"That's their business. Chester Arthur hasn't been President long enough after poor Garfield's assassination to tell whether he'll be a credit to the office or the Republicans, but I'm more concerned with the local situation. Tammany Hall controls New York City, and you've got to admit they're a disgrace, Bob."

"Graft in politics is natural, Theodore."

"I disagree. I feel something must be done to curb the corrupt Tammany dictatorship of this city. That's why I've joined the Twenty-first District Republican Organization."

"I hope you realize," the young investment banker said, speaking with great care, "that most of your colleagues are horsecar conductors, saloonkeepers and the like. I mean, they aren't the sort you'd meet anywhere else."

"What you really mean is that the people you and I know socially aren't members of the governing class. If we abdicate to them, we deserve graft and tyranny."

"You can't change human nature."

"You forget that in England men of personal background, education, and means go into politics. They take their responsibilities as citizens seriously."

"We can do anything they can. And someone must make a start."

Bacon was disturbed but amused. "I'll grant that you're high-minded. But that isn't your only reason."

Theodore became calmer, and his teeth showed as a slow smile spread across his face. "I'll admit that I intend to become a member of the governing class."

"Now you're being honest," his friend declared. "You aren't the first to be intrigued by the thought of holding high office, and I don't suppose you'll be the last. What's your goal," he added in a teasing vein, "a United States Senatorship, or the Governorship of New York?"

Theodore's smile faded. "I haven't thought that far ahead, Bob. I've only gone to a couple of meetings, and I've met very few men. I still don't know whether they'll accept me, or whether I'll find them too hard-bitten to tolerate. If I can't get along with them, I'll quit, but not until I find out whether I'm really too weak to hold my own in the rough and tumble."

A saloon occupied the ground floor of the building on the corner of Fifth Avenue and 59th Street, and the headquarters of the Twenty-first District Republican Organization was conveniently located directly above it. Consequently the members made it a habit to stop off at the saloon to find their colleagues before climbing the narrow stairs to the barnlike chamber above it. And, since the only heat in the huge room was provided by a single, inadequate hearth, the faithful found it helpful to fortify themselves before braving the wintry blasts.

The saloon was cozily warm, however, its windows frosted and the pungent odors of wine, whiskey, and beer permeating the atmosphere. As usual, it was filled to capacity by the early evening crowd of drinkers, and Theodore, unbuttoning his greatcoat, removed his misted spectacles in order to wipe them clean as he peered myopically into the dimly lighted room.

"Ah, there you are, Teddy! Let me buy you a beer."

Theodore recognized the voice of Joe Murray, the local ward captain, an Irish immigrant who had been a member of Tammany but had left in disgust to become active in the opposition. "I'm afraid beer would spoil my appetite for dinner, Joe." Theodore replaced his glasses and shook hands. "But I'll buy you a glass."

"I always forget that folks of your class don't eat your supper until the night is half-gone." Murray drained his glass and put it down on the bar.

"Maybe you'd like something stronger."

"I lost my appetite for the hard stuff years ago, Teddy lad." Murray pushed back a mop of black hair and linked his arm through that of the younger man. "We'll go upstairs for a chat, before it gets too crowded, and I thank you for coming around so soon after I dropped off a message at your house."

They started up the stairs together. "You said it was urgent, Joe."

"Well, now. Maybe it is, and maybe it's only me that thinks so. What's important to one man don't mean a tinker's damn to another."

Theodore laughed heartily. He enjoyed the company of the ward captain, and, somewhat to his own surprise, found himself able to relax in Murray's company.

"That speech you made on civic reform went down pretty good with the boys, Teddy. Jake Hess didn't like it much, but Jake doesn't understand that times are changing."

Theodore placed his hat and coat on a wall hook, and wandered across the cuspidor-strewn clubroom toward two straight-backed chairs in a dusty, far corner. "I didn't want to antagonize Mr. Hess, Joe. It does no good to turn the District chief against you. But I had to say what I believed."

"It made sense, Teddy lad. The Diamond Back District is in trouble, and Jake is in personal hot water." Although there was no one else in the room, Murray lowered his voice. "Jake thought there would be jobs a-plenty for the boys when Garfield became President, but he was straight, and President Arthur is continuing the same policies. It isn't enough these days for a man to do party work so as to get a U.S. job. He needs to have the ability, too."

"President Arthur is taking a big step in the direction of clean government," Theodore said enthusiastically.

They sat, and Murray offered the younger man a cigar, but knew it would be refused. "Jake promised jobs to some of the men who live in the Sixth Avenue tenements, and they're sour on him. So are the folks like yourself who have moved into the fine new houses on Fifth

Avenue, and on Madison. It won't be easy for Jake to keep his own place as head of the District. They're against him on all sides."

Theodore nodded, but remained silent. He was learning that a valuable asset in politics was an ability to look sympathetic while saying nothing.

"Right now Jake is making his biggest mistake," Murray continued. "We held a meeting of ward captains today, and he insisted we nominate Assemblyman Trimble for another term in Albany."

Theodore knew so little about politics that the idea of refusing a new term to an incumbent shocked him. "Has Trimble been disloyal to the party?"

"No, but that's about all we can say for him. Have you read of even one constructive bill Dick Trimble has sponsored in the legislature?" Murray blew a thick cloud of cigar smoke, then answered his own question. "No, sir. You haven't! Teddy lad, the only way we can beat Tammany, and keep it beaten, is to run candidates who are really dedicated to the principles of civic reform and good government. The only difference between Trimble and the Tammany men is his party label. That's why I want to run you."

Color drained from Theodore's face. "I couldn't," he said at last. "I'd be accused of having joined this club because I wanted a public office."

"In this business you'll soon learn to ignore gossip. There are two reasons I want you as our candidate. You'll do well in the legislature. And I believe you can win."

Theodore remained unconvinced. "If Hess wants Trimble, he'd oppose me, and I couldn't win without his support."

"No man is too big for the boots he ought to wear, Teddy lad. The ward captains are unhappy, and I'm sure I can win them over to you. Then Hess will either work with us, or he'll find himself in the street." Murray's ruthlessness was tempered by a cordial smile.

His logic was unassailable, but the proposition was so unexpected that Theodore was shaken. Standing abruptly, he walked to the ice-covered window and tried to peer through it. "I've been meaning to tell you, Joe, that my friends don't call me Teddy. I'm Theodore, or TR, if you prefer."

Murray knew little about the gentry, and wondered if all members of the class were endowed with such pedantic vanity. Swallowing his amusement, he merely said, "As you will, TR." Teddy was an easier, more familiar name for a politician than Theodore, but his disciple would learn.

Theodore tried in vain to rub frost from the windowpane. His inner struggle took no concrete form, but he realized that his ambition was warring with a fear that he would be called an opportunist and, consequently, would be defeated.

Murray knew it would be unwise to use persuasion, and remained quiet, blowing streams of cigar smoke at the ceiling.

In spite of his reluctance, Theodore felt he would be unable to live with himself if he refused to meet the challenge. "If Jake Hess and the boys will have me," he said at last, "I'll do it."

Murray crossed the room and clapped him on the shoulder. "Just leave everything to me."

The revolt of the ward captains forced Jake Hess to capitulate, and he agreed to accept the candidacy of the untried amateur politician. Theodore's endorsement by a club caucus was a formality, and his nomination was announced in the late spring of 1881. Joe Murray appointed himself manager of the neophyte's campaign, and Theodore assured the friends who teased them that the career he had chosen was not a passing fancy.

The Democrats named a Tammany stalwart to oppose him, and the campaign began immediately. Theodore delivered an address before the Council for Reform, which announced it would endorse him, and the newspapers swiftly indicated their own support. *Mr. Roosevelt,* the *Times* said, *does not need a seat in the Assembly to support himself and his wife. The doors of every bank and office in the city would open to him if he sought a career in commerce or industry. Instead, he prefers to work for the good of all our people. He is a public-spirited citizen, not an office-seeker.*

The *Tribune* was equally generous. *If every District nominated a candidate of the caliber of the Twenty-first's Theodore Roosevelt, the future of New York City would be made secure, and her problems would be solved.*

Theodore was pleased, as were Alice, his mother and other relatives, but Joe Murray, who called for his protégé one hot summer afternoon, took a more cynical view. "Don't let all that sweet talk go to your head," he said as they walked toward Sixth Avenue. "The folks who read the newspapers will support you, no matter what. And organizations like the Council for Reform don't have enough members to mean much. You'll need the votes of the plain people if you hope to win."

"It was Lincoln who said that God must love the plain people because he made so many of them. He—"

"Never mind Lincoln or anybody else," Murray said brusquely. "Get them to like you. And trust you. Make them think of you as their friend. That's what we're going to do this afternoon, and every afternoon from now until election. We're going to visit every voter in the District."

Theodore saw he was heading toward a Sixth Avenue saloon, and put a restraining hand on his arm. "Wait, Joe. I can't afford to be seen in a place like that!"

"Why the hell not? Carl Fischer not only runs a respectable beer parlor, but he's loaned money—without interest—to everybody in that whole row of tenements. If he's on your side, they'll be on your side. And even though you don't like to drink, order a small glass of beer. Let it sit on the bar, if you don't want it. But I beg you, start no temperance crusades there!"

They entered the crowded saloon, and when Theodore was introduced to the proprietor, the rotund Fischer wiped his hands on his apron, then raised them over his head. "Boys!" he shouted. "Meet Teddy Roosevelt, the Republican candidate for the Assembly."

For a moment Theodore stood very still, his face frozen. Then, abruptly, he grinned and began to pump the hands of the patrons, asking each his name, his occupation and the size of his family. Many were German immigrants, and he surprised them by addressing them in their native tongue. His jokes were feeble and sometimes painful as he struggled in vain to establish a rapport with men of a class he had never known, but the laborers appreciated his efforts.

Murray stood at the bar, sipping a beer and watching him.

"I think you got yourself a live one, Joe," Fischer said, leaning on the far side of the bar.

"I didn't know he was going to wade into the mob like this. I just hope they don't think he's looking down his glasses at them."

"He's stiff, all right, but the boys know he isn't afraid he'll get his hands dirty shaking with them. He'll do fine, Joe."

Theodore joined them after conscientiously speaking to every patron in the saloon, and his wooden smile was still on his face as he joined Murray at the bar. "These men are splendid fellows," he said, an undertone of wonder in his voice.

"Give him a glass of lager, Carl," Murray said hastily.

"Have a stein, Mr. Roosevelt. On the house." Foaming beer spewed from a tap, and Fischer was careful to wipe the stein with his apron.

"Thanks, Mr. Fischer. Here's to you." Theodore forced himself to take a large swallow, then made a supreme effort to hide his distaste for the stuff.

The proprietor rested his elbows on the bar. "I hope you'll do something for us when you get up to Albany, Mr. Roosevelt."

Theodore looked faintly perplexed.

"Carl is speaking of saloon owners," Murray interjected.

"I'll be pleased to do anything that's equitable, sir." Even if he lost as a result of his lack of conviviality, Theodore could drink no more beer. "What is your complaint, Mr. Fischer?"

"Beer parlors are forced to pay taxes much higher than anybody else who deals with the public. The grocer next door, the butcher across the street, everybody—even the people who opened that new store that sells clothes to ladies and gentlemen—pay lower taxes than I do! It just isn't fair."

"Well, Mr. Fischer," Theodore said, "there's a philosophy that governs taxation. Groceries and meat and clothes are considered necessary essentials, but beer isn't."

"Some think it is," Murray said, nudging the candidate with his foot.

Theodore was too absorbed to heed the warning. "How high are your taxes, Mr. Fischer?"

"I have to pay two hundred dollars a year for the privilege of keeping my doors open."

"Why, that's not enough!"

Murray became voluble, changing the subject and delivering a long monologue until some new patrons entered and required the saloon-keeper's attention. Then, firmly grasping his candidate's elbow, the campaign manager guided him into the street.

"You're not happy with me," Theodore said.

Murray shook his head. "Maybe," he said, "taxes really should be raised on saloons. I wouldn't know about things like that—"

"I've made it my business to study the tax structure, and they're paying an absurdly low fee!"

"Maybe so, TR," Murray said dolefully, "but you don't win votes by telling people their taxes should be raised. Keep thoughts like that strictly to yourself, and if you can't give a man like Carl Fischer the encouragement he wants, say something vague that will make him think you're on his side."

"But that wouldn't be honest!"

"I'll square things with Carl. Later. When I'm alone." Murray looked at the well-dressed passengers in a carriage rumbling across 57th Street. "Those folks yonder, they're your type, TR."

"As a matter of fact, they happen to be friends of my sister, Anna."

"Exactly what I mean. Beginning right now, we're going to run a different kind of campaign than I planned. I'll look after this end— the ordinary people. You go see your personal friends, the kind who'd slam their doors in my face, and between us maybe we'll make out all right. You'll do fine in the Assembly—but first we've got to get you elected."

The tension in the second-floor sitting room of the house on 57th Street was almost unendurable. Corinne and Douglas Robinson, the handsome and energetic young financier to whom she was engaged, sat together on the window seat, holding hands but rarely speaking. Martha Roosevelt tried to keep occupied by sewing, but could pay little attention to what she was doing, and Alice was even more agi- tated, frequently dropping stitches as she made a futile attempt to finish the winter scarf she was making for Theodore.

Only Anna remained tranquil. Comfortably seated in the chair near- est the glowing hearth fire, she read calmly, completely absorbed in Henry James's new novel, *The Portrait of a Lady*.

Conie's patience, like that of most Roosevelts, was limited, and suddenly she exploded. "How can you sit there, enjoying yourself, as though this were an ordinary evening, Bamie?" she demanded, ignor- ing Douglas's futile attempt to silence her.

Anna remained tranquil as she looked up from her book. "Either he'll be elected, or he won't. Driving ourselves half-mad won't change the outcome."

Alice was unable to control a tremor in her voice. "When they first made him a candidate, he didn't much care what happened. But by now he'll be crushed if he's beaten. You have no idea how desperately he wants to win."

"Theodore always wants to win," Anna said complacently, "even if it's just a boat race or a boxing match or a shooting contest. The need to win is part of his nature."

Conie became angrier. "Are you criticizing him for it?"

"Hardly," her older sister replied. "I'm merely explaining that's the way he is. When a man chooses a career in politics, even a temporary career, he must be prepared to accept failures that are no reflections on his ability or integrity."

"Don't quarrel, girls," Martha said automatically, only half-hearing the argument.

"Theodore will be destroyed if he loses," Alice said, and put aside her knitting.

"Stop worrying about him," Anna assured her. "He's far tougher and more resilient than you think. At breakfast this morning, before any of you were awake, he showed me a chart he worked out, giving the percentage possibilities, ward by ward and precinct by precinct. He's prepared to accept any outcome. Not that he'll give up if he's beaten. I'm sure he'd run again next time, and try twice as hard."

Conie turned on the window seat to face the young man she planned to marry. "Douglas, it's only a two-minute walk to Republican headquarters. Would you mind going there again to see if the results have come in?"

Robinson smiled and shook his head. "I wouldn't mind in the least, if it would do any good, even though I'm an outsider. Elliott is there with Theodore, and has promised to come straight home the moment the official returns are tabulated."

The women lapsed into silence again.

"Mother, would you like some tea?" Anna asked.

"I think not, dear. I'm far too nervous," Martha said.

"Alice?"

The candidate's apprehensive wife appeared to have lost her voice, and could only shake her head.

"Conie?"

"The very thought of tea makes me ill!" Corinne jumped to her feet. "How anyone could think of holding a tea party at a time like this is beyond my understanding!"

Alice couldn't help laughing. "You and Theodore are alike in so many ways. It's remarkable."

Martha raised her head as she heard the front door open and close. "Someone is coming," she said, her poise restored, at least on the surface.

They looked at one another, and Robinson took Conie's hand. Martha pretended she was concentrating on her sewing, but Anna closed her book, neither realizing nor caring that she had lost her place. Alice rose to her feet, her yarn and needles falling to the floor as she dug her nails into her palms. She had turned very pale, and looked as though she might faint.

A dog raced down the stairs, barking happily, and an indistinct male voice could be heard greeting the animal.

After what seemed like an interminable wait, the door opened, and Theodore stood in the frame, Elliott behind him in the corridor. He looked around the room, his face somber, then he embraced his wife and bent to kiss his mother. "I've won," he said, "by fifteen hundred votes, the biggest majority in the history of the Twenty-first District."

They heard the news in stunned silence, almost unable to grasp it.

"From your expression," Alice murmured, "I was afraid you'd lost."

"They're going wild at headquarters," Elliott said, "but he wouldn't stay for the party."

"I don't believe this is an occasion for a celebration," Theodore declared, still unsmiling. "I hoped I'd win, but the size of my vote makes me realize how much I owe the people. Wanting to become a member of the legislature and suddenly finding I am one are very different. I've got to study every bill passed at the last session and every one pending. I need to learn what I can about the characters of the other members—and where they stand on important issues. Now that I'm an Assemblyman, by jingo, I'm going to be a good one, the very best any district has ever sent to Albany!"

II

1882–1896

I will not stay in public life unless I can do so on my own terms.

THE WINTER of 1881–82 was viciously cold, snow fell steadily, and by the time the New York State Assembly convened in Albany, early in January, the town's hills were covered with snow and the Hudson River was frozen. Newspaper reporters shivering on the slippery walks outside the huge state capitol, under construction for fifteen years but not yet completed, held their interviews with arriving Senators and Assemblymen to a minimum so they could retire to a tavern at the first opportunity. Albany, with a population of about seventy-five thousand, reputedly boasted more drinking establishments per capita than any other community in the state, and the reporters, weary of political clichés as well as numbed by the cold, could scarcely wait to finish their late morning assignments and take advantage of the opportunity to wander off to the nearest spa.

But even the most jaded forgot their boredom when they saw a dapper young man marching toward the capitol steps at a hiker's pace. He wore no greatcoat, hat or boots, and a fine layer of powdered snow covered his wind-ruffled brown hair. Attired in a handsomely tailored suit of unmistakable English cut and cloth, with a pearl-gray waistcoat and a silk cravat of dazzling scarlet and white polka dots, he wore spats over shoes that had not lost their high gloss in the snow, he carried a walking stick which he was swinging jauntily, and suspended from the glasses perched firmly on the bridge of his nose was a long ribbon of black silk that was looped through the buttonhole of his jacket.

Of equal interest was the fact that he approached from the direction of the hills behind the town, and it seemed strange, too, that he was enjoying himself, grinning broadly as he breathed deeply and exhaled long streams of vapor.

"Good Lord," a veteran reporter from Buffalo muttered.

Another, from Troy, announced to no one in particular, "I saw him on a road out in the country a couple of hours ago, as I was driving in. As nearly as I could make out, he seemed to be taking some sort of constitutional, and I thought he was a madman."

"He is," said the political editor of the New York *World*, a newspaper that always supported the Democrats. "It's Assemblyman Roosevelt, and if you ask me, he ought to go back to Harvard. He looks like he's dressed for a dinner party of his society friends, and the boys in this town won't tolerate a dude. They'll slice him to ribbons like that silk string on his glasses!"

The group, sensing a story, surged forward.

Theodore raised his walking stick in greeting. "Good morning, gentlemen!" The unexpected attention pleased him, and although he had no idea why he had aroused the interest of the press, his instinct prompted him to pretend he was unaware of it. Nodding affably, his grin broader, he did not halt until the newsmen closed in around him.

"Mr. Roosevelt," the political editor of the *World* asked solemnly, "did anyone tell you it's only eight degrees above zero this morning?"

"No, but there does seem to be a nip in the air." Theodore was surprised by their laughter.

"You didn't leave your hat and greatcoat at home, by any chance?" The reporter for the *Post* not only worked for a Democratic newspaper but was a close friend of Tammany Hall leaders.

Theodore immediately understood that the opposition was trying to embarrass him, but he saw no reason to lie about his personal habits. "Hardly, sir. I find I perspire when I take a brisk walk, so it was more convenient to leave my coat and hat at the hotel."

The reporters crowded still closer.

"Do you always walk in weather like this, Mr. Roosevelt?" the man from Buffalo wanted to know.

"In any weather."

The young reporter from Troy was overcome by personal curiosity. "Do you mind telling me how far you walk?"

Theodore saw the questioner was someone of his own age, who appeared friendly. "I don't anticipate the chance to follow my usual schedule when I'm in Albany, so I've set myself a goal of twelve miles every morning. I advocate exercise for everyone, gentlemen. The stronger our bodies, the more vigorous our minds. Any and all of you are welcome to join me tomorrow morning, gentlemen."

A few groans mingled with the laughter.

The political editor of the *World* looked innocent. "I don't suppose you plan to introduce legislation making constitutionals compulsory for all able-bodied citizens."

"Although I'm concerned about the health of everyone in the state, sir," Theodore replied instantly, "I'm not a fool. To answer your specific question, I emphatically do not propose to submit such a bill. To generalize, I'm a freshman in the legislature, gentlemen, and I want to learn a great many things before I start introducing bills on the floor of the Assembly."

"But you do have some bills in mind, Mr. Roosevelt?"

"I would imagine," Theodore replied caustically, "that every member of the Assembly has ideas on ways to improve the lot of our people, encourage the growth of industry and commerce, and create a graft-free government!"

The reporter for the Republican New York *Tribune* came to his aid before others could draw him out and, perhaps, trick him into revealing specific objectives. "Wouldn't you say, Mr. Roosevelt, that your policies here will be identical with those of the Republican party?"

Theodore knew the man and recognized his motives, but honesty compelled him to reply with care to a question he considered too sweeping. "Since I was elected by Republicans, I have an obligation to my party. But I represent all the voters of my district, and I must keep faith with every last one of them. I hope—and certainly anticipate—that I'll be able to support the Republican position on every issue, but no honorable, thinking man can accept his party's stand automatically before that stand has even been determined."

The man from the *Post* chuckled.

Theodore's amiability vanished. "Only a corrupt organization—a Tammany Hall controlled by men whose close friends and associates tolerate and perhaps encourage the criminal element—can force its puppets to support its position in advance. We who want to reform the government of our state, and I'm sure there are many of us, must follow the dictates of our own consciences."

There was an immediate clamor, and someone called, "Are you planning to lead a reform movement, Mr. Roosevelt?"

"I've just arrived in Albany," Theodore replied irritably. "I have no more than a nodding acquaintance with one or two of my colleagues, and I have no idea what reforms are being contemplated, although

I'm positive that the Republicans—who are always interested in good government—will have many plans."

Only the reporters from New York City were bothering to take notes.

But the incensed Theodore was speaking too rapidly for them, and refused to slow his pace. "As you gentlemen know, a caucus of Assembly Republicans will be held this evening, and I assume the party's attitudes on various matters will emerge at that time. I assume the Speaker will hold a meeting with you, and will tell you whatever he deems proper, and I wouldn't presume to step into his shoes or make rash predictions. Good day, gentlemen." Still aroused, he stomped up the capitol steps.

The reporter from Buffalo broke the silence. "He's not only a dude, but bad-tempered. God preserve us from amateur politicians."

The *World* editor watched the receding figure. "Unfortunately, he's sincere. And a reformer. I haven't seen many of them, and they don't stay around long, but they can sure cause trouble before the voters grow sick of them."

The young reporter from Troy shook his head. "Don't be too sure he'll be as harmless as the other reformers. He may be a Harvard gentleman, but so is Henry Cabot Lodge, who is causing such a stir over in Massachusetts. If this Roosevelt were just another rich reformer, he'd be just another nuisance, and the professional politicians could squash him. But there's an outside chance he may be clever as well as sincere, and that's a dangerous combination."

Theodore found his new life exhilarating. He spent four days of each week in Albany, returning for long weekends to his bride in New York and his weekly drill sessions as a lieutenant in the National Guard. He discovered that, as the only member of the young social set in Manhattan who held public office, he had acquired a faint sheen of glamour, but he was indifferent to the admiration of his peers. Others in Albany were making newspaper headlines, and he wanted the respect of professional politicians of both parties.

He waited in vain for an opportunity to make a name for himself, meanwhile dutifully voting with the Republicans and conservative Democrats of the Assembly against bills granting pay increases to New York City's overworked firemen and transit workers. He was disgruntled and restless, Alice wrote to her family, and even the favorable press reception accorded his *Naval War of 1812* failed to satisfy him. *He's afraid they're laughing at him in Albany,* she declared, *and I've never seen him so angry. He wouldn't mind their hatred, but can't tolerate ridicule. Theodore gives all of himself to everything he does, and demands the respect that is his due. I'm proud of him, as you can well imagine.*

In the spring of 1882 Theodore heard vague rumors at weekend social outings that aroused his indignant curiosity and made him wonder if he might be able to create the political opportunity he was seeking. Control of the Manhattan Elevated Railway Company, long debt-ridden, had been assumed by a syndicate headed by financier Jay Gould, and some of the stories seemed incredible to the young Assemblyman. Gould and his associates, Theodore heard, had deliberately manipulated the company's bonds, depressing their worth in order to buy the corporation for a fraction of its value. And they had succeeded, these stories indicated, only because they had been aided by Hamilton Ward, who had just retired as New York State Attorney General, and by New York Supreme Court Justice T. R. Westbrook.

Unwilling to believe the tales, yet determined to find out for himself whether they were true or false, Theodore "conducted an investigation," which, as he told Alice, meant that he discreetly questioned relatives and friends who might know the truth of the situation. He made better progress than he had expected: his financier uncle, Robert B. Roosevelt, had heard similar stories, and privately made an appointment for Theodore to meet several editors of the New York *Times*, who had been conducting an investigation of their own.

The *Times* had just learned that the deal had been closed in Gould's office, where Judge Westbrook had secretly and illegally held a session of his court. The newspaper had not yet been able to prove the allegation, but a member of the Assembly had access to the court records, and when Theodore returned to Albany he went straight to the state archives.

There, in a dark, musty room, with volumes of court proceedings piled high beside him, he began his search. He was so engrossed in his reading that only when he heard someone sneeze did he realize the adjacent table was occupied. Readjusting his glasses, he recognized a fellow Assemblyman, also a first-term Republican, whose name he could not remember.

"Roosevelt, New York," Theodore said, grinning politely.

"Yes, I know." The other man, only a few years his senior, spoke with a slow drawl. "I'm Isaac Hunt."

Theodore looked him up and down, unaware that his study was insulting. "From the country, aren't you?"

Hunt tugged at the lapels of his new suit, the first purchased in a store he had ever owned. "Jefferson County."

Conscious of his hurt pride, Theodore became contrite. "I—ah—I've been looking for a suit just like that for a long time."

Hunt smiled, appreciating the effort. "Come with me to Watertown," he said dryly, "and you can get its twin at Jansen's Drygoods Store. For eight dollars and twenty-five cents."

Theodore's roar of laughter as he bounded to his feet brought an alarmed archivist to the door. "You're all right, Hunt." He extended his hand. "Some of us are born snobs and some grow into it. I'm afraid I've done both. When we leave here, let me buy you dinner."

Hunt knew he meant well, even though the offer itself was condescending. "Thanks. But I may be here for some time. I'm searching some court records, but I don't know some of the details I need, and I may have to search the full proceedings of the Supreme Court to locate what I want."

Theodore eyed him speculatively. "Sounds interesting."

"It could be, if I can lay my hands on what I need." Hunt became cautious, too.

"These records," Theodore said after a heavy silence, "go all the way back to the early days of the Republic. Over one hundred years. I'm amazed to discover," he continued slowly, "how many Indians were hauled into court on charges of scalping. I guess it never crossed my mind that anyone would seek legal retribution for a scalping."

"There are still Indians in my part of the state," Hunt replied, equally careful, "and scalping traditions haven't died out there yet."

"Ever since the end of the Civil War there's been talk of scalping knives being whetted again right here in Albany. But nobody has done anything. A real reformer has to be willing to use a knife."

Hunt chuckled.

"It could be we're hunting the same scalps," Theodore said.

"The Mohawk who operated hereabouts had the right idea. They always sent out strong war parties when they attacked heavily defended stockades."

"I'll welcome reinforcements," Theodore said.

"You've met Billy O'Neil, I know. He's sat next to you at several caucuses."

"He's a country fellow, too, but very energetic." Theodore would have been horrified had he known how patronizing he sounded.

Hunt was willing to overlook the newest insult. The young Republican reformers needed a leader, someone willing to take chances and antagonize the established hierarchies of both parties, and Roosevelt wasn't forced to live on his income from the Assembly. "I'm sure Billy will stand with us."

"So will some anti-Tammany Democrats," Theodore added, surprising his colleague. "I've sounded them out, and they're spoiling for a fight. So am I."

Assemblyman Roosevelt startled the legislature and made newspaper headlines everywhere in the state when he submitted a resolution demanding the impeachment of Justice Westbrook. Supported by a dozen young Republicans and a smaller but equally enthusiastic nucleus of Democrats, he and his lieutenant, Isaac Hunt, submitted to the Assembly a carefully documented bill of particulars against Westbrook, and implicated former Attorney General Ward so thoroughly that the press demanded punishment for him, too.

The senior members of both political parties heard the charges in polite silence, however, and the resolution was tabled "in order to give its sponsors time to reconsider."

Theodore sputtered angrily, in spite of the efforts made by Hunt, O'Neil, and others to restrain him, and finally called a meeting of his friends in his hotel room. "Boys," he said, "the newspapers have said flattering things about us, but that doesn't change the basic situation. Judge Westbrook and Ward are going to escape."

"We've bitten off more than we can digest, maybe," Hunt replied, mixing himself a drink of the whiskey that Theodore always kept on hand for others. "Our problem is that we're naïve, and it hadn't crossed my mind that so many key Republicans and Democrats have been bought off."

O'Neil, a burly young farmer who had studied law, chewed on an unlighted cigar. "Our problem," he said sourly, "wasn't a lack of ammunition. We just didn't credit the other side's strong defenses."

"You aren't planning to stop now?" Theodore asked incredulously.

"We haven't done too badly for one session," Hunt said, adding a measure of water to his drink. "We've opened the eyes of a great many people, and I'm sure there will be more reformers coming here after the election this autumn."

"What's more," added the usually silent Tim O'Connor, a nominal Democrat, "they're scared. I've had a couple of quiet offers from Tammany, wanting to buy me off."

"Every last one of us has had offers," O'Neil said, taking a candle from its wall socket to light his cigar. "And when the high muckamucks wave dollar bills under our noses, you know they're on the run."

Theodore pounded the arm of his chair, his face growing scarlet. "You're being fooled and cajoled and pushed back into a corner, all of you," he shouted. "Don't you see we'll be playing into the hands of the enemy if we do nothing?"

"We'll be stronger next year, TR," Hunt said. "There's no more we can do now."

"If we wait until next year, the issue will be dead! The time to strike is right now, when the newspapers are supporting us and public interest is strong."

"Jay Gould and his friends own a majority in the present Assembly, unfortunately." O'Neil shrugged and puffed hard on his cigar.

"They don't own me!" Theodore sprang to his feet and, without realizing it, assumed a boxer's stance.

Hunt, who had grown fond of him, was afraid to laugh. "They know it, never fear."

"They'll know it even better before I'm through with them!"

"Hold on, now." Hunt, who had admired his recklessness, couldn't help wishing he would display more common sense. "We blundered into a situation with more ramifications than any of us recognized. There's an alliance between the politicians of this state and at least one group of very powerful financiers in New York City that we can't fight until we get some more recruits. Only one thing counts in the business we're in. Votes."

"I'm going to fight," Theodore shouted, his voice rising a half-octave, "if I've got to do it alone!"

"Sit down, TR," O'Neil said gently.

"You don't want to be a damn fool," Hunt added. "You'll only ruin yourself."

"How?"

"They'll find some way to beat you for re-election. I have no idea what they'll do, but those boys are experts. And you'll find yourself on the outside, TR. They have too much at stake to let a reformer with his head up in the clouds destroy what may be the most foolproof graft system ever developed in this country. Do you realize that just about everybody involved in the Manhattan Elevated Railway deal—in that one swindle alone—has made millions?"

"I do," Theodore said in a choked voice, "and that's all the more reason why I won't wait, I won't keep quiet, and I won't play their game."

Hunt sipped his drink and sighed. "What do you have in mind?" he asked in resignation.

Theodore made a herculean effort to calm himself, opened the small drawer of the desk behind him and brought out a sheaf of papers. "I wrote this on the train coming up here on Sunday night," he said. "The Assembly can table our resolution, but nobody can stop me from making this speech on the floor of the legislature!"

Hunt took the sheaf and, as he finished each page, passed it along. Soon everyone was reading, and the silence was punctuated by soft whistles and muffled exclamations.

Theodore was unable to sit still, and was forced to climb over the legs of his colleagues as he roamed the room.

"Listen to this," Hunt said. " 'Jay Gould is part of that most dangerous of dangerous classes, the wealthy criminal class.' That's strong language, TR."

"It was meant to be strong."

"Gould may sue you for libel," O'Connor said.

"He might, but I doubt it. He knows I'd present all of our evidence in the Elevated deal. If he did sue, so much the better. I'd prove every word against him."

O'Neil became thoughtful, his face obscured behind a cloud of cigar smoke. "I hold no brief for Jay Gould, but I don't see what you—and we—stand to gain by a speech that makes a direct attack on him."

"Public feeling is in our favor," Theodore explained. "The Elevated swindle—and many others like it—are actually complicated financial maneuvers. But Gould and a few others like him are responsible for them, so it doesn't stretch the truth to simplify for public consumption. No individual, no group and no political party can defy an aroused electorate. By concentrating on the chief villain we'll win more than the impeachment of Judge Westbrook. This is the opening wedge, and we'll really be in a position to push reforms through the Assembly."

"You may be right," O'Neil said, "but you'll have to brace yourself for a lambasting from Gould and his Wall Street friends."

"They'll want your blood," O'Connor said.

"They won't get any." Theodore's lips parted in a humorless grin.

"If I let them beat me, just once, I'm finished. I've got to prove to them, once and for all, that they can't shut me up!"

Hunt, hearing his stubbornly aggressive tone, couldn't help wondering whether victory for its own sake wasn't as important to TR as the principles for which he was fighting. Although the goals he sought were beyond reproach, the methods he was using would draw his irate criticism if the opposition employed them. Hunt had come to know him well during the weeks they worked together, but couldn't decide whether he was naïvely cunning or inspired by a calculated ruthlessness that would permit no one to block his path. The truth, in all probability, was that he himself didn't know what inspired him.

Jay Gould and his colleagues emerged unscathed from an investigation conducted by the Assembly's Judiciary Committee, but Theodore suffered no loss of prestige. On the contrary, he was universally regarded as one of the Republican party's future leaders. *Harper's Weekly* published an article about him that called him to the attention of the entire nation, and he was deluged with letters of congratulations. *If you want it,* wrote Henry Cabot Lodge, who was corresponding with him regularly, *you have won yourself a life career in politics.*

Even New York City's Democratic newspapers gave him unstinting praise. *Roosevelt's courage and candor have changed the very nature of political methods employed in the state,* the *World* wrote. The *Post* was even more laudatory, declaring, *He has accomplished more good than any man of his age and experience has accomplished in years.*

Theodore accepted his sudden fame with becoming modesty, but a brief entry in his diary revealed a private attitude of laconic smugness. *In my first term,* he wrote, *I achieved all I had set out to do.*

Reform was in the air, and Grover Cleveland, the Democratic candidate for Governor, made the promise of clean government the central theme of his campaign. Theodore accepted the Republican nomination for a second term in the Assembly, but found no need to conduct an active campaign. Every newspaper in New York City gave him its unqualified support, and his friends tendered him a testimonial dinner at Delmonico's, which made headlines throughout the state because General Carl Schurz, the vigorous civil service reformer and Secretary of the Interior in President Hayes' cabinet, was the principal speaker.

"Teedee," said Elliott, who had recently become engaged to marry an attractive girl of impeccable social background, Anna Eleanor Hall, "is the first professional politician in the family. I'd be upset if I weren't convinced that one of these days he'll decide he wants to become President of the United States. And, if he does, he'll persuade the people he's the only candidate in the country worth electing. I'm willing to bet on it."

Theodore was unruffled by his brother's mild sarcasm. "I'm still an undergraduate in the school of politics," he said, "so I can't think seriously about the presidency. Besides, the Constitution is very specific. I won't be eligible to run until I'm thirty-five."

Only the lower-class laborer had reservations about sending Theodore back to Albany for another term. He had consistently voted against every bill granting higher wages, shorter hours and improved working conditions to men employed either in private industry or by the municipalities. And there had been considerable resentment felt when he had declared on the floor of the Assembly, "Only the lazy are afraid to work long hours. Honest sweat never hurt anyone, and a man who wants a better life for himself and his family must earn it."

But labor, both organized and unorganized, did not oppose him, thanks to the quiet intervention of thirty-two-year-old Samuel Gompers, who had been elected president of the American Federation of Labor earlier in the year. The English-born Gompers, himself conservative by nature, interrupted his effort to organize the workers in every American craft and trade, and called a private meeting of his New York lieutenants.

"I've met Roosevelt several times," he said, "here in town and up in Albany. His heart is in the right place, but he's never been forced to earn a living himself, and simply doesn't understand that the laborer on starvation wages has no chance to improve his family's situation. What he needs is a little education."

The aides protested.

"I'm not asking you to support Roosevelt," Gompers declared. "I merely suggest that you take no stand either for or against him. And if he's re-elected, I'll attend to his education myself."

"Why bother?" someone asked.

"Look at the record he made in just a year. If he stays in politics, we'll need him—and he'll need us. I'll grant you I might waste my time, but if he continues to develop as a leader, every hour I spend with him will be a good investment."

Organized labor took no stand in the Twenty-first District.

On Election Day, November 7, 1882, Grover Cleveland won an easy victory, and the supporters of reform were encouraged when anti-Tammany Democrats doubled their seats in the State Senate and Assembly.

Theodore made a succinct entry in his diary. *I was re-elected by a two to one majority, even though Cleveland carried my district by eighteen-hundred votes. I led the whole Republican ticket throughout the state.*

The Republicans retained a majority in the Assembly, and Theodore believed the showing he had made warranted his election as Speaker. He was supported by the Hunt-O'Neil reform group, but quickly discovered that the men he had offended the previous year had long memories.

"Out of sheer spite," he told Alice, "the old line Republicans and Democrats banded together to beat me."

His wife tried to sympathize, although she had gained virtually no understanding of politics.

But Theodore cut her short before she could say more than a few words. "If I were in banking or the law, I'd rise on merit, but I've chosen a strange profession. I'll have to be content with the support of the people, and hope that public approval will force my fellow-politicians to accept me as a leader. Meanwhile, I can promise you, every Assemblyman who voted against me is going to regret it."

Alice didn't know what to reply; the vindictiveness he displayed in politics was alien to the Theodore she knew, and often frightened her.

Governor Grover Cleveland was a broad-faced man with a receding hairline and walrus mustache, piercing eyes and a double chin that softened the lines of his face. "He's a gentleman, and he really wants to improve the state government," Theodore told Conie during a weekend visit to New York. "I suspect he belongs to the wrong party."

"I've heard the same thing said about you," his sister replied.

Theodore winced. "I'm a pure Republican—in everything!"

Governor Cleveland drew no sharp party distinctions, however, when he invited Assemblyman Roosevelt to visit him in his office. "Roosevelt," he said, "you and I need each other."

Theodore felt uncomfortable in the room that was furnished simply, almost sparsely. Either Cleveland lacked taste or deliberately kept the room bare in order to convince poor constituents that he was a man of the people. "I'm always anxious to work for the general good, Governor," he said cautiously.

"That's why I sent for you. Tammany and the old-line Republicans are banding together to prevent change. I don't have the strength in either the Senate or the Assembly to push through my reform program until I've convinced them they can't pass their bills over my veto. If you'll help me, the reformers can take the reins."

Not even the most open-minded Republican could make a blanket agreement with the titular head of the opposition, and Theodore hesitated.

The Governor, aware of his inexperience, smiled blandly. "I'm not asking you to sign a pact," he said, showing a rare flash of humor.

Theodore's laugh was louder than the little joke warranted.

"What I do suggest is that we work together whenever it's in our common interest."

"Fair enough, sir." Theodore considered it unlikely that they would think alike on many issues. He had formed a grudging admiration for Cleveland, who refused to compromise his principles, but no politician, including the state's first citizen, would seek help from the opposing party unless he had no choice.

"As I understand it, you can deliver about thirty Assembly votes."

"I can guarantee no vote except my own." Theodore spoke more sharply than he had intended, and a quick grin indicated that he had not meant to rebuke the Governor.

The seasoned Cleveland took no offence. "What I should have said is that twenty-nine other Republicans think as you do on matters of reform."

"More or less, sir." The figure was accurate, but Theodore hated to play all his cards.

"When it's important, I can count on about that many Democrats. And I happen to believe the question of the reduction in the New York City transit fares is a matter of paramount importance."

Theodore nodded, immediately on guard. A bill reducing the city's Elevated fare from ten to five cents was pending, and he had assumed it would benefit everyone in New York who relied on public transportation. "I know very little about the issue, Governor." He refrained from adding that any legislator who opposed the bill would arouse the ire of the voters.

"On the surface the proposal looks harmless, but in reality a pernicious scheme has been plotted. The sponsors of the bill will take a head count in the next few days, and then want to announce they have enough votes to reduce the Elevated fare. But before they call up the matter for passage, they'll hold committee meetings to see if the reduction is in the general public interest."

Theodore nodded blankly.

"I needn't tell you that Jay Gould and the other stockholders want no reduction."

"Obviously, Governor. Their own profits will be cut."

"Correct. So the sponsors of the bill, after holding long hearings that the press will publicize, will announce that the financial condition of the Elevated doesn't warrant the cut."

"I don't see—"

"With all due respect, Roosevelt, you're still new to politics. Between the time the hearings open and the day the announcement is made that the fare cut will be abandoned a great deal will be happening behind the scenes. Gould's representatives will offer the sponsors a large, quiet bribe to abandon the project, and the sum will be raised and raised until the boys are satisfied that they've milked the Elevated of all they can get."

Theodore blinked indignantly behind his glasses. "Then this becomes a case of one set of robbers stealing from another!"

"Precisely." Cleveland was giving him ample time to sort the facts in his own mind.

"The best way to prevent this sort of flagrant graft is to demand an immediate vote on the bill—and defeat it."

"I told you we'd be in agreement." The Governor was jovial, but his smile faded. "However, since the New York City voters will believe they're being cheated of a fare cut, the whole question will need to be handled with great delicacy, with finesse, one might say."

Theodore's mind was racing, but he kept his thoughts to himself. *I don't share Governor Cleveland's lack of faith in the intelligence of the electorate,* he wrote in his diary that night.

The reform Republicans held several secret meetings, and the day after Theodore sent a message to the Governor saying he was ready for action on the transit question, he arose in the Assembly to demand an immediate vote on the Elevated fare reduction. The sponsors of the bill were taken by surprise, and tried to stall, but he circumvented them by making a brief but impassioned speech in which he revealed their real motives and intentions.

Then, before they could recover from his attack, which broke the unwritten rule that no legislator ever accused another of chicanery, he formally moved that the vote be taken. The reform Republicans and Governor Cleveland's Democratic supporters carried the day, and Theodore was elated.

Cleveland, however, was astonished. "I've never known a legislator to behave so recklessly," he said. "Roosevelt has not only made permanent enemies of senior Assemblymen who can hurt him, but he's destroyed his own popularity in New York. People who have been looking forward to paying a nickel instead of a dime for an Elevated train ride aren't going to forgive him."

The Governor was mistaken. The newspapers made the most of the story, blowing it up to spectacular proportions, and Theodore won universal press approval. Even the *Tribune*, which was on friendly terms with Gould and the sponsors of the defeated measure, called him *a young St. George who has slain the dragons of corruption.*

I gambled, Theodore wrote in his diary, *and won.*

That weekend, in the city, he offered a fuller explanation to Douglas Robinson. "If they'd been clever they could have denied the whole thing and made me look like a fool. I had no proof that they were going to hold up Gould, and no money had actually changed hands. The newspapers would have been reluctant to support me, and the voters would have sworn I cheated them out of a lower fare. I had to surprise those robbers by attacking them unexpectedly and putting the question to a vote before they could rally."

"What would you have done if you'd lost?" his brother-in-law wanted to know.

Theodore grinned, but his eyes remained serious. "I was risking the possibility," he admitted, "of being forced to look for another career. But I weighed my chances pretty carefully, and didn't see how I could lose."

In the summer of 1883 Alice learned she was pregnant, and Theodore, surprised to discover he felt tired after a long and grueling session of the legislature, went alone to the Dakota Territory, where, he had heard, the hunting was good, for a holiday. There he rode, hunted and hiked, was introduced to the business of cattle raising in the little town of Medora, and accompanied a party of ranch hands on a roundup, living and eating in the open.

Immediately after his return to New York, tanned and full of enthusiasm for life in the West, he paid a call at the Wall Street office of his uncle, James Roosevelt, who was the executor of his father's Will. Too impatient for more than a token exchange of courtesies, Theodore immediately came to the point. "Uncle James," he said, "I want fourteen thousand dollars of my money."

"That's a fairly large sum." The elder Roosevelt refrained from repeating the family rumor that Theodore had vetoed the purchase of an English baby carriage on the grounds that it would cost twenty dollars more than one made in the United States.

"I'm planning to make an investment that will pay for itself fourfold."

The banker was unimpressed. "I wouldn't mind making that sort of investment myself."

Theodore was too excited to hear the sarcasm in his uncle's voice. "I'm buying a herd of cattle in Dakota."

The older man stared at him. "Do you know anything about cattle?"

"I learned a great deal this summer."

"Enough to protect an investment of that size?"

"Enough to recognize a good thing when I see it!" Theodore retorted.

"The money belongs to you, of course, and you're free to do what you please with it. A man of twenty-five isn't a child. But you may lose every penny unless you can make regular trips out there to see how your herd is faring. The men who are looking after your cattle might not be too industrious in caring for someone else's property."

Theodore became still angrier. "In the first place, I believe my judgment of human character is sufficiently good for me to have made my arrangements with honest men. And I can assure you that I have every intention of making frequent visits to Dakota!"

His uncle's expression was that of a banker, not a sympathetic relative. He carefully refrained from asking, however, how a young man who would soon become a father and who was immersed in a political career could take the time to travel across two-thirds of a continent on more than an irregular schedule. "Do I glean you've already committed yourself in this venture?"

Theodore curbed his temper, reminding himself that he was addressing his father's older brother, who deserved respectful treatment, even though he was poking his nose into matters that were none of his concern. "Yes, sir. I closed the deal before I came home. I signed a very simple agreement—" He broke off, patted his pockets and smiled apologetically. "I didn't remember to bring it with me, but if you'd like to see it—"

"Don't bother showing it to me. If you've made a deal you'll have to honor it. I'll have the auditor give you a check and charge fourteen thousand dollars to your account. For your family's sake, I hope it turns out to be a wise investment."

"It will, Uncle James!"

The elder Roosevelt wisely remained silent. Theodore's impulsiveness was certain to cause him difficulties, and if he learned a lesson after losing the relatively small sum of fourteen thousand dollars, the price would be well worth the failure. The newspapers could hail him all they pleased as a rising political star, perhaps because there were so few New Yorkers of courage and intelligence in the profession, but only a close relative who was also a banker knew he was monumentally ignorant in matters of finance.

Theodore had agreed to make the private investigation into working conditions in the cigar-making industry after Samuel Gompers had appealed to his sense of fair play. Just re-elected to his third one-year term in the Assembly, he knew he would sit on a committee that would pass on the merits of a new bill designed to establish new labor and health standards for cigar-makers, and although he privately thought his effort a waste of time, he would lose only a morning.

Besides, he enjoyed the company of the American Federation of Labor President, and Gompers' sportsmanship had been impossible to resist. Theodore had selected the factory they would visit, choosing it at random from a list containing hundreds of names, and the labor leader had promised him he could go to others as well, as many as he pleased, if he shouldn't be satisfied.

The autumn afternoon was warm, and children from the shabby tenements that lined both sides of Water Street, on Manhattan's Lower East Side, spilled out from the sidewalks into the cobbled street itself, indifferent to the danger of being run down by an occasional carriage and making life hazardous for the pushcart vendors peddling everything from clothing to wilted vegetables. Boys and girls were equally energetic, throwing homemade balls made of rags, with rock centers, or kicking small, empty cartons of heavy wood.

The odors of the district were overpowering. Uncollected garbage and rubbish lay piled in the gutters, ignored by everyone, and cooking smells, mingling with rancid, unidentified scents, came from the open windows of the four- to six-story buildings. Men in drab work clothes wandered aimlessly up and down the street, apparently with nothing better to occupy them, and confirming Theodore's opinion that they were inherently lazy. Surprisingly few, however, frequented the saloons where steins of beer sold for five cents and free lunch counters were piled high with inexpensive cheeses and sausages, pickled eggs and day-old bread. Still fewer responded to the blandishments of the women who lounged in doorways, most in their mid-teens, all heavily rouged and wearing sleazy, tight-fitting dresses of shockingly short calf length.

In the main, the respectable women of Water Street displayed the greatest energy. Some haggled vigorously with the pushcart vendors for turnip greens and sprouting potatoes, others were hanging threadbare clothes they had just washed on ingeniously devised poles that protruded from windows, and even those who were taking advantage of the sunshine to sit on the steps of the stone and wooden tenements were busy mending already patched shirts and undergarments.

Few of the slum inhabitants looked twice at the soberly dressed Gompers, whose black suit and cravat, white shirt and modest top hat of dark gray felt identified him as a minor member of a profession, perhaps one of the struggling lawyers, physicians, or undertakers who sometimes visited the district. Almost without exception, however, adults and children alike stared at Theodore, dapper in a handsomely cut suit of blue wool, with a pearl-gray waistcoat, polished boots and a high top hat that matched his waistcoat. He pretended to be unaware of the stir he was creating, but occasionally touched his silk cravat or the brim of his hat, which, he suspected, the older boys were sorely tempted to knock from his head.

"This neighborhood must be very strange to you, TR." Gompers still spoke with a trace of a near-Cockney accent.

"Not at all." Theodore enjoyed surprising him. "I know every inch of Water Street."

The astonished Gompers knew that, if he said nothing, an explanation would be forthcoming.

"When I was a boy I went every day to the Fulton Street fish market looking for specimens. For my natural history collection. I still work on it when I have the chance, but I've had to put it aside until Mrs. Roosevelt has had her baby. She says the odors make her ill."

"I see. You don't mind the smells of Water Street, then."

"I taught myself to overcome them many years ago. I'm not even aware of them, Sam." Theodore inhaled deeply, by way of illustration, unaware that the asthma he had suffered in childhood and adolescence had in some way permanently impaired his sense of smell.

Gompers, conscious of his companion's vanity, managed to look duly impressed.

"Water Street hasn't changed, but I have. I don't mind confessing to you that in the years before I learned to protect myself with my fists, I sometimes ran for my life from the young rowdies who would have beaten me to a pulp. For no reason, other than my glasses and clothes, which made me a bit different, but mainly because they had nothing better to do. The laziness of these people has always astonished me."

Gompers had hoped they could avoid the subject of the area's poverty and the problems it caused, preferring to let the young aristocrat draw his own conclusions after their tour, but he could not permit the assertion to pass unchallenged. "Their difficulty is an inability to find work, TR, not laziness. Most of them are unskilled laborers, and many are immigrants."

"You migrated here, and have had no trouble. Carl Schurz has had a magnificent career. I could name scores of others." Theodore's jaw jutted forward, as it always did when he became combative.

"I was already literate, and so was General Schurz. The adults in these families usually aren't, and have no chance to learn English. And the children must work, even if it's for no more than a short time each day, doing anything, no matter how menial or low the pay. They rarely become literate, either, because there aren't enough schools in the slums, and the few that have been built are badly understaffed."

Theodore could think of no immediate, countering arguments, and frowned.

"Here we are."

"This is a tenement, Sam, not a factory." Theodore's frown deepened as he looked at the dilapidated wooden building.

"There isn't a house in the district that isn't being used for manufacturing of some sort. You'll see what I mean." Gompers sounded cheerfully casual as he led the way into the building.

In spite of Theodore's impaired sense of smell he found the odors that assailed him almost unbearable. The combination of fetid airlessness, heavy grease, garlic and decomposing food, combined with the unmistakable scent of unwashed human bodies, turned his stomach, and he fought a growing queasiness. Picking his way past rotting garbage that littered the areaway, he followed the labor leader up four flights of creaking stairs, taking care not to step through holes in planks or touch the sagging handrail that looked as though it might come apart if tugged.

A babble of voices in many tongues assailed him, and he wondered if all the inhabitants of the tenement spent their days shouting at one another. It did occur to him that the walls, from which layers of old, cracked paint were peeling, might be very thin, but he told himself firmly that not even the most wafer-like partitions could account for the noise.

Gompers halted at the fourth floor landing and tapped on a door.

A frail man in his mid-thirties, dressed in filthy trousers and shirt, answered the summons and, coughing so hard that his whole body trembled, stared at the visitors.

The labor leader said a few words to him in a strange language, obviously speaking it with difficulty.

The man's attitude changed, and he bowed from the waist, an incongruously courtly gesture, and waved the two visitors inside.

"Both families are Bohemian," Gompers said. "One comes from Prague and the other from a small town about forty miles from the city. I'm not sure which is which, but they both migrated here about five years ago."

Theodore was so astonished that he was rendered speechless during their inspection of the premises. The apartment consisted of two rooms, both facing an inner court, and was so dark that he needed several minutes for his eyes to become accustomed to the gloom. Eight people obviously lived and worked in these cramped quarters, four of them adults, the others ranging in age from a boy of about six or seven to a girl of perhaps fourteen or fifteen.

All slept on narrow, dirty pallets, and aside from a work table of raw, stained pine, the only furnishings were a small wood-burning stove that stood in a corner of the inner room and several oaken buckets, some of which were used as slop jars, while the others contained water. Bales of both long-leaf and shredded tobacco occupied most of the available space, and its smell, combined with the other odors, made Theodore want to retch.

The man who had admitted him returned to his work at once, and no one else paid any attention to the newcomers, either. All eight worked in a silence broken only by an occasional word in Bohemian from one of the two men. A crude assembly line of sorts was in operation, the three smallest children gathering shredded tobacco which they placed in small, remarkably neat mounds at one end of the table, while the older girl carefully unwrapped longer leaves. The two men cut the leaves with broad-bladed knives, interrupting their labors occasionally to move another bale closer to their immediate area. And the two women, who never raised their heads, stuffed the filler tobacco into the wrappers, rolling each cigar and sealing it with saliva before dropping it into an empty container.

Theodore took a deep breath, and instantly regretted it. "May I speak to them?" he asked.

Gompers, who was watching him, said nothing.

The teen-aged girl glanced up from her work. "I am the only one who can speak a little English," she said, her accent heavy.

"Do all of you live here?"

She nodded, surprised by the question.

"You cook all of your meals on that thing?"

Again she nodded.

He started to inquire about sanitary facilities, realized there were none and started again. "Where do you get your water?"

"In the—how do you say?—courtyard there is a tap." The girl did not interrupt her work.

Theodore watched in silence for a few moments. "How much are you paid?"

She repeated the question in Bohemian to one of the men, and his reply was curt. "My father, he says for each day one dollar."

Theodore blinked, and removing his glasses, polished them with a clean handkerchief before resettling them on the bridge of his nose.

"I assume," he said, speaking rapidly, "that each person engaged in this—ah—enterprise is paid wages of one dollar per day."

The girl, unable to follow him, looked puzzled.

Gompers broke his silence, repeating the observation in simple terms.

Again the girl acted as interpreter, and this time the other man replied, saying a few words in a harsh voice. The girl's face remained expressionless as she translated, "My uncle, he says for all. Together."

Theodore began to sputter. "This is preposterous!" He reached into the inner pocket of his jacket for his pigskin wallet.

Gompers touched his arm. "They may live and work like animals, TR, but don't deny them their pride. It's all they have."

Theodore forced himself to put away the wallet. "I wonder how many of these infernal cigars they make," he said to no one in particular.

The girl replied without referring his remark to either of the men. "The company takes from us five thousand cigars every day. But on Sunday we go to church, so they take only three thousand."

Theodore was stunned by the figures, as well as by the realization that these people worked six and one-half days every week. Although he knew nothing about the cigar business it was obvious that the profits earned at their expense were enormous. "What would happen if you refused to work for such rates?" he demanded.

"They find somebody else." The girl shrugged, looking much older than her fourteen or fifteen years. "And we starve."

Indignation and pity made Theodore speechless, but at last he turned to Gompers. "We've intruded long enough, Sam."

The two Bohemian women looked up from their work long enough to smile shyly, the girl curtsied, and the men, bowing, formally shook hands with the visitors.

Theodore curbed a desire to wipe his palm on the side of his trousers, and felt ashamed of the urge.

"They work from sunrise until sunset," Gompers told him as they descended the rickety stairs. "They have no gaslight, of course, and can't afford to burn either oil lamps or candles, so they're forced to stop at nightfall. I do know of families that work even longer hours, however."

Theodore, no longer conscious of his surroundings, loudly cleared his throat. "I want to send these people a basket of fruit. And I'll ask Mrs. Roosevelt to buy that girl a dress. It's disgraceful to see someone of her age in rags!"

"I'll send someone from my office to deliver your gifts, TR," Gompers said quietly.

Theodore didn't speak again until they had walked more than a block down Water Street. "Forgive me for being so naïve, Sam, but I had no idea such conditions existed in New York today!"

"There are scores of families in the same situation. Those who have been able to afford to join the union live and work in slightly better circumstances, but the improvement is infinitesimal. Would you care to drop in on some of them? I'll show you the whole membership list, and you can take your pick. Most of them live in this part of town."

"I've seen enough for one day, thanks," Theodore replied grimly.

They headed toward the financial district, where they found a carriage for hire, and Gompers deliberately allowed his companion to fume in impotent, silent rage.

All at once, typically, seemingly out of nowhere, Theodore's wrath exploded. "How can the United States live up to her potential? How can we become one of the greatest, wealthiest nations on earth when conditions like this exist in our most important city?" Ignoring the stares of the carriage driver, who half-turned on the board to peer at him, he continued to shout. "I have no use for the Socialists and their like—men who preach disorder—but what we've just seen is abominable! Those men and women will die of consumption in the next few years, and not one of those children will survive until adulthood."

"I dare say you're right, TR." It surprised and dismayed Gompers that an Assemblyman could be so uninformed about the poor.

"Do you happen to recall what the bill that the Assembly will consider this winter provides?"

The labor leader concealed a smile. "Every cigar worker must be paid a minimum wage of two dollars for a twelve-hour day. Cigar making is permitted only in lofts and factories, not in dwellings. And children under twelve years of age cannot be employed."

"Sound provisions, all of them. The bill will not only have my vote, Sam, but my active support."

"In that case, it will pass." Gompers silently congratulated himself; the morning's lesson had been effective.

Theodore's anger subsided, and he stared with unseeing eyes at the pedestrians on the busy city streets. "You know," he said at last, "I'm relieved I never took up the habit of smoking cigars. The way they're made just isn't sanitary."

We've never been so happy, Theodore wrote in his diary on New Year's Day, 1884, and his family, friends, and political associates agreed he had every reason to rejoice. Alice's baby was due the following month, and the young mother-to-be was weathering her pregnancy in good health and humor, although she took fewer walks than her energetic husband recommended. The couple's formal social life was curtailed, but friends frequently dropped in for an evening at the house on 57th Street, and everyone remarked on the high spirits of Theodore and Alice.

Certainly Theodore had ample reason to be satisfied with his vocational progress. He had become the undisputed champion of the reform Republicans, and was seriously thinking of taking the advice of Henry Cabot Lodge that he move to a larger arena, Washington. Perhaps, after the Republican National Convention met later in the year and nominated a candidate for President, he would assess his own situation and run for a seat in the House of Representatives. His future, he told Alice, depended on whether he became a leader of the state delegation to the Convention, a post he felt certain he would win.

Corinne and Douglas Robinson had a fine, healthy baby, Elliott was married, and there were rumors in the immediate family circle, not denied, that Anna was growing interested in an eligible gentleman. "I couldn't ask more for my children," Martha said, and they agreed that their lives were rich and full.

Early in February Conie left her baby at the 57th Street house while she accompanied Douglas on a short business trip, and when Theodore left for Albany on February 10 he predicted there would be another infant there by the time he returned. He proved to be an accurate prophet.

On the afternoon of Wednesday, February 13, he was on the floor of the Assembly when he received a telegram informing him that Alice had given birth to a baby girl. Both mother and infant were in good health, Anna said in the wire.

Debate on a bill intended to deprive the New York City Board of Aldermen of their right to approve appointments made by the Mayor was interrupted, and members of both parties offered the beaming young father their congratulations. "Speech!" someone shouted, and others took up the chant as the Speaker gaveled for order.

Isaac Hunt, who had the floor, chuckled and turned to his friend. "Mr. Speaker, I yield to the gentleman from the Twenty-first District. He's never been bashful about talking, but from the looks of him right now, he doesn't have much to say."

Theodore stood, causing a wave of laughter when he ran a finger inside his collar. "Fatherhood is new to me, Mr. Speaker, so I beg your indulgence. To all of you, my thanks. Mrs. Roosevelt decided that if we had a daughter we'd call her Alice, so I guess that'll be her name. To be honest with you, it didn't cross my mind that I wouldn't have a son."

Again there was a roar of laughter.

Theodore held up a hand. "There are refreshments waiting in my office, and all of you are cordially invited to join me there after we finish our day's business. Now, I hope, nobody will be offended if I suggest we get on with our work. I needn't tell you I'd like to catch the nine o'clock train to the city this evening."

The debate was resumed, and after a brief celebration in his office, Theodore dined with Hunt and Billy O'Neil, who escorted him to his train. His mood was one of restrained exuberance, and when he reached New York he walked home from the station, whistling so loudly that passing pedestrians stared at him.

Lights were burning in virtually every room in the house, which he found normal under the circumstances, but he was mildly surprised when he recognized the Robinson carriage in the street. As he remembered it, Conie and Douglas had planned to remain in Baltimore until the end of the week. Several other horses were tied to hitching posts, too, but he paid no attention to them, assuming that callers had already descended on the establishment.

It didn't occur to Theodore that he was excited until he began to fumble in his pockets for his latch key, and he chuckled when he couldn't locate it.

Suddenly the door opened, and a white-faced Elliott stood in the frame. "There's a curse on this house," he said. "Mother is dying, and so is Alice."

Theodore stared at him in horror, too numb to grasp the full import of his words.

Anna appeared, and for the first time since her father's death had been weeping. "I've been waiting for you, Teedee," she said. "Alice became ill a few hours after the baby was born."

Theodore's lips moved, but he could not speak.

"The doctors say she has Bright's disease."

His eyes indicated he knew nothing about the ailment.

"It's a kidney disease. They're doing all they can for her, but they don't hold out much hope." She took a long, tremulous breath. "Mama has typhoid fever. The doctors have tried everything, but it hasn't helped."

Theodore found his voice. "There *is* a curse on this house," he whispered.

"Mama doesn't—know anyone by now. Go to Alice."

He ran toward the stairs, mounting them two at a time as he climbed to their suite on the third floor. Halting for a moment in the open doorway, he saw several figures clustered around the bed.

Conie came to him, taking his arm, and two physicians moved aside to make room for him.

Alice appeared to be asleep, and her waxen face shocked him. Her breathing was shallow, labored, and he turned to the doctors.

The senior of the pair answered his unspoken question with a resigned shake of his head.

Veins bulged at Theodore's temples, and his face grew red as he tried in vain to cope with a situation he had no power to alter.

"She was already weakened, Mr. Roosevelt," the doctor said.

Someone pushed a chair close to Theodore, and he sat down, staring at Alice's face, then taking her frail, limp hand in his and trying, through sheer force of will power, to communicate his strength to her.

He had no idea how long he sat there, but his legs and back were stiff when Elliott came for him.

They went together to their mother's room, where Bamie and Conie were standing at the bedside. The brothers joined them, and Martha's children hovered above her as she died quietly in her sleep. Much later someone told Theodore that she passed away at three o'clock in the morning.

He staggered back up to the stairs to his vigil in the room he had shared with Alice, and occasionally a coherent thought went through his mind. At dawn it occurred to him that he hadn't yet seen his daughter. An hour or two later he realized it was St. Valentine's Day, the fourth anniversary of his betrothal.

A short time before noon Alice opened her eyes, recognized him and smiled, then dropped off to sleep again.

Theodore had no idea he was weeping, but eventually it occurred to him, vaguely, that his glasses were smudged and his face wet.

At 2:10 P.M. on February 14, 1884, less than twelve hours after her mother-in-law's death, Alice Lee Roosevelt breathed her last.

For five days there were no entries in Theodore's diary.

At last the ordeal of the double funeral and its aftermath was ended. Anna volunteered to take care of the newborn infant, flowers and letters of condolence were acknowledged, and the shattered Roosevelts made an effort to settle down again in their daily routines. Theodore published, for family and friends, a little booklet containing the messages he, his sisters and brother had received, and on its first page he wrote his own valedictory to Alice:

She was beautiful in face and form and lovelier still in spirit; as a flower she grew, and as a fair young flower she died. Her life had been always in the sunshine; there had never come to her a single great sorrow; and none ever knew her who did not love her for her bright, sunny temper and her saintly unselfishness. Fair, pure and joyous as a maiden; loving, tender, and happy as a young wife; when she had just become a mother, when her life seemed to be but just begun, and when the years seemed so bright before her—then, by a strange and terrible fate, death came to her.

And when my heart's dearest died, the light went from my life forever.

For the rest of his own days, Theodore did not speak of Alice again, never mentioning her name to anyone, even those closest to him, including members of her own family with whom he remained on intimate terms.

"I think I should go mad if I were not employed," Theodore told Carl Schurz, and returned to his work with a vigor and dedication that surprised even those who knew he thrived on activity.

On the surface his routines were unchanged; he spent several days each week in Albany, returning to the house on 57th Street for weekends. But he had become indifferent to the progress the builders were making on the house under construction at Oyster Bay, and in subtle ways his personality was altered. Eventually he laughed again, as loudly as ever, but his mirth had been sapped of its spontaneity; in time he became bouyant again, enjoying life, but his impulsiveness was restrained by a new, almost hidden depth of maturity.

"Theodore *is* changed," Henry Cabot Lodge said when they met later in the year. "I sometimes think that even his impetuous gestures are calculated."

Fortunately, there was enough to occupy the mind of any ambitious politician in 1884. A presidential election was looming, and the Republicans were conducting an earnest search for a candidate capable of competing with Grover Cleveland, who seemed assured of the Democratic nomination and had won favor throughout the country because of his stand in favor of reform. President Chester A. Arthur, who had succeeded to the nation's highest office six months after the assassination of President James A. Garfield, was hard-working but colorless, and had built up almost no personal following. Most members of the Republican hierarchy leaned toward the handsome James G. Blaine of Maine, but the younger men in the party had little use for him.

Blaine, Theodore wrote to Lodge, *is a weakling. We need a candidate as attractive as Cleveland, who'll press just as vigorously for governmental reform.*

Together the pair searched for a candidate, with the encouragement of such Republican reform leaders as Carl Schurz, Charles W. Eliot of Harvard, and the party's younger element, which included the vocal Nicholas Murray Butler, an instructor at Columbia University. By early spring Lodge found the man who appeared best qualified to lead the Republicans out of what he and Theodore considered "the morass of machine politics." United States Senator George F. Edmunds of Vermont had a solid voting record, was an independent who neither sought nor gave political favors and long had advocated the extension of the Civil Service in the Federal Government.

Theodore went to the New York State party convention at Utica, in late April, committed to the cause of Edmunds. But there, in spite of his popularity with younger colleagues from the Assembly, he found himself in immediate conflict with the more important members of the state's Republican hierarchy, principally United States Senator Warner Miller and the man being groomed to succeed him, State Senator Tom Platt.

On the night of his arrival he received an invitation to visit the hotel suite of the gray-haired, rotund Miller and, as he suspected, Platt was there, too, tight-lipped and sallow. Senator Miller offered his young guest a glass of whiskey, which was politely declined, and smiled when Theodore asked for coffee instead.

"I hadn't known you reformers are teetotalers, too," he said.

"It's a matter of personal preference, Senator." Theodore appeared at ease, but spoke very slowly, a sure sign that he was wary.

Miller ordered coffee sent to the room, and after chatting about inconsequentials, came to the point abruptly. "I've been told that you're seeking revenge against the men who beat you for Speaker of the Assembly, Roosevelt."

The idea was preposterous, and Theodore laughed. "If I haven't learned to accept a defeat with good grace, Senator, I have no place in politics."

Platt nodded, seemingly pleased by the reply, but Miller tugged thoughtfully at his beard. "Then I can't understand why you're playing into the hands of the New England cabal. This fellow Lodge, who served a term or two in the Massachusetts House, is going to throw the nomination to President Arthur if he keeps pushing the candidacy of Edmunds. I don't believe you want Arthur as our man, Roosevelt."

"No, sir, and I don't want Blaine, either!"

The Senator tried a different approach. "I assume you're a friend of Edmunds'. Well, I've known George for years. We've served together on a good many committees, and I like him, you understand, but— speaking as one professional to another—he has such a simple approach he couldn't be elected to any office outside of Vermont."

Theodore recognized the attempt to flatter him by calling him a professional politician, but was unimpressed. "I've never met Senator Edmunds, sir, and I have no idea whether Cabot is personally acquainted with him."

Platt poured his coffee and handed him the cup. "It's the privilege of someone your age to be an idealist, TR," he said in his rasping voice. "But the situation at the Chicago convention is going to be very tight. President Arthur has no personal following, but anyone in his position can command a respectable number of votes. Neither he nor Blaine can win the nomination without the support of you young idealists. We need your help."

"And you won't suffer, I can promise you," Miller added, sipping his drink.

Theodore gulped his coffee. He hadn't expected a pledge of personal support from the leaders of the state hierarchy, and supposed that, under the circumstances, it would be easy enough to obtain the nomination for Congressman-at-Large. But the very idea of making such a deal violated the principles in which he believed, and infuriated him. "My friends and I," he said briskly, "are convinced we can nominate Senator Edmunds."

"Don't be a fool," Miller said bluntly. "All you can do is cause trouble."

Theodore tried to remain civil. "That remains to be seen, Senator."

Miller lost patience. "I'm trying to deal with you reasonably, Roosevelt. You've won support from the newspapers and the professors and the people who always respond to appeals for honesty in politics. You'll have a real career if you'll remember that party loyalty is the first obligation of every man in this business."

"It's because of my loyalty to the party that I'm supporting Senator Edmunds," Theodore said, his voice rising a half-octave.

Miller grimaced. "Apparently I haven't made myself clear. You have an opportunity to advance yourself, but if you miss the chance, you'll suffer; I won't. I didn't inherit a fortune that would support me in retirement if I guess wrong. I can't afford to guess. Or gamble."

"I don't regard the presidency of the United States as a form of lottery or horse race." Theodore was too incensed to realize how pompous he sounded.

"You can go in either of two directions, Roosevelt. Up. Or out."

Theodore lost his temper as well as his sense of propriety. "You can't frighten me, Miller, any more than you can buy me!" Arms flailing, he stormed out of the suite.

Tom Platt followed him into the hotel corridor and halted him. "I know you're upset," he said, "but come back and apologize, even if you vote against Blaine. Nobody in this state who wants to stay in politics can wave a fist under Senator Miller's nose. He won't forget this scene tonight."

"Neither will I, and I refuse to grovel before any man." Theodore shouted so loudly that a delegate from Long Island opened the door of his room, decided it was better to hear and see nothing, and disappeared again.

"The Senator isn't young, and he doesn't like personal insults."

"I may be less than half his age, but neither do I!" Theodore stomped off down the hall, his face scarlet.

Platt watched him as he turned a corner, still talking angrily, and shrugged. No matter how great the popularity Theodore Roosevelt had attained in a few years, it was absurd to think of him as anything but an amateur. No man, not even a charming aristocrat who had won the support of the press, could survive in public life if he became emotionally involved in the issues for which he fought.

They met beneath the hissing gas jets of the chandelier in the main lobby of the Prairie Inn, and delegates from a score of states as well as newspaper reporters who had come to Chicago from every part of the country witnessed the reunion. Henry Cabot Lodge, dignified in black frock coat and striped trousers, was trying to persuade two delegates from Pennsylvania to support Senator Edmunds when a dapper young man bounded across the lobby and enveloped him in a bear hug.

"Cabot, you rascal!" Theodore roared, pounding him on the back.

Lodge disengaged himself, smoothed his waistcoat and coolly shook hands. "You haven't changed, have you, Theodore? It's good to see you."

A prominent Blaine supporter, Congressman William McKinley of Ohio, missed no detail of the scene. "Edmunds will be no threat," he said. "His campaign managers probably won't be on speaking terms with each other by tomorrow."

His friend, Mark Hanna, who had made a fortune in coal, iron, and Great Lakes shipping, didn't agree. "If they're strong, it's because they're so different, but they have two things in common that make them dangerous. They're visionaries who dream of creating a new world, and they're gentlemen, which means they obey no rules except their own."

Hanna proved himself an astute judge. While the Blaine forces quietly used persuasion and influence to gain votes, Theodore Roosevelt and Henry Cabot Lodge told every newspaper correspondent they could find that victory was assured for Senator Edmunds. New to the national political scene, they generated an aura of excitement that attracted the younger men from every state delegation, and they lost no time demonstrating their power.

To the astonishment of delegates from the South, Lodge nominated Thomas R. Lynch, a Negro from Mississippi, as temporary chairman of the convention. Theodore jumped onto his chair and, sending his straw hat skimming across the heads of the delegates, seconded the nomination in a brief but impassioned address. Lynch won by a close vote, and the professionals grudgingly admitted that the Lodge-Roosevelt coalition was stronger than any of them had been willing to believe.

Unwilling to hand the Republican party reins to untried young idealists, the leaders of the delegations held a series of secret meetings, and Blaine was nominated on the fourth ballot. Hundreds, including the working press, saw Theodore Roosevelt of New York stalk from the convention hall.

Republican advocates of reform protested violently, but in vain. William Lloyd Garrison sent an angry telegram to the Massachusetts delegation, as did President Eliot of Harvard. The New York *Herald,* the Chicago *News* and Boston *Advertiser,* among many prominent Republican newspapers, announced editorially they could not support Blaine. Carl Schurz organized a mammoth protest rally in New York.

Theodore, bitter and discouraged, retired to his hotel room, locked his door and refused to see anyone. The press, hoping to obtain a statement from him, besieged him in vain, and he deliberately let it be known through the hotel management that he had departed for home. Then, his privacy assured, he went to Lodge's suite.

"You look as though you had no sleep last night," the former Harvard instructor said accusingly.

Theodore removed his glasses and pressed his fingertips to his eyes. "I didn't get much," he admitted.

"What did you have for breakfast?"

"I saw the editorial in the Chicago *Tribune* asking whether you and I would support Blaine," Theodore said glumly, "and I lost my appetite."

Lodge pointed to rolls, butter, and jam on a room-service table. "Eat!" he commanded.

Theodore ignored the order. "Blaine really is third-rate, a miserable excuse for a candidate. I think too much of the presidency to help elect him."

"Eat!"

Theodore spread butter on a roll and stuffed a piece into his mouth. "What are your plans, Cabot?" he asked, swallowing with difficulty.

Lodge pointed to a stack of telegrams on a table. "Nearly everyone I respect is wiring me, demanding that I disavow Blaine. But I can't do it." Although his dilemma was painful, he spoke with cool detachment. "As chairman of the Massachusetts Republican Committee, it's my duty to hold the party together, not split it. And, since I'm running for Congress myself, I'd be committing suicide if I failed to support my party's candidate for President."

"Then you advise me—"

"I can't tell you what to do, Theodore," Lodge said sharply. "Don't expect me to act as your conscience. I'm doing what I must, for reasons I consider valid. But you'll have to work out your own problem."

Theodore finished the roll, buttered another but looked at it without appetite. "You aren't the only one hearing from friends." He pulled a sheaf of telegrams from his pocket and threw them onto the table. "Schurz. Thomas Nast. Harper, the publisher. George Putnam. Classmates like Bob Bacon. Men of integrity. All of them begging me to announce that I won't support Blaine."

"It's a crucial decision."

"I'd be a traitor by default, even if I didn't say a single kind word about Governor Cleveland."

"Your real decision," Lodge said, "is whether you want to stay in politics."

"Of course I do!"

"You're sure?"

"Positive, Cabot! I drifted into this career almost by accident, but I've made it mine, and I don't intend to be squeezed out or frightened out, not even by myself."

Lodge stared up at the ceiling for a moment, then carefully clipped off the end of a thin cigar.

"I know the cardinal rule of the game. Senator Miller and Tom Platt made it very clear to me at Utica. But none of the people whose support and respect I want will ever take me seriously again if I work for Blaine's election."

Lodge struck a match and held it to the end of his cigar.

"I'm trapped."

"If you plan to stay in politics, I'm afraid it won't be the last time."

"Probably not, which doesn't make my present dilemma any simpler." Theodore heaved himself to his feet and moved wearily toward the door. "I don't know what I'll do, but I'll work it out in some way."

For twenty-four hours Theodore pondered alone, wrestling with his conscience. Then, after writing to his sister, Anna, thanking her for the loving care she was devoting to his infant daughter, he quietly vanished from Chicago.

The following day a Minnesota newspaper editor, arriving home from the convention, recognized him on a railroad station platform in St. Paul, where he was changing trains. Sensing a story, the man hailed him.

Theodore turned, and his broad grin indicated none of the turmoil he had undergone. "Well," he said, "this is convenient!"

"I wasn't sure you'd think so. There must have been fifty newspapermen looking for you in Chicago."

"I had no statement to make then."

"But you do now, Mr. Roosevelt?"

"Of course. The Republican party has made its selection. I'm a Republican. It's that simple." Although Theodore spoke casually, he had worked out the wording in advance, and was careful not to praise the Republican candidate by name.

The editor was quick to recognize the evasion, but was equally clever. "I assume, then, that you'll campaign for Blaine."

"I have business interests in the Dakota Territory, and my personal situation has been so chaotic this year that I've had no chance to look after them. At the moment I can't say how long I'll be out there, but when I return East I'll put myself at the disposal of the Republican leaders for any task they may want me to perform." Still smiling, he picked up his leather handbags and boarded his train.

But he became somber again after settling on the heavy plush that covered his horsehair-stuffed seat, and he remained bitter as his thoughts returned to the convention. It was best that he had no intention of seeking re-election to the Assembly; the party wouldn't support a man who side-stepped, and the reformers like Schurz, who had been counting on him, would be as disgusted with him as he was with politics.

That evening, as the soot from the locomotive rolled past his window and the train bounced and swayed on the tracks laid across the prairies, he confided his inner thoughts to Anna in another letter. *The voice of the people,* he wrote, *might be the voice of God in fifty-one cases out of one hundred; but in the remaining forty-nine it is quite as likely to be the voice of the devil, or what is still worse, the voice of a fool.*

The western portion of the Dakota Territory, near the Montana border, was still a frontier land where few could read or write, where itinerant cowhands worked for a season or two before drifting elsewhere. Every man carried firearms to protect himself from greedy two-footed foes, and game was so plentiful that no one who could shoot went hungry.

The land that stretched out toward the horizon from the village of Medora, on the swift-running Little Missouri River, was an endless prairie interspersed with buttes, cliff-like hills, each standing alone. Only along the banks of the river were there stands of trees; elsewhere, stretching out toward the horizon in all directions, only the oddly shaped buttes broke the monotony of the endless sea of prairie grass.

Only the hardy could withstand the elements. Rainfall was sparse, water was a precious commodity and in dry spells cattle were forced to wander for miles in search of fodder. In the summer, when the temperature soared above one hundred degrees, there was no shelter from the sun burning down through the dry air; but the winters tried the souls of even the most courageous. Then the thermometer plunged to lows of forty to fifty degrees below zero, and high winds that blew steadily for days at a time made it dangerous for anyone to venture outdoors for even a short time. Snow fell infrequently, but the wind made every snowstorm a blizzard, and drifts were often piled as high as the buttes.

Perhaps the worst scourge of the western Dakota Territory was loneliness. It was not uncommon for a settler to see no other human being for weeks at a time, and many who had come to the area were compelled to retreat to more hospitable regions. A. T. Packard, editor of the only newspaper in the region, was fond of saying that a man needed two qualities to survive there: physical strength and a craving for solitude.

The usually gregarious Theodore felt at home from the day of his arrival, although Medora entertained its private doubts about a man who wore eyeglasses and expensive clothes, spoke with an aristocratic Eastern drawl and assumed he would be accepted simply because he bought himself a ranch. Bets were made that he would become discouraged and leave within a few months.

To the surprise of virtually everyone but Theodore himself, he stayed. Recovering from his grievous personal losses and the political defeat that still smarted, he relished solitude as much as he enjoyed working with the men he had hired to build him a bigger house than the shack in which he lived. By the standards of the East he was an accomplished rider, but horsemanship in the West was more than a sport, and a man needed stamina, strength, and courage as well as skill to qualify. Not until Theodore made several long journeys across the prairies with herds of cattle and accompanied cowhands on roundups did he become proficient at the grueling trade of the wrangler. On these expeditions he slept and ate in the open, taking his turn on duty, and frequently spent periods of twenty-four hours and even longer in the saddle. To the astonishment of his neighbors and employees, he found these experiences exhilarating.

He enjoyed hunting, too, shooting antelope, bear and buffalo, learning to treat the wild boar with respect and to exercise caution when

he encountered rattlesnakes. The hunt, he discovered, was a necessity when men went hungry, and became more than a pastime.

In spite of Theodore's eagerness to learn and share in the hardships
of the frontier, the Westerner regarded him with suspicion, and he
long remained an outsider. He had come to Medora as the proprietor
of a large herd of cattle and immediately thereafter became a ranch
owner. His cultivated, polysyllabic speech made men uncomfortable,
and many in the region continued to regard him as someone who
was playing at being a frontiersman.

But his willingness to seek no favors on the trail, share work burdens
without complaint, and, in the area's disputes with the railroads and
the stockyards of the Midwest over beef prices, to take up the West's
cause, gradually won him a grudging measure of acceptance.

In his enthusiasm, and to the dismay of his banker uncle in New
York, Theodore bought a second ranch and brought Bill Sewall, the
Maine guide, and his nephew to the Dakota Territory to operate it for
him. No man worked harder in an attempt to make a success of cattle
raising in a region where drought and too many herds were causing
grass to disappear at an alarming rate, and Theodore's earnestness,
combined with his scrupulous treatment of all men as his equals, slowly
enlarged his circle of new friends.

He joined the Montana Stockgrowers Association, and made such
a thorough study of the cattleman's problems that he soon became a
member of the organization's executive committee. He enjoyed the
long rides across the butte-covered prairies to the Association's meetings, but on one occasion found reason to wish he weren't traveling
alone.

Returning to his ranch, he halted at the end of a long day's ride in
the little town of Mingusville, and after stabling his horse entered the
lobby of the only hotel there. Even before the door closed behind him
he knew something was wrong: Gus Grisy, the proprietor, ordinarily
an affable man, waved to him feebly from the far side of the room, and
Minnie Grisy, his wife, seemed frozen behind the bar that ran the
length of the lobby. At least fifteen patrons were standing at the bar
or sitting at small tables near it, and they, too, were unusually silent.

The reason quickly became apparent. A powerfully built cowhand,
a two-day growth of beard on his florid face, was stalking up and down
near Grisy, his thumbs hooked in the gunbelt from which two pistols
protruded. Apparently he had paused for breath, but started talking

again as Theodore came into the lobby, and his speech consisted of an unintelligible string of oaths.

Theodore, preferring to avoid unpleasantness when possible, wanted to leave, but could not make an exit without calling undue attention to himself. Also, as he well knew, the night was too cold to sleep in the open, and there was no other lodging house within fifty miles of Mingusville. So he walked quietly to a table near the end of the bar, and, speaking in a low, conversational tone, asked Minnie for a mug of coffee.

But the cowhand had become aware of his presence, and pointed a grimy finger at him. "Well, we got more company! Four Eyes is here. You going to buy drinks for everybody, Four Eyes?"

Theodore pretended not to hear him.

"I say you're going to buy a lot of drinks!" The man drew one of his pistols and flourished it to emphasize his shouted words.

Theodore continued to stare off into space, hoping he looked calmer than he felt.

The cowhand, shoving his pistol back into its holster, crossed the lobby, staggering slightly, and came to a halt directly in front of the Easterner's table. "Are you deaf?" he demanded.

Theodore managed to look up at him and grinned painfully.

"Then do what I tell you. Buy drinks for everybody here, and do it now!"

Theodore realized that the man could draw one of his own pistols far more rapidly than an inexperienced outsider could pull his own pearl-handled pistol, which he carried principally for show, from its holster. Besides, the prospect of a shooting match in which a number of people might be killed or injured was as stupid as it was frightening.

On the other hand, he realized that if he permitted himself to be bullied he would lose whatever reputation he had managed to build up during the long months he had spent in the West. The codes of the region were still primitive, and no one would respect him, regardless of the danger, if he submitted meekly.

Swiftly he estimated his chances. He was no match for the taller, burlier man, but two factors were in his favor. He could box, and considered it unlikely that his antagonist had been trained in the sport. Equally important, he was sober, and therefore could move more quickly.

Still grinning, he pushed back his chair and rose slowly, hoping he was giving the impression that he intended to obey the order. Then, putting all of his strength behind his blows, he lashed out with his left to the side of the man's hand, following with a harder punch that caught the cowhand on the chin.

Taken by surprise, the man fell backward, his head crashing against the edge of the bar as he lost his balance. He was unconscious as he landed on the floor.

The triumphant Theodore could not resist the opportunity to play-act. "Throw him out, will you, boys?" he called.

"Hold on." Gus Grisy bent down and removed the pistols from the man's holster. "You don't want him gunning for you when he wakes up, Mr. Roosevelt."

Theodore's elation vanished, and he watched in a chastened mood as two of the other guests carried the unconscious man out of the lobby and deposited him in the dusty hotel yard.

Everyone started talking simultaneously, and the din filled the room. Grisy insisted on buying a round of drinks himself, his wife thanked Theodore at length, and the others crowded around him to slap him on the back and shake his hand.

When the excitement finally subsided, Theodore assessed his situation as he sipped his scalding coffee. He had done more in a few minutes than in all the previous months he had been in the Dakota Territory to win the unqualified acceptance of the settlers. And the chances were slight that the cowhand, after the effects of the liquor he had consumed wore off, would seek revenge against him.

Above all, Theodore knew, he had been very lucky. It had been the blow on the edge of the bar, not his punches, that had knocked his foe unconscious, and it was improbable that he could have accomplished the feat without the aid of the fortuitous accident, regardless of whether the man had been drunk or sober. He saw no reason, however, why an awareness of his own limitations should prevent him from exploiting the incident.

The Dakota Territory cast aside the last of its reservations and accepted Theodore as a true Westerner. Men began to speak of sending him to Congress when the Territory became a state, and he thanked his neighbors, but privately knew that Dakota would not become his permanent home, that his real roots lay in the East. During the long winter months he returned to an earlier profession and worked hard

writing two books, one a life of Thomas Hart Benton, a great frontiersman and colleague of Andrew Jackson who had become a distinguished United States Senator from Missouri.

He understood Benton and wrote about him with gusto, but the
other task he had set himself, a biography of the Revolutionary War
financier, Gouverneur Morris, proved more difficult. Morris, a man of
conservative temperament and limited horizons, had been something
of an enigma to his contemporaries, and Theodore found it hard to
sympathize with him.

In addition to the preparation of the two biographies, Theodore
found himself compelled to make frequent notes on frontier living and
the character of his neighbors. Gradually the conviction grew in him
that the American wilderness had been responsible for the strong sense
of individualism, love of liberty and intellectual independence that
had so long shaped the nation. Eventually, he knew, he would want
to put these beliefs on paper, and it was in his Dakota cabin, while
temperatures dropped far below zero and winds howled across the
prairies that he planned the most ambitious of his projects, *The Winning of the West.* He thought of writing the book in two volumes, but
soon found he could not handle the subject in such a limited space,
and reluctantly expanded the idea to a four-volume series.

More than all else, while working on the ranch, writing or hunting,
Theodore took care to keep in close touch with friends and associates
in the East. He maintained a steady correspondence with Henry Cabot
Lodge, and wrote steadily, although less frequently, to New Yorkers
who had supported his political career. *It wouldn't surprise me,* he said
in a letter to Corinne, *if I come home and run for office again some
day. I love my life here, but I feel closer to the problems of New York.*

During a sojourn of a little more than two years in the Dakota Territory he made several trips home, always eager to see his little daughter,
and, while in New York, took care to confer with leaders of the Republican party. Time, he found, was healing rifts he had believed impossible to reconcile. The members of the party's reform wing had
forgiven him for his refusal to repudiate James G. Blaine, while the
orthodox Republicans, although still somewhat uneasy in their dealings
with him, admitted their willingness to maintain relations because of
the possibility that he might become an attractive candidate for public
office at some future time.

Suddenly, in the early autumn of 1886, an opportunity arose. In the same sack of mail dropped from a train passing through Medora were letters from two reform Republicans he liked and respected. Chauncey Depew, who had been a friend of his father's, the vice-president and general counsel of the New York Central and other Vanderbilt railroad interests, urged him to come home in order to run for Mayor of New York later in the autumn. Elihu Root, a highly successful corporation lawyer, made the same suggestion.

How odd, Theodore wrote to Lodge, *that both of these gentlemen would like to promote the candidacy of someone who is no longer in politics. There is more happening than meets the eye of a simple cowboy with an insatiable bent for oratory. Since Anna is being married to W. S. Cowles, and I cannot reasonably expect her to remain the custodian of little Alice, whom I long to see, I shall go to New York, and there hope to discover why a Dakota rancher should have become a favorite of his one-time associates for a juicy plum of an office.*

A maid admitted Theodore to the Robinson house on Madison Avenue, and telling her he would announce himself, he started toward the stairs that led to the second-floor parlor, whistling tunelessly under his breath. He had good reason to be satisfied with all he had found since his return: Alice was thriving at the Oyster Bay house, Anna was in good health and happy, and he had been fortunate in piecing together information regarding the mayoralty race.

Bounding up the steps two at a time, he heard his younger sister's familiar laugh, and couldn't resist shouting to her.

"On your guard, Conie! There's a wild cowman from the Dakota Badlands after you!"

He charged into the parlor, stopped short when he saw that Corinne was having tea with another young woman, and turned scarlet when he recognized Edith Carow.

Conie was equal to the situation, and crossing the room quickly, greeted her brother with a kiss.

Edith, always dignified and reserved, looked even more attractive than Theodore had remembered, and managed a self-conscious smile. "Do all cowmen from the Dakota Badlands wear London-made suits?"

"I've kept my city clothes. For my visits." He couldn't recall when he had felt so ill at ease, but did not forget his manners. "You're looking well, Edith."

Corinne knew her friend had been avoiding Theodore for years, and tried desperately to think of a diversion that would relieve the tensions of the accidental meeting.

But Edith needed no help. "Thank you. I must say you seem in good health, Theodore."

"I've been in the open for months. Range life is guaranteed to put muscle on a man."

"I like your mustache, too."

"I'm not sure I do," Conie said, surveying her brother critically. Suddenly aware that neither heard her comment, she wisely subsided.

"I was thinking of shaving it off," Theodore said, beaming, "but maybe I'll keep it." He struggled to overcome a wave of shyness. "You've lost weight, Edith."

She refrained from saying she had taken off a few pounds several years earlier, but realized he wouldn't remember her appearance at the funeral, the only time since his wedding that they had met.

Suddenly Theodore became conscious of a bundle under his arm. "I brought one of my deerskin shirts to show Conie. Would you like to see it?" Not waiting for a reply, he unfolded it and held it up.

He looked and sounded precisely like a small boy showing off. Corinne, suppressing a laugh, glanced at her friend, and was fascinated when she saw that Edith was inspecting the shirt with a solemn air.

"It's very handsome, Theodore."

"Not really. But it's useful." He began to fidget.

All at once Edith appeared to have nothing to say, either.

Corinne stepped into the breach. "Why don't you stay for dinner, Edith? Theodore and Douglas are planning to have a political talk, but it shouldn't keep them busy too long."

"It'll take no time at all," Theodore said earnestly.

Edith's regret was genuine. "I'm so sorry, but I promised my mother I'd be home in time to help her select the steamer trunks she's had sent to the house. We're going to England next month," she added when Theodore looked blank.

"The weather will be getting a bit unpleasant for a visit by then."

Obviously he hadn't heard that her father had suffered financial reverses and was planning to work in London. "We aren't going on a visit. In fact, we may stay more or less permanently."

Theodore had no idea how dismayed he looked, but he recovered swiftly. "If you don't have a carriage, mine is at the door, and I'd enjoy paying my respects to your parents. I haven't seen them in a long time."

"I'm sure they'll be pleased." Edith glanced out of the window. "And I would appreciate a ride. I hadn't realized it was growing so late."

Corinne saw them to the front door, and wasn't in the least surprised when Theodore made no mention of returning. It was probable that the Robinsons wouldn't see him again that night, just as it was certain that most of his evenings would be occupied in the weeks ahead.

The hotel on 14th Street made a half-hearted effort to keep up appearances, but European aristocrats and merchant princes from other American cities had moved to newer hostelries uptown. The rugs were faded, the gas jet fixtures needed polishing and the furniture was threadbare. But Tom Platt was indifferent to elegance; he found the place both comfortable and convenient, and a few scuff marks on the tables meant nothing to him.

Sipping the one mild drink of whiskey and water he allowed himself late in the day, he smiled at his guest. "I've been looking forward to this meeting, Teddy."

Theodore cautioned himself not to take offense. Platt had no idea he loathed the nickname, and was merely trying to be friendly. At this juncture there was much to be gained and little to lose by adopting the same attitude and hearing what he had in mind. Grinning, Theodore hoped he looked at home in the parlor of the dingy hotel suite. "I've been anxious to get together, too. From what I hear, this has become Republican headquarters, Tom."

Platt grimaced, making his long face look even more lugubrious. "There are some who claim the party doesn't exist in New York any more, and I can't really blame them for feeling the way they do. I spent just enough time in the U. S. Senate to develop a liking for the place, but the voters didn't want to keep me there. The Democrats sent Dave Hill to Albany as the governor with a huge majority last year, and I still feel as though I've been kicked by the Democratic mule when I think of the beating Levi Morton took from William Evarts for the Senate seat."

"I've been away, of course, so I'm not familiar with the specific situation," Theodore said, and sounded convincing.

"It's simple. We fought among ourselves, and the people lost faith in us. But I'm devoting myself to rebuilding the party. And I'm positive," he added firmly, "that we'll eventually regain all we've lost."

Theodore quietly tucked away what he considered the key word, "eventually."

"We've got to work together, all of us, no matter what wing of the party we support. It's too much to hope we'll win anything big in the state during the next couple of years, but we have our chance here in the city."

Theodore nodded, but remained silent. Platt, he had learned since coming home, had been responsible for the letters suggesting he run for mayor, and he wanted to find out more before making any comment.

Silence did not make Tom Platt uncomfortable, and he sipped his drink, then suddenly said, "I suppose you've met Henry George."

"We spoke at the same dinner three or four years ago."

"He's a damned radical, a Socialist."

Theodore refused to pin false labels on anyone, even a man he disliked. "I'm no economist, but George's ideas on taxation and the reversion of land to the public don't strike me as Socialism. I'd call him a muddle-head. He likes to advertise himself as a reformer, but he's a cheap opportunist who'll change his theories and do anything to advance himself."

"Whatever he is, he's running for mayor as an independent, and he's won the solid support of every labor union in town," Platt said.

"He can't be allowed to win. The day he took office, New York would become the joke of the country."

"I suppose you've heard that some of the financial people would move to Philadelphia or Boston."

"So my brother-in-law tells me." Theodore refrained from adding that Bob Bacon, now a junior partner in J. P. Morgan's office, refused to take the threat of Henry George's possible election seriously.

"Wall Street is afraid, the shipping and railroad people are afraid, manufacturers are afraid," Platt said ominously. "The ordinary citizens —honest, decent people who work hard for a living—are damned scared, too."

The situation wasn't as black as Platt was painting it, Theodore believed.

"Dick Croker of Tammany has pulled a rabbit out of that old hat he wears," Platt said, unable to conceal his envy. "It was real genius to persuade Abe Hewitt to run as the Democratic candidate for mayor. You know Hewitt?"

Theodore merely nodded, seeing no need to reveal that Abram Hewitt, a wealthy manufacturer of steam engines and iron girders, for-

mer United States Congressman and one of the city's leading philan-
thropists, had served with his father as a trustee of various charitable
institutions.

"He has a great record," Platt continued. "There's never been a
strike in one of his plants, and everybody old enough to remember the
Civil War knows he refused to accept one penny of profit on the cannon he made for the Union Artillery. What's more, he's so damn rich
that even with Tammany support everybody in town knows he
wouldn't steal a nickel."

Hewitt, in Theodore's opinion, would be New York's best mayor in
many years.

"But he has one liability that not even Croker could wash away.
Hewitt is old. In his sixties. So our tactics become obvious." Platt spoke
confidentially, leaning forward and putting a veined hand on his visitor's knee. "This is the year everybody wants reform. Hewitt is an old
reformer. Henry George is a crazy reformer. So the Republican party
puts up a young, fighting reformer, Teddy Roosevelt! We beat age
with youth and vitality. We beat George because he isn't sensible—and
because Sam Gompers likes you, which I happen to know. Here's the
chance to hold a major office, to jump to the top of the party. You'll
be the only Republican in all of New York State to be in a front-rank
office." Platt leaned back, looking smug. "Say the word, and you'll have
the job, Teddy."

"First," Theodore replied quietly, "I'd have to be elected."

"Leave that to me. With you as our candidate, the boys will work
—right down to the precinct level—as they've never worked before!
And we can count on heavy campaign contributions. Elihu Root and
Levi Morton tell me they can set up a war chest in less than twenty-
four hours."

"It's tempting," Theodore said, showing no emotion.

"I suggest we call a press conference for tomorrow to announce your
candidacy."

"I'll need more time," Theodore said.

Platt was surprised and annoyed. "Every day of delay gives Hewitt
—and Henry George—more of an advantage."

Theodore's jaw jutted forward. "It will take me another week to assess the situation. If you can't wait that long, Tom, I suggest you find
someone else."

Platt's expression indicated that, if he could, he would be delighted to work with anyone else. But his need was too great, and he surrendered. "Give me your answer a week from today," he said.

The weather was still warm, but the traditional fire of hickory logs burned in the library hearth at the Union League Club. It was said that no known Democrat had set foot in the place since it had been founded during the Civil War, and even political independents were regarded with distrust when seen with members in the oak-paneled dining room. The massive, overstuffed furniture, heavy drapes and thick rugs created an oppressive atmosphere, and in the library, lined with shelves of leather-bound books which were dusted regularly but read infrequently, no one had ever been known to speak above a low murmur. A few bankers, brokers and corporation executives were glancing through the day's newspapers, and there was no sound but the crackling of the burning logs and the occasional rattle of a newspaper page being turned.

Theodore found both the heat and silence stifling, and moved toward an open window at the far end of the room from the hearth, and Elihu Root, his host, followed him. Ponderous and square-faced, with impressively bushy side whiskers, looked like the legal representative of the wealthy he had become, but his eyes, often amused, sometimes sympathetic and always sensitive, revealed other, unexpected facets of his nature. Lowering himself into a heavy leather chair, he tugged at the gold watch fob hanging from his waistcoat and asked, "Would you like a glass of wine before lunch?"

Theodore spoke even more loudly than usual in order to compensate for the library's quiet. "I never cared for wine, and I haven't been able to tolerate it since drinking nothing but water or coffee in Dakota. But don't let me stop you."

Root signaled to an attendant, and smiled when he saw the glares of the newspaper readers. He had expected his guest to upset the decorum of the club, and was not disappointed. "You started to tell me about the private survey you conducted."

"In the past week I've spoken to scores of people, perhaps hundreds." Theodore demonstrated a surprising awareness of his surroundings, and although still speaking more loudly than the traditions of the club dictated, lowered his voice slightly. "I've talked with everyone from Joe Murray and my old friends in the Twenty-first District to bartenders, members of Sam Gompers' unions, even some of the fish sellers I knew as a boy on Fulton Street."

"Chauncey Depew and Levi Morton expected you to call on them," Root said, a gleam of humor appearing in his eyes.

"I know how they intend to vote, so I didn't waste my time. I'd expect the support of Republicans, including every member of this club." Theodore grinned amiably at an elderly gentleman who was glowering at him over the top of the *Tribune*. "What I wanted to find out was where I'd stand with men who belong to no political parties or organizations. They're the ones who'll decide this election."

He was right, Root thought, and wondered how he had acquired an almost uncanny ability to locate and analyze the core of a political problem. "At dinner last night, John Hay said the same thing." Hay, President Lincoln's secretary, had served abroad in various legations, written editorials for the *Tribune* and, more recently, acted as President Hayes' Assistant Secretary of State. "He's convinced that neither we nor Tammany can win without the help of the independent voter."

"There's no question about it. People in this town don't follow the patterns that have developed in other places. Oh, we have our hard-core Republicans and Democrats, but most New Yorkers reserve judgment, vote for the individual and let the party go hang."

Two of the newspaper readers had overcome their annoyance and were eavesdropping shamelessly.

"I've never bet on an election," Theodore continued, "but I'm so sure of the results this time that I could almost be persuaded to put up a small sum."

"You think Hewitt will win?" Root asked.

"Without question!" Theodore forgot his surroundings, and his voice soared. "Men who have never voted for a Democrat in their lives—and who hate Croker and Tammany Hall—are giving him their support. I'm inclined to vote for him myself," he added with a chuckle.

Amusement showed only in Root's eyes. "You aren't afraid that organized labor support will put George into the mayor's office?"

"The support isn't that strong. Labor has too much respect for Abe Hewitt, and it wouldn't surprise me if Gompers himself votes for him."

"Even if you're a candidate?"

"I refused to embarrass him by asking him that personal a question. All he told me, and my own investigation confirmed it, is that the labor unions aren't too well acquainted with me, and don't really like what they know. They approve of the cigar-making bill I pushed through the Assembly, but they haven't forgotten or forgiven my opposition to pay increases for the city's firemen. If I had to vote on that bill again tomorrow," he said, thumping the arm of his leather chair, "I'd still vote against giving them higher wages."

One of the elderly newspaper readers nodded in approval.

Root sipped his glass of wine. "What have you decided, Theodore? Will you accept the nomination?"

"I'll see Tom Platt."

The attorney was silent for a moment. "You don't think you can be elected?"

"No one stands a chance against Hewitt. And I think Henry George's vote would be bigger than mine."

"Then you'll refuse." Root was openly disappointed.

"No." Theodore sat back in his chair and grinned, enjoying his host's bewilderment.

AM BADLY DEFEATED. WORSE EVEN THAN I FEARED, Theodore said in a telegram to Henry Cabot Lodge. According to the final tally in the race for Mayor of New York, he ran thirty thousand votes behind Abram Hewitt, and trailed Henry George by eight thousand.

Nevertheless he had accomplished his basic purpose, as he told Lodge in a confidential letter written the same day. *I have returned to the thick of the battle in New York. I'm recognized everywhere, and have won, even though I've lost.*

A few days later he sailed for England to marry Edith Carow, who, with her family, had preceded him to London. Never had a couple who had known each other so long made a vital decision so quickly and without fuss.

On board the ship was a slender, dashing young English diplomat, Cecil Spring-Rice, a close friend of Lodge's, with whom Theodore was acquainted. Rice was willing and able to take any position in a debate, and the two men, arguing interminably, were on such good terms by the time they reached London that Theodore asked Rice to act as his best man.

The wedding was scheduled to take place at St. George's, Hanover Square, at noon on December 2, 1886, but that morning a panicky Anna Roosevelt Cowles, who had accompanied her brother, was afraid it would not take place. An hour before he was expected at the church, Theodore, unshaven and still clad in pajamas and dressing gown, lingered at the breakfast table in the parlor of his hotel suite.

"Springy," he said to his best man, "you're living proof that Eton and Balliol don't educate a man. They merely stuff you with the facts

of ancient history to the tune of *God Save the Queen*. Every word
you speak condemns you. It's obvious and incredible that you know
nothing about the Hawaiian Islands since the reign of Kamehameha I
more than three-quarters of a century ago."

Spring-Rice smoothed his ascot and tugged at the lapels of his frock
coat. "I pity you, Theodore, for being a bombastic American ignoramus. Hasn't anyone ever told you they're properly called the Sandwich Islands?"

Anna looked at them in helpless consternation. Although she had
become accustomed to their violent exchanges of insults, this was no
time for mutual harangues.

Theodore jumped to his feet, tugging at the sash of his robe. "If you
don't mind, sir, I prefer the name the natives give their kingdom,
Hawaii."

"Call it what you will, I represent that British influence is growing,
and they'll enter into a permanent association with us." Spring-Rice's
tone was withering.

"Arrogant as well as ill-informed." Theodore's sigh was exaggerated.
"I assert, as a fact, not a prediction, that the Hawaiian Reciprocity
Treaty with the United States will be renewed this coming year."

"Please, Theodore, get dressed," his sister said.

He ignored the interruption. "The union of Hawaii and the United
States is inevitable because of the identicality of our interests. You
English own half the earth already. Be satisfied and stop reaching out
those greedy lion's paws for more territory!"

"Aha!" Spring-Rice was triumphant. "At last you reveal your true
colors. You're nothing but a damned, territory-hungry jingoist."

"You try to tar me with your own imperial brush, but you fail," Theodore shouted. "What you can't or won't understand is that the Hawaiians want our protection, not as colonials, but as free and equal
members of our Union."

"Cecil," Anna said in despair, "he'll keep this up all day unless you
help me."

Both men became aware of her presence, and looked at her sheepishly.

"I beg your pardon, Anna." Spring-Rice bowed stiffly, the correct
and proper Third Secretary of the British Embassy in Washington.

Theodore ran a hand through his hair. "What time is it, Bamie?"
he asked, trying without success to sound unconcerned.

"Almost ten past eleven, and you have an appointment to be married in fifty minutes. I don't believe Edith will appreciate being kept waiting because of a nonsensical discussion of Hawaiians, or Sandwich Islanders, or whatever they're called."

Theodore fled in the direction of his bedroom, shedding his robe. "Hawaiians! Springy, will you lay out my suit and put the studs in my shirt?"

"Certainly, old boy. I'm here to do odd jobs." Spring-Rice followed him, calm and cheerful.

Anna looked after them shaking her head, and didn't envy the bride. But she remembered what Conie had said to her about her best friend: "Don't waste sympathy on Edith. Ever since we were children she's understood Teedee better than anyone, and she's the one person on earth who can handle him."

"What strikes you as most remarkable about Venice?" Theodore, hatless and waving both arms, appeared blissfully unaware of the tourists and priests, strolling Venetian citizens and beggars in the square outside St. Mark's Cathedral. Squinting at a pigeon that landed at his feet, he repeated the question in a booming voice.

Only Edith could have remained unflustered. Accustomed to his idiosyncrasies since childhood, she reflected calmly, looking at the Cathedral, then at the Ducal Palace. "There's so much here—the Grand Canal, the paintings, those clever artists who blow glass." She was willing to play the game because it amused him, and considered the matter seriously. "I find myself thinking of Shakespeare's play, too. It's astonishing that a man who never saw Venice, who probably never left England, could have so captured the spirit of this place."

"Everything you say is true, but you're missing what's really remarkable." Theodore waved energetically to some fellow-Americans who had shared a gondola with the Roosevelts on a tour of Venice's canals.

"If I've missed something," Edith said dryly, "I'm sure you'll correct me."

"I'm not thinking in aesthetic terms, or even of the fact that this church was modeled after the church of Saint Sophia in Constantinople. Did you know it was?"

"Yes, dear. You told me about it at breakfast." Edith took his arm and started to walk again before a swarm of beggars could descend on them.

"The population of Venice has been stabilized at about one hundred and forty thousand since the beginning of the seventeenth century. And it wasn't much lower for the previous five hundred years. In other words, it's about the size of a comfortable American town like Buffalo. If you prefer, it has only fifty thousand fewer people than the District of Columbia."

"Comparative population figures were the very last thing on my mind." She began to laugh.

Had anyone but Edith mocked him, he would have been outraged, but he grinned at her. "Venice was a city-state. One of the most powerful on earth. Think of it!"

"Must I, Theodore? I'd much rather see the sculptures we missed in the Doge's Palace."

"How did they manage it? That's the question. How did this city-state succeed where others failed?"

She tried to reconcile herself to the inevitability of a history lecture. "If you insist on delivering a speech, let's go somewhere for coffee. I'll be much more attentive if I'm sitting down. These shoes pinch."

"The Venetian character did it!" Theodore sounded triumphant.

Edith guided him toward a cafe.

"I'm thinking of the United States, not Venice."

"I know."

He stopped short, blinking at her. "How?"

"I couldn't possibly explain it." She took his arm again, more firmly.

"My point is that when a people have character, their nation achieves greatness as it matures. I can cite you twenty examples—"

"Forty, probably. In full detail." They reached the cafe, and she found a vacant table beneath a faded awning.

Theodore, speaking rapidly, as he always did when he became excited, told her that President James K. Polk was one of the most maligned men in American history because his doctrine asserting the manifest destiny of the United States had been premature by more than a half-century.

Edith nodded as he talked, meanwhile quietly ordering two cups of coffee and, for her husband, several of the Venetian plum tarts he loved.

"Think of our energy!" he boomed. "Think of our growing industries and our dedication to liberty! We're unique!"

"You might lower your voice slightly. Everyone in the place is staring at you!"

"You miss my point." He was stubborn, but nevertheless spoke more quietly. "European travel is making me realize our own national potential. I'm turning into a patriot."

"You've always been a patriot, Theodore."

"No, I—"

"The summer when you were ten," she continued, "your family and mine were visiting someone or other on Independence Day. They had an old cannon and some iron cannonballs decorating their yard. I couldn't possibly tell you how old they were."

"The War of 1812," he said promptly.

"You stuffed an iron ball into the cannon, and you found some gunpowder in the room where hunting rifles and things like that were kept."

Theodore grinned sheepishly.

"You wanted to fire the cannon as a Fourth of July salute, and you were very indignant when the adults stopped you."

"I remember. My father put me on restrictions—all sorts of restrictions." Theodore thought for a moment, then shook his head. "He was wrong."

"He was right. You could have blown up all of us children."

"Aside from the fact that I knew how to handle gunpowder—"

"You didn't, Theodore. Not at the age of ten!"

"—I should have been encouraged, not punished," he continued, ignoring her interruption. "My father was a pure American. No man was more devoted to the United States. But he might have made me feel less enthusiastic."

"No one," Edith said, "could do that. I don't think anyone could love his country more than you do."

His eyes were solemn behind his glasses. "You know my feelings before I realize them myself."

"Some of your feelings, I suppose."

"Most of our friends are inclined to take the country for granted. I've been accused of being naïve."

"You won't change, Theodore." Edith saw that he was disturbed, and, although she disapproved of public gestures of affection, put her hand over his. "Educated men from far more sophisticated countries than ours make no secret of their patriotism. There's no need for you to be ashamed—"

"Ashamed?" His voice rose again. "I'm proud! I'd like to tell the whole world it's grand to be an American!"

"You're making a good beginning." She was still sympathetic, but her expression was wry.

Theodore looked blank for a moment, then realized that everyone in the crowded cafe was staring at him and smiling. His own principles were unalterable, however, and Edith approved, so he was indifferent to the reactions of others. "You know," he said, making a sudden discovery, "I'm homesick. Instead of going back to Geneva and Paris, let's go home."

The winter of 1886–87 was the most severe Dakota had known since the first settlers had established homesteads there, and both cattle losses and property damage were catastrophic. As soon as the Roosevelts reached New York, Theodore made a hurried trip to his ranch, and learned that the worst had happened. His own herds had been virtually destroyed, and, in all, he had lost about eighty thousand dollars, approximately the sum he had inherited from his mother.

"Unless you badly need cash, which I doubt," Douglas Robinson advised him when he returned to New York, "don't sell out. Statehood for North and South Dakota will be a stabilizing influence, and property values are certain to go up in the next ten to fifteen years. Wait, and you'll recoup most of what you've lost."

A loss of any kind, in finances, politics or the boxing ring, was intolerable to a man whose hunger for victory was insatiable. "I'll try to hang on," Theodore replied gloomily, "but it won't be easy."

Nothing in his style of living indicated that he was embarrassed by a lack of funds, however. He, Edith, and his little daughter took up permanent residence in the house at Oyster Bay that he had built for Alice Lee, and he spent thousands on furnishings, hired a staff of servants and bought a stable of horses. He couldn't resist the temptation, either, to fill the shelves of the library with new additions to his already considerable collection.

"The library is so big," he explained, "that my books don't fill more than half the space, and the sight of empty shelves makes me uncomfortable. Besides, there's so much I want to read."

Only when Edith went into New York to buy material for new summer wardrobes for herself and her stepdaughter did he protest that they were living in straitened circumstances.

Edith smiled in resignation, but returned none of her purchases.

Theodore named the gabled house Sagamore Hill, and settled into a new life. The house itself filled the needs of a man who had accustomed himself to the vast spaces of the West. The parlor was enormous, as were the dining room, library and kitchen, and the bed-chambers were spacious. "This place was built to last," Theodore told the visitors whom he insisted on showing through the place. "Why, the foundations are twenty inches thick!"

Alice bloomed under Edith's care, and spent much of her time play-ing with her cousin, Eleanor, Elliott's shy little daughter, who was almost precisely her own age. "The house is big enough for an army of children," its master declared, and the nursery was put to use when Theodore, Junior, was born in the autumn of 1887.

Theodore loved to entertain, and Edith soon acclimated herself to his ways, becoming what Cecil Spring-Rice, a frequent visitor from Washington, called "a perfect hostess." The variety of guests was be-wildering, and reflected Theodore's ever-broadening interests and in-satiable curiosity about his fellow humans.

One never knowns whom one will find there, Spring-Rice wrote. *One expects to see Vanderbilts and rising young men in the empires of Morgan, Harriman, et al., and does. One also sees authors, renowned and unknown, horse trainers and Maine woodsmen, university profes-sors, and even saloon-keepers and the like from New York, who mangle the Queen's English. Edith treats them all with gracious se-renity, and is magnificent. She alone prevents a degeneration into the Bedlam that Theodore seems intent on creating.*

Few men active in politics made the journey to Sagamore Hill. Theodore's name had become known in New York, thanks to his candidacy for mayor, but the Democrats were riding high, and the Republicans, it appeared, had little use for a loser. The one exception was Henry Cabot Lodge, who was quietly making himself the master of the Republican party in Massachusetts. He and his gentle wife, Nannie, paid frequent visits to Oyster Bay, but it was a strain to dis-cuss politics with a man whose party didn't want him, and Lodge usually chatted with his host about their other mutual interest, history.

With no other vocational interests to occupy his energies, Theodore returned to his writing with a vengeance. He published his biography *Thomas Hart Benton,* which received a limited but enthusiastic critical acclaim. Polishing his biography of Gouverneur Morris, he wrote a small volume, *The Wilderness Hunter,* describing his adventures in the West, and then turned out a *History of New York* that was ac-curate but lacking in exuberance. And, discussing the project with no one, he continued to work on *The Winning of the West.*

Still devoted to strenuous physical exercise, he hiked, swam, and sailed, boxed with anyone he could persuade to don gloves, played tennis and rode. His love of competition made riding for its own sake dull, so he persuaded his neighbors to ride to hounds, and organized a polo club, too. Thrown frequently because of his recklessness in the saddle, he endured a broken arm without complaint, and told no one of the injury until he had remounted and finished the chase.

No matter how crowded his athletic and social schedules, no matter how furiously he wrote and read, sometimes devouring three books in a single evening, he always found ample time to play with the children, and habitually set aside the early morning hours for them. "I honestly believe," the bachelor Spring-Rice said, "that he enjoys a romp as much as the children do. When he plays with them he forgets he's an adult. That's the secret of his success."

In 1889 Edith gave birth to her second son, Kermit, and the delighted Theodore wrote the good news to everyone he knew. Little Ted was moved out of the nursery, and Theodore taught him to ride, but was forbidden by Edith to buy him a gun of his own until he was a few years older.

The youngsters were given increased paternal attention during the summer, and were joined by the children of relatives, friends, and Oyster Bay neighbors. Swarms of them accompanied Theodore on hikes, picnics and, on rainy days, at violent games in the barn. He particularly enjoyed anchoring a sailboat offshore and swimming with them, and in the summer of 1889 took an enthusiastic group with him every day.

One very hot afternoon he set his usual example for them by diving from the boat into the water, and the competitions he invented for them were endless. Eventually, however, he hoisted himself back onto the deck to rest for a few minutes, and was surprised to see his niece sitting alone in the stern, staring moodily across the calm water.

Her loneliness immediately reminded him of his own childhood, and he felt a quick stab of sympathy. "Eleanor!" he called.

Showing a dignity beyond her years, she looked at him, stood and slowly went to him.

He was puzzled when he saw that her bathing suit was dry. "Aren't you feeling well?"

"I'm fine, Uncle Theodore."

"Then why aren't you with the others?" He gestured toward the splashing, shrieking youngsters who surrounded the boat.

Eleanor hesitated briefly. "I can't swim."

"Poppycock! All Roosevelts can swim!" he insisted.

The little girl's expression remained calm. "Well, I can't," she replied stubbornly.

"Why not?"

"Because I'm afraid." She spoke without shame, in a matter-of-fact tone.

Theodore was torn, but quickly decided a drastic cure was necessary. "We'll soon take care of that," he said, and, picking her up, threw her overboard.

Eleanor thrashed wildly, the water around her turning white.

Watching her, Theodore chuckled aloud. Within seconds she would be dog-paddling, and before the day ended would be swimming as expertly as the rest. One of the greatest advantages of childhood was a youngster's ability to learn quickly.

Eleanor made no sound, and all at once, her flailings ceasing, she sank below the surface.

The alarmed Theodore jumped into the water, scooped her under one arm and deposited her, coughing, on the boat. Hauling himself onto the deck, he peered at her anxiously, unable to see her expression clearly without his glasses. "Are you all right?"

She continued to sputter for a moment, but when she spoke there was no panic in her voice. "I swallowed some water, but I'll be all right."

"You almost drowned!" Recovering from his fright, he became accusing.

"I told you I couldn't swim," the little girl replied logically.

"But you didn't cry out or shout to me!"

"I didn't want you to think I was a baby."

He regarded her thoughtfully. Eleanor wasn't like his extroverted, athletic children or Corinne's, but she had her own brand of iron-willed Roosevelt courage, and although still badly upset, he couldn't help feeling proud of her. At the same time, however, an immediate goal remained to be accomplished. "I'll take you ashore, and we'll go into the shallow water. One way or another, you'll learn to swim before dinner time tonight."

Republican hopes revived in 1888, a presidential election year, and the party was gaining strength in key states. Tom Platt felt certain New York would return to the Republican banner, McKinley and

Hanna were confident that Ohio would turn out the Democrats and
Matthew S. Quay, a new leader in Pennsylvania, was building a solid
organization. The Republicans nominated General Benjamin Harrison
for President, and his background was sure to appeal to the country.
A Civil War hero, he was the son of President William Henry Harrison, who had attained legendary fame as an Indian fighter in the
Midwest.

Theodore suddenly showed a renewed interest in politics, and in
the weeks prior to the election made a speaking tour of New York
State, attacking President Cleveland's stand in favor of lowering
tariffs. Harrison was elected, and Theodore promptly informed his
political friends that he was interested in a return to public service.

The President-elect appointed James G. Blaine as his Secretary of
State, and Nannie Lodge, reminding Blaine that Theodore had resisted the attempts to persuade him to leave the party in '84, suggested
he might make an excellent Assistant Secretary.

Blaine wrote her a reply that threw cold water on the idea. *I do
somehow fear that my sleep in Augusta or Bar Harbor would not be
quite so easy or refreshing if so brilliant and aggressive a man had
hold of the helm. Matters are constantly occurring which require the
most thoughtful concentration and the most stubborn inaction. Do
YOU think that T.R.'s temperament would give guaranty of that
course?*

Theodore's friends went to Harrison, saying that the loyalty of an
energetic, prominent young Republican should be rewarded, but the
General displayed no enthusiasm over the prospect of finding a place
in his Administration for the thirty-year-old New Yorker. "He's a
storm-maker," he said, "and I don't think anyone could control him."

Lodge persisted, as did Root, Depew, and the other reform leaders
in New York, and a month after Harrison's inauguration in the early
spring of 1889 he reluctantly offered Theodore a place on the four-man
Civil Service Commission. Certain that the post was insufficiently important to satisfy an ambitious young man, Harrison believed that
Theodore would decline, and was appalled when he received an immediate letter of acceptance.

On May 13, 1889, Theodore arrived in Washington to take the oath
of office, rent a house for his family and upset the equanimity of the
nation's capital. Harrison, unfamiliar with Theodore's brief record of
public service, did not know that the reform and extension of the Civil

Service, which had been strengthened by new laws during Cleveland's Administration, were keystones in the New Yorker's developing philosophy of government. He and job-hungry Republicans throughout the United States were about to receive an education.

I am a great believer in practical politics, Theodore wrote to Lodge, *but when my duty is to enforce a law, that law is surely going to be enforced, without fear or favor. I am perfectly willing to be turned out or legislated out—but while in I mean business.*

The rented house off Connecticut Avenue soon became an active social center. The Lodges and Cecil Spring-Rice were frequent guests, and Theodore formed a new, close friendship with Richard Harding Davis, an energetic newspaper correspondent who also wrote books of action-packed adventure. Rudyard Kipling, England's most famous author, was paying an extended visit to the United States, and Theodore, who had admired his work, saw him often, but developed a personal contempt for him. "I admire his writing," he said to Owen Wister, who was creating a new brand of fiction by writing about the West, "but I can't tolerate any man who constantly criticizes the United States!"

In the unique atmosphere of a city devoted exclusively to government, where men thought in national and international terms, Theodore's circle expanded rapidly. An amiable, food-loving Ohioan, William Howard Taft, son of President Grant's Attorney General, Alphonso Taft, was approximately Theodore's age, and the two discovered they shared many ideals when Taft was appointed Solicitor General. Jim Garfield, son of the assassinated President, became one of Theodore's admirers and confidants. And no man was more fascinated by the explosive New Yorker than the cynical Henry Adams of Boston.

Great-grandson of President John Adams, grandson of President John Quincy Adams and son of the distinguished diplomat, Charles Francis Adams, Henry had much in common with Theodore. A Harvard graduate who later had taught there, he had achieved renown as a historian and biographer, and was generally regarded as the leading authority on the Administrations of Jefferson and Madison. Theodore admired his biographies of Albert Gallatin and John Randolph, leading statesmen in the early days of the nation, and Adams, in turn, enjoyed *Thomas Hart Benton* and *Gouverneur Morris*.

"We've formed a very small, exclusive society devoted to mutual admiration," Theodore said.

Adams explained their friendship in different terms. "I've heard people wonder how Washington will change Theodore. It won't. But I can hardly wait to see what Theodore will do to Washington."

Theodore, behaving as though he were the only Civil Service Commissioner, threw himself into his work with a fury that left easygoing Washington aghast. Convinced there would be a strong demand for reform if the people understood what was at stake, he took it upon himself to educate the American people on the subject, and gave so many lively interviews to the press that even Edith finally protested, telling him he was making too many enemies in a city where scores of officials sought the newspapers' headlines.

Gradually, amid the din, the outlines of a pending battle took shape, and it was inevitable that Theodore's foe should be Postmaster General John Wanamaker. One of the country's wealthiest drygoods merchants and a major contributor to the Republican party, Wanamaker was so dedicated to the spoils system that he dismissed thirty thousand postmasters and replaced them with faithful party workers.

A conflict became unavoidable when Charles J. Bonaparte, a young Baltimore lawyer, came to the Civil Service Commission with evidence indicating that Post Office Department officials in that city who had been appointed by Wanamaker rarely visited their offices, left their responsibilities to untrained subordinates and were making a shambles of mail collection and delivery. Theodore went to Baltimore, made a personal investigation and called a press conference as soon as he returned to Washington.

CIVIL SERVICE COMMISSIONER DEMANDS CONGRESSIONAL INQUIRY OF P.O. MALPRACTICES, newspaper headlines screamed.

Wanamaker promptly sent Theodore a curt note: *My Dear Roosevelt—Be good enough to let me run my Department. J.W.*

Theodore, reacting just as quickly, cranked his recently installed telephone and called the Postmaster General. "Mr. Wanamaker," he said, "I'm not attacking you, but I'm convinced that the abuses in Baltimore—and in hundreds of other communities—won't end until Congress passes a new law requiring all Government appointments to be made on the merit system."

"I wish you'd see me," the Postmaster General said, "before you give any more press interviews."

A quarter of an hour later Theodore presented himself at the surprised Postmaster General's office. A huge oil painting of President

Harrison dwarfed the diminutive figure of the Philadelphia merchant, who greeted his visitor with chilly reserve.

Theodore took what he considered a diplomatic approach. "Mr. Postmaster General," he said, "I've been your admirer for a long time. Your work for the Young Men's Christian Association will benefit the whole world, and your reorganization of the Presbyterian Sunday school curriculum was a masterpiece."

Wanamaker did not thaw. "But you don't approve of me as a Cabinet member."

"Well, sir, I believe flaws that have existed since the Administration of Andrew Jackson—and that are no reflection on you—will disappear when all Post Office appointments except those at the very top are determined by examinations."

"Young man, you're fortunate that your father left you comfortably fixed, or you'd starve. You've never had to earn a living, and you have no idea of what makes the world turn. Thousands of men worked hard for the election of President Harrison, just as they've worked for every other President who has ever held office. They have rents to pay, food and clothing to buy for their families. They deserve their rewards."

Theodore found it difficult to remain civil. "In my opinion the spoils system corrupts the foundations of democracy!"

The Postmaster General lost his temper. "You weren't brought into this Administration to disrupt it. If you don't like practical politics, resign and go home."

Theodore no longer cared that he was dealing with one of President Harrison's intimates, a cabinet member and the single biggest contributor to the Republican party's campaign fund. "Practical politics can be raised from the gutter, sir! I not only obey the law, but intend to do everything in my power to get stronger laws that will prevent abuses and corruption."

"I warn you, stay away from Congress! You've already caused enough trouble!"

"I've been invited to appear before two House committees and one in the Senate." Theodore stood, leaned across the desk and shook his fist under the nose of the Postmaster General. "I'll keep those appointments," he continued, relishing his histrionics, "no matter what the cost!"

"The cost—to you—will be dear. Good day, Mr. Roosevelt."

President Harrison sent for Congressman Henry Cabot Lodge, who was considered certain to become a Senator from Massachusetts in the next election. "You brought Roosevelt here," he said.

Lodge coughed behind his hand. "Theodore is determined to win your Administration a high place in history, Mr. President."

"Tell him to let history take care of itself."

"His reforms are very popular, and every newspaper in the country is supporting him, Mr. President."

"The newspapers don't have to live with John Wanamaker—and all the good people who worked for me."

Lodge doggedly continued to defend his friend. "His aim, sir, is to make it unnecessary for any President to pay off such embarrassing political debts. He believes it's degrading for the office of the President to engage in that sort of traffic."

"I'd like to sit him behind this desk for just twenty-four hours."

"I'm sorry, Mr. President."

"The only trouble with Roosevelt," the mild-mannered Harrison said, "is that he wants to put an end to all the evil in the world between sunrise and sunset."

"I've asked him to be circumspect in his appearances before Congressional committees."

"He must be intelligent enough to know that the House is dominated by the Democrats, and that they've struck gold when they've found a member of my Administration who discredits me."

Lodge found it impossible to explain that Theodore, fighting for a principle in which he believed, thought the issue more important than partisan considerations. "Many of his friends—and of yours, sir—are asking him to be careful."

"He doesn't know the meaning of the word. I don't suppose," Harrison said delicately, "that he could be persuaded to resign."

Lodge displayed his own brand of finesse. "He enjoys Washington, Mr. President, and so does Mrs. Roosevelt."

"I was afraid of that," Harrison said gloomily. "I'd be tempted to discharge him, but he's become such a favorite of Congress and the press that I'd only succeed in making him a martyr, and hurting myself that much more. I'm afraid I'll have to put up with Commissioner Roosevelt."

Whenever Congressional committees wanted to create news or tried to embarrass the Administration, Theodore was called to testify on

Civil Service abuses, and became a star witness at hearings that lasted through the years of the Harrison Administration. "Postmaster General Wanamaker," he trumpeted, "is trying to provide a shield for subordinates who are guilty of slanderous falsehoods. It grieves me that fellow Republicans could be derelict in their duty, but the welfare of the people must be our paramount consideration."

"Theodore," Henry Adams observed, "is St. George fighting an army of dragons, and what makes the spectacle extraordinary is that St. George is breathing the fire."

In 1892 the Democratic majority of a Joint House and Senate investigating committee supported Theodore's charges, and the embarrassed Republican minority, unable to deny concrete evidence, gave its half-hearted consent. The question of Civil Service reform became a major issue in the presidential campaign of that year, and Harrison was defeated by Grover Cleveland, long an advocate of Civil Service extension, who returned in triumph to the White House he had been forced to vacate four years earlier.

"Theodore has made a place for himself in American history that's unique," Henry Adams said. "But I'd advise him not to buy any merchandise in Mr. Wanamaker's store."

The Roosevelts found themselves reluctant to leave Washington. Theodore was fascinated by the operations of the Federal Government, but was not confined by life in the capital. He traveled to the West on hunting trips, spent a part of each summer at Oyster Bay, to which Edith retired with the children for several months each year, and, in Washington itself, found the rugged terrain of Rock Creek Park perfect for his daily hikes. The family had grown again—a daughter, Ethel, was born in 1891—and he argued that the children enjoyed cultural advantages in Washington that were unknown elsewhere.

"Alice," he said, "goes to school with children from a dozen embassies and legations, and Ted plays with boys of more nationalities than I can count. Living here is like making a long trip around the world."

Traveling to New York for the purpose, Theodore asked Carl Schurz, Cleveland's old friend, to sound out the President on the possibility of reappointing him.

Grover Cleveland was pleased. Not only could he retain the services of a man who had won wide popularity, but the presence of a Republican on the Civil Service Commission would give the reform cause a bipartisan flavor. "Tell Roosevelt," he said to Schurz, "that we worked together harmoniously for the good of New York, and we can do it again for the benefit of the entire country."

Theodore signed a new lease on the house that was too small for his family, but was otherwise perfect because of its central location. But a personal problem troubled him in the spring of 1893, and he sat down with Edith after dinner one evening to discuss it. "Douglas Robinson went over my accounts with me when I was in New York," he said, "and we may have to stop entertaining."

His wife knew that filling the house with friends was one of his greatest joys, but remained calm.

"We're spending more than I earn. My income from my books is a little less than a thousand dollars a year—I don't know where I got the idea that it was much more—and combined with my salary it isn't enough. Douglas says I went into the red by twenty-five hundred dollars last year."

"Oh, dear," Edith said, thinking it wise not to mention all they spent out of the large interest that his inherited income drew. It annoyed him, she had discovered, to be reminded that money he himself had not earned enabled him to enjoy luxuries denied to others.

"Of course," he continued, "we don't want to do anything too drastic. We must be indebted to a dozen people—"

"Many more than that. I can show you the list."

"No, that isn't necessary. We can't eliminate our social life. If we don't entertain we'll have to refuse invitations, too, and that would be absurd. No one can live the life of a hermit in this town." He readjusted his glasses on the bridge of his nose, stood and paced the length of the parlor. "If we entertain, and we must, we'll need the cook. How much do you pay the upstairs maid?"

"Twenty dollars a month."

"Well, we need her, too, and the savings would be paltry." Clasping his hands behind his back, he walked more rapidly. "I'm sorry to say I bought my new rifle before I learned we were in difficulty, but I've used it, unfortunately, and wouldn't get back more than a small fraction if I tried to sell it."

The conversation was settling into the groove of all their previous talks on the subject of economy, and Edith was tranquil.

"I promised the children a pony, you know. It's wrong to deny them the pleasures of riding just because I selfishly insist on living here and force them to spend the better part of every year in a city. If I hadn't given them my word, I might reconsider." Theodore frowned, then brightened. "However, the expenses of keeping a pony are minor."

Edith knew he would become upset if she told him the groom earned the highest wages of anyone on the household staff.

He halted in front of her and struck a tragic pose. "We might have to sell Sagamore Hill."

She knew what was expected of her. "I won't hear of it!" she said firmly.

Theodore sighed. "We'll have to do something."

She had bought almost no new clothes in months, but realized he'd fret until she made a gesture. "Alice and I," she said, "could cut down on our wardrobes."

An unbearable weight was lifted from his shoulders. "How easy it is to solve even the most difficult problems when our thinking is directed into the right channels."

"I've never believed that Alexander the Great really wept when he had no more worlds to conquer," Henry Adams said in the spring of 1895. "It simply isn't consistent with what we know of his character. But with my own eyes I've seen Theodore Roosevelt reduced to boredom *in extremis* because no one will quarrel with him. President Cleveland, both Houses of Congress, the press and the people are supporting his campaign for Civil Service reform with single-minded determination. He's still wearing his boxing gloves, but no one will fight him, and he's alone in the ring. If there's one thing Theodore can't tolerate it's loneliness, and I'm afraid Washington will soon have seen the last of him for a time."

In April 1895 Theodore resigned from the Civil Service Commission to accept an appointment he regarded as an exciting challenge. Newly elected Mayor William L. Strong of New York offered him a post as a member of the city's four-man Police Board, and, seeing an opportunity to extend his concept of reform into new areas, he eagerly took the position.

Edith had given birth to her third son, Archibald, in 1894, the Washington house had grown impossibly small, and she heartily endorsed the move. *To tell you the truth,* she wrote Corinne Robinson, *it will be a relief to get back to my own kind of living.*

Theodore regarded the future in less gracious terms. *I shall be spend-*

ing all my days and nights, he declared in an exuberant note to Anna Cowles, *fighting vile crime and hideous vice.*

Three other men already had received appointments to the Board. Colonel Frederick D. Grant, son of the former President, was a Republican, his father's party, and it was expected that he and Theodore would work well together. Unfortunately, Grant had lived in the shadow of his renowned father, and deeply resented publicity given to anyone else. The others were nominal Democrats. Andrew D. Parker, a foe of Tammany, was quick-tempered, imperious and stubborn, and newsmen assigned to Police Headquarters privately wondered how long he and Theodore would remain on speaking terms. Major Avery D. Andrews, a firm advocate of reform, had admired Theodore's work on the Civil Service Commission and formed a close friendship with him.

In matters of policy each of the four members had an equal vote, while the executive administration was left largely in the hands of the President, whom they elected from their own number. No one was surprised when, at their first meeting, Theodore became President, without discussion, after Andrews nominated him.

The Headquarters building on Mulberry Street was an ancient, crumbling structure, Board members occupied gloomy offices with filthy walls and cracked ceilings on the second floor, and reporters had become accustomed to drab, almost meaningless routines. But Commissioner Roosevelt, calling a press conference within minutes of his election, promised brighter days ahead.

"My aims are simple," he said. "I'm going to drive professional criminals out of the city. I'm going to close the brothels that are a disgrace to American womanhood. I won't tolerate corruption, no matter what its source, or any connection between the Police and political parties. Members of the Department will be promoted on merit alone, and every member, from the Commissioner down, will enforce the law."

The press quickly discovered he meant every word, and a group of brilliant young reporters, all of them personally devoted to reform, soon became his partisans. Jacob Riis and Lincoln Steffens formed personal friendships with him that lasted for many years, and Arthur Brisbane, although less close to him, remained his lifelong admirer.

Theodore wasted no time providing news. He appointed as his secretary the first woman ever employed by the Police Department, a competent girl recommended to him by Joe Murray. He conceived the idea of making personal investigations to insure that patrolmen were on the job, and the technique he developed was extraordinary. Around midnight, often following a dinner party and wearing dress clothes, he donned a "disguise" consisting of a broad-brimmed slouch hat, long cape and a cummerbund sash with a tassel that drooped below his knees. Then, appropriately attired, he wandered about the streets of the city, checking on the activities of policemen on duty.

Steffens promptly dubbed him "Haroun-el-Roosevelt," and the other reporters adopted the nickname, too. Brisbane summed up the sentiments of his colleagues in a piece he wrote in the *World: We have a real Police Commissioner. His teeth are big and white, his eyes are small and piercing, his voice is rasping. He makes our policemen feel as the little froggies, but no matter. He is a man of strength, a determined man, a fighting man, an honest, conscientious man. He is the man to reform the force.*

Patrolmen dreaded his unexpected appearance, flinching under the barrage of questions he shot at them, and when it became known they kept watch for the telltale sign of his exposed teeth, newspaper cartoonists began to portray him with teeth bared. Street peddlers suddenly appeared on the city's streets, their carts laden with whistles called, "Teddy's Teeth," and it was rumored, without proof, that Tammany had paid for their manufacture.

Theodore was shown one of these supposed replicas at a press conference, and roared with laughter. "They're—ah—very pretty," he said.

Riis, approving of his ability to laugh at himself, dared to ask him why he so frequently bared his teeth.

Theodore sobered and considered the question. "I suppose," he said, "it is more habit than anything else. All shortsighted men have some facial characteristic of which they are unconscious. I cannot be blamed for having good teeth, or this characteristic of a shortsighted man."

That ended the subject—in his presence. But the patrolmen continued to keep sharp watch for a set of gleaming teeth, and the efficiency of the force improved markedly. But the problems the Commissioner was forced to solve were many, varied and unending.

A few months after taking office Theodore was surprised, one morning, when his secretary announced that Jacob Schiff, the head of the private banking firm of Kuhn, Loeb & Company, was paying an unexpected call on him. The surprised Theodore jumped to his feet and hurried into the anteroom to greet the banker and escort him into the inner office.

"This is quite an honor!" Theodore pumped his visitor's hand.

"Don't be too sure of that," the modestly dressed Schiff replied dryly, speaking with a slight German accent. "Forgive me for not making an appointment, but something important has just come up. I tried to telephone you, but the exchange isn't working well today."

"I know. I haven't been able to use the telephone all week." Theodore offered his visitor a chair somewhat less dilapidated than the rest of the furniture in his office.

"I'm not here on my own behalf alone. Some of my friends wanted to send a delegation to see you, but in my experience committees often do more harm than good trying to solve delicate problems." Schiff leaned forward in his chair. "It's no secret to you that I'm Jewish."

"No, of course not." A man's religion meant nothing to Theodore, but he saw no reason to defend himself by explaining that he frequently deplored the anti-Jewish and anti-Catholic attitudes of some of his Oyster Bay neighbors.

"The Jewish community of New York is very disturbed. Does the name of a German clergyman named Ahlwardt mean anything to you, Commissioner?"

"No, Mr. Schiff. Should it?"

"Rector Ahlwardt landed here from Europe late yesterday. He has a number of speaking engagements in the city, most of them before German-American groups. He's a violent anti-Semite, Commissioner, who advocates driving the Jews from New York by force."

"I see."

"I wonder if you do. A great many Jewish immigrants here, men who suffered from pogroms in Russia and Poland, have no intention of allowing this bigot to stir up new trouble for them in a free land. In the interests of peace, Mr. Roosevelt, and to prevent a rise in anti-Semitism here, I hope you'll refuse to let this man Ahlwardt make a single speech."

"I know very little about the prevention of bigotry," Theodore said, "although I do believe it spreads more rapidly below the surface when it isn't allowed to come into the open. But that's irrelevant, Mr. Schiff. The Bill of Rights, the first ten Amendments to the Federal Constitution, specifically grant all Americans freedom of assemblage and speech. I'd be breaking Federal law if I tried to gag this fellow Ahlwardt."

"You don't understand," the banker declared. "Ahlwardt will stir up audiences who have brought their own anti-Semitism with them from Europe. The Jews of New York haven't endured great hardships and traveled thousands of miles to begin new lives in America just to suffer from the same hatreds that made life a hell for them in the Old World. There will be riots, Commissioner, and bloodshed."

"I'm sworn to uphold the Constitution, Mr. Schiff. Even if I agreed with the wisdom of silencing this man, which I don't, I have no authority for gagging him."

The banker stood. "You must do what you think right," he said stiffly, "and I'm sorry you can't see there will be a breakdown in public order here because of your refusal to help."

Theodore surprised him by laughing. "Now you're the one who doesn't understand, sir. All I've said is that I have no right to stop Ahlwardt from keeping his speaking engagements. But I'll do everything I can to prevent riots and curb the spread of anti-Semitism!"

Schiff looked mystified.

"One of my recreational hobbies is hunting," Theodore said, "and I've learned the truth of the saying out in the West that there's more than one way to skin a bobcat." He pressed a buzzer, and, enjoying the dramatic situation he had created, sat back in his chair and grinned.

A uniformed captain came into the office.

Theodore did not present him to the visitor. "Do you know anything about a Rector Ahlwardt who landed in town last night?"

"You bet I do, Commissioner," the officer replied. "There's a meeting scheduled in the Detective Bureau later today to figure out ways to keep his followers and the Jews of the Lower East Side under control."

"There will be no need for such a meeting. I want forty patrolmen commanded by a sergeant assigned as Ahlwardt's bodyguards while he's here. They're to protect him twenty-four hours a day."

"Yes, sir." The captain obviously thought the order inadequate.

"Make certain," Theodore said, "that all members of the force— the sergeant and every patrolman—are Jewish."

The captain stared at him for a moment, then chuckled as he saluted. "Yes, sir!" Still laughing, he left the office.

Theodore turned to Schiff, who was smiling broadly. "I may go to hear Ahlwardt myself. It'll be difficult for anyone to take the hatreds he preaches seriously when he's being protected by forty Jewish policemen."

In the autumn of 1895 zealousness caused Theodore to make his first serious mistake. New York law prohibited the sale of alcoholic beverages, including beer, on Sundays, and he ordered the police to make certain that every tavernkeeper in the city obeyed the injunction. It quickly became evident that the law could not be enforced. Corruption spread when saloon owners paid patrolmen to look the other way, and the newspapers, even those that had been consistently friendly to Theodore, began to attack him.

Mayor Strong, trying to disclaim any responsibility for the uproar, made a pointed remark in a public address, saying, "I'm sorry the Dutchman I appointed is trying to turn New Yorkers into Puritans."

Theodore's response was predictably stubborn. "I didn't make the laws. I'm obliged to reform them. If the people don't want a law, let them change it. Until they do, I have no choice, and will continue to close the taverns and saloons."

His jealous fellow Board member, Parker, saw an opportunity to hamper his effectiveness, and moved boldly to force a deadlock. Theodore, in his efforts to reform the Police force, had weeded out large numbers of incompetents, many of them men who had owed their appointments to Tom Platt's influence, and Platt was offended. So Parker entered an informal alliance with him, Platt persuaded Colonel Grant to stand with Parker, and Theodore, supported only by Major Andrews, could not win an affirmative vote on any of the ever-increasing number of changes he wanted to institute.

The New York Assembly further complicated the issue by passing a new law, in 1896, allowing any "hotel" to sell alcoholic beverages on Sundays. A hotel was described as any establishment that offered ten or more rooms to rent, and, suddenly, every brothel in New York City obtained a liquor license. Vice became almost impossible to control unless the Police Board interpreted the law liberally, and Theodore's efforts were hampered when Parker and Grant consistently voted against such interpretations.

The beleaguered Commissioner continued to work for reform, within the limitations imposed on him, but the frustrations were overwhelming, and his achievements steadily dwindled. The newspaper

reporters sympathetic to him wanted to help, but were equally power-
less, and began to hint he might be wise to look elsewhere for a post.

"If the Democrats don't put William Jennings Bryan into the White
House," Jacob Riis said to him one afternoon, "you could do worse
than return to the Federal Government."

Lincoln Steffens agreed. "McKinley knows your brand of reform.
He'd be sure to give you a good job. But I don't think he'll be elected."

Theodore leaned back in the swivel chair he had bought with his
own money, and clasped his hands behind his head. "Bryan's speeches
arousing the silver states are dramatic, but I don't believe he can beat
McKinley, although—not for publication, boys—I think Mark Hanna's
campaign to sell McKinley to the country like some brand of shaving
soap is tasteless and lowers the dignity of the presidency."

Riis looked at him. "We have an idea you'll run for President some
year, provided you have the ambition. Do you?"

To the astonishment of both reporters, Theodore's feet landed on
the floor with a crash. Baring his teeth, he moved around to the front
of his desk, and began to pound it in an inarticulate rage.

Steffens, afraid he intended to strike Riis, braced himself as he prepared to intervene.

"Don't you dare ask me that!" Theodore shouted, his temper completely out of control. "Don't you put such ideas in my head! No
friend of mine would ever say a thing like that, you—you—" He choked
back his anger, walked stiff-legged to a carafe for a drink of water,
and then turned back to the astonished newsmen, his face white.

"I didn't mean to offend you, Theodore," Riis said. "What on earth
did I—"

Theodore tried to force a laugh, but made only a rasping noise. To
show he bore no grudge, he threw an arm around Riis's shoulders,
and with his free hand patted Steffens on the back. At last, his breathing normal, he returned to his chair.

"Never, never," he said, "you must never, either of you, remind a
man at work on a political job that he may be President. It almost always kills him politically. He loses his nerve. He can't do his work. He
gives up the very traits that are making him a possibility."

They stared at him, wondering if he realized how clearly he was
revealing his private dreams.

"I, for instance," he continued, "still hope to do great things here,
hard things that require all the courage, work, ability that I'm capable

of. I can do them if I think of them alone. But if I get to thinking of what it might lead to—" He broke off abruptly.

Riis started to reply, but thought better of it when he saw that Theodore hadn't yet finished.

"I must want to be President." Although speaking through clenched teeth, Theodore sounded astonished. "Every young man does." Again he halted, slowly shaking his head. "But I won't let myself think of it! I mustn't, because, if I do, I'll begin to work for it. I'll be careful, calculating, cautious in word and act—and I'll beat myself. See?"

Theodore made a number of speeches in behalf of the Republican candidate for President, William McKinley, and almost immediately after the defeat of Bryan concluded that his friends had given him good advice. The deadlock on the Police Board remained unbroken, and it became difficult to maintain even the ordinary routines of police work.

"I'm handcuffed," he told Edith, "and I'm wasting my time as Commissioner."

Although she would soon give birth to another son, Quentin, she faced her husband's uncertain future with equanimity. "I'm willing to go anywhere," she said, sure he was thinking of applying for a post in McKinley's Administration.

Theodore felt the need to justify himself. "If I could do some good here, I'd stay. But Mayor Strong won't support or repudiate me, and I'm wasting my time on the Police Board when I could be helping the country prepare for war with Spain."

"The newspapers may be exaggerating, and there may not be a war," Edith said hopefully.

"It can't be avoided." Theodore's tone left no room for argument. "It's bad enough that the Spaniards are demonstrating the very worst of their colonial policy by repressing the free people of Cuba, but it's even worse when they use Cuban soil as a base to challenge American strength less than one hundred miles from our own coast. I'm positive we'll be forced to take a strong position, and I'd feel like a shirker if I didn't do my part."

Henry Cabot Lodge, now United States Senator from Massachusetts, Speaker Thomas B. Reed of the House of Representatives, whom Theodore would have preferred as the Republican candidate for President, and a number of other friends bombarded McKinley with requests that the New York Police Commissioner be given a place in the new Administration worthy of his talents and energies. McKinley, however, was not anxious to bring a controversial public figure into his official family.

"The truth is," the President-elect told William Howard Taft early in 1897, "Roosevelt is always in such a state of mind."

The newspapers agreed, but took a different approach. *Roosevelt is a fighter, and the country needs him,* the Washington *Post* declared.

McKinley repeatedly assured the American people that he wanted peace, and would work to achieve an understanding with Spain. Meanwhile Theodore, in several bristling interviews that did nothing to advance his own cause, expressed the opinion that war with Spain was inevitable.

I'll see McKinley and do what I can to obtain a high post for you, Lodge wrote his friend, *but I beg you, grant no more interviews until an appointment is assured.*

The President-elect received the Senator from Massachusetts cordially when Lodge came to his Canton, Ohio, home for a visit, but displayed nervousness when Theodore's name came up. "That man," he said, "has enlisted the support of half the country. I'm pestered every day of the week by campaign contributors, Congressmen, friends —everyone, all of them urging me to give him a job."

"He's earned a place," Lodge replied, "and certainly no one is more popular with the reform Republicans in New York. Do you have any specific reason for keeping him out?"

"Not really," the stolid McKinley said, "but I hope he has no preconceived plans which he'd wish to drive through the moment he got in."

"Oh, you can take my word he'd be loyal, and wouldn't try to strike out on his own." Lodge knew it wouldn't be sufficient to repeat the conversation. He'd need Theodore's promise to abide by Administration policies, but realized that even such a pledge might prove worthless if his friend became aroused.

McKinley continued to hesitate until Tom Platt, who had been returned to the Senate, saw an opportunity to rid New York of the one man who might interfere with his own plans to consolidate his control of the state's Republican party. He, too, urged McKinley to find a job —in Washington—for Theodore.

The President-elect capitulated, but revealed his uneasy frame of mind to his Senator Mark Hanna, his intimate friend and campaign manager. "I'm not sure," he said, "that anyone has the strength, stamina, and patience to curb Roosevelt's enthusiasms. I'll make a place for him to stop his admirers from badgering me, and I just hope I won't regret it until the end of my days."

III

1897–1900

A life of slothful ease, a life of that peace which springs merely from lack either of desire or of power to strive after great things, is as little worthy of a nation as of an individual. I ask only that what every self-respecting American demands from himself and from his sons be demanded of the American nation as a whole.

I N THE LATE AUTUMN of 1896 President-elect William McKinley was bombarded by friends of Theodore Roosevelt who asked that the volatile New Yorker be given a high place in the new Administration. Senator Henry Cabot Lodge of Massachusetts maintained insistent pressure on the incoming President and his closest associate, Senator Mark Hanna of Ohio. Socially prominent Bellamy Storer of Cincinnati, a major contributor to McKinley's campaign fund, made a quietly fervent plea. John Hay, the most distinguished of the Republican party's elder statesmen, added his voice to the clamor, as did William Howard Taft, Elihu Root, and many others.

McKinley had good cause to hesitate. Relations with Spain were deteriorating rapidly because Madrid's strict control of her Caribbean colony, Cuba, conflicted with American commercial ambitions in the West Indies. Talk of war was being heard everywhere in the United States, and the President-elect, who was determined to settle the Spanish-American dispute peacefully, knew Theodore was one of the most vellicose of his compatriots.

Theodore's record, loudly proclaimed, indicated he carried a large chip on his shoulder. On various occasions in recent years he had advocated the annexation of the Hawaiian Islands and the building of a shipping canal in Nicaragua. When Great Britain and Germany had become involved in a complicated dispute in Venezuela, he had urged President Cleveland to invoke the Monroe Doctrine and warn both European powers that they risked war with the United States unless they withdrew immediately. And, in a fiery speech delivered at the

Republican Club in New York, he had demanded the modernization and enlargement of the Navy to "sustain the honor of the American flag."

Anxious to obtain a post in the new Administration, Theodore assured the President-elect, in a letter he wrote to Cabot Lodge, promising he would behave. McKinley remained unconvinced. "I hope he has no preconceived plans," he told Lodge, "which he would wish to drive through the moment he got in."

McKinley resisted the pressures, and Theodore was still a private citizen when the new President was inaugurated on March 4, 1897. But the place he coveted, that of Assistant Secretary of the Navy, had not yet been filled, and he wrote to Lodge, asking him to enlist the help of the new Secretary, John D. Long. Begging his friend to assure Long he would cause no problems, Theodore wrote, *I want him to understand that I shall stay at Washington, hot weather or any other weather, whenever he wants me to stay there, and go wherever he sends me, and my aim should be solely to make his administration a success.*

Long, a courtly gentleman who had no desire to change the habits of a lifetime, was hoping to spend at least part of the summer at his estate in Maine, and recommended Theodore's appointment. He found a totally unexpected ally in Senator Tom Platt of New York.

Busily reorganizing the Republican party in New York, Platt repeatedly found his efforts blocked by very vocal reformers. And in almost every incident, Theodore played an active role in demanding graft-free government. Finally it dawned on Platt that he would have a far easier time if Theodore were in Washington rather than peering over his shoulder in New York. He added his recommendation to the already impressive list, and on April 5, 1897, President McKinley capitulated, sending Theodore's nomination to the Senate.

The appointment was confirmed by a voice vote, without debate, on the morning of April 8, and late that same day an exuberant Theodore arrived in Washington. Edith and the children would follow as soon as he found a suitable house to rent.

Secretary Long, a former Governor of Massachusetts and member of the U. S. House of Representatives, was a mild-mannered gentleman who soon discovered that his assistant was virtually impossible to control. Convinced it was the duty of the United States to protect the Western Hemisphere, Theodore at once advocated the strengthening of the Navy, and transmitted the views of admirals and captains to leading members of Congress.

But he did not make his opinions public until, early in June, he found himself unable to remain silent any longer. In an address before the Naval War College at Newport, Rhode Island, he declared, "If we mean to protect the people of the lands who look to us for protection from tyranny and aggression, a strong Navy is essential. Our choice is clear. Let us give the Navy the sinews to wage war, or let us abandon all talk of devotion to the Monroe Doctrine or to the honor of the American name."

The nation was unprepared for violence, newspapers attacked Assistant Secretary Roosevelt as "bellicose," and the President was disturbed. Secretary Long was even more upset, but accepted his assistant's explanation that all he sought was an enlarged Navy. In fact, Long was sufficiently mollified to go off for his delayed holiday, and Theodore found himself in charge of the Navy.

The Acting Secretary became furiously busy. He made a whirlwind inspection of Navy Yards on the Eastern seaboard, urged an increase in the pace of construction of new ships and astonished officers and naval architects alike with the technical knowledge he had acquired by spending his free evenings reading all he could find on the subject. Advocating a pay increase for all Navy officers, he drew up a bill for the purpose, and passed it along to friends in both the Senate and House to introduce.

Taking advantage of an invitation to address members of the Naval Reserve in Ohio, he made a speech in which he renewed his plea that the United States annex Hawaii. State Department officials shuddered when they read the passage, "I am told that Japan would consider such annexation an unfriendly act. Let her feel as she pleases. We must do what we believe right for the people of the United States and of Hawaii, regardless of the consequences. We fear the armed might of no nation."

Nothing he did in the busy summer of 1897 was more significant than the summoning of an officer who held views similar to his own, Commodore George Dewey, to his office for a private conference. Although the stocky, sixty-year-old Dewey belonged to another generation, the two men were completely at ease with each other, and the Commodore made himself at home in an overstuffed leather chair.

"Mr. Secretary," he said, "you have no idea how much your pay increase bill has done for morale."

Theodore grinned at him. "I've hoped it would. Men whose families are on the verge of starvation don't put their hearts into a fight."

Dewey tensed. "Are there new developments in the Spanish situation?"

"There's nothing specific yet," Theodore replied, "but I'm finding it easier to win Congressional support for our campaign to build more battleships."

The Commodore was pleased. "We need them."

"We've always needed them. The situation is the same now as it was a century ago, in the days of Admiral Nelson. It's the fire power of big ships that wins major battles." Theodore was silent for a moment, then asked abruptly, "Assuming a war breaks out with Spain, and it's a fair assumption, where do you believe the critical battles will be fought?"

"The main Spanish fleet is stationed at her Far Eastern colonial base in Manila," Dewey replied quickly. "There's been speculation that we'd need our greatest strength here at home, and some of our Commodores agree."

"But you don't."

"Certainly not, Mr. Secretary, unless she shifts her forces. The Spanish squadron in Cuba is so small she'll cause us no real trouble. Her main fleet will be our real worry."

"It seems to me that our Far Eastern squadron should keep a close intelligence watch on that fleet to report any large-scale transfers of ships."

"We don't have enough ships in the squadron to spare any for reconnaissance duty."

"We will, and soon." Theodore handed him a single sheet of paper. "This is an order to the Bureau of Operations, transferring our strongest ships to Hawaii and Hong Kong. The Hawaiians will be delighted to cooperate with us, and once the ships are at sea, the British won't be able to deny us anchorage privileges at Hong Kong."

Dewey obviously approved of his tactics. "Only the Japanese may protest."

"If you were in command of the squadron, how would you handle a Japanese protest, Commodore?"

Dewey thought for a moment. "I think I'd ignore any communication from them. If I acknowledged a protest, even to the extent of refuting it, I'd be granting Tokyo the right to have a voice in the matter. But if I said nothing at all in reply, the Japanese wouldn't have grounds to take action themselves without running the risk of a war with us, and I don't believe they're ready for war. I'd just go about my business."

"Bully!" Theodore's eyes gleamed behind his glasses. "I didn't ask you to drop in this morning for a theoretical discussion, as you'll realize in a moment. Suppose war with Spain were declared, and you were commanding the squadron. What would you do?"

"I'd sail every ship I could muster to Manila, and I'd blow the Spaniards out of the water."

Theodore slapped his knee. "We speak the same language, sir! Could you bring off a victory?"

"Our gunnery is superior, and from the reports I've read of Spanish movements, her commanders stay in port when they can and put out to sea only when they must. If I could catch her Pacific fleet at anchor, I could destroy it."

"You shall have the Far East, Commodore." Theodore was equally positive.

Dewey was overwhelmed, but cautious. "I hope Secretary Long and the Operations office agree."

"I'm Acting Secretary." Theodore settled the question of authority with a sharp, chopping motion that resembled a wave. "I made up my mind yesterday, but thought I should have a last talk with you. Senator Lodge approves, and so does Senator Proctor of Vermont. You have friends in Congress, Commodore, so I suggest you talk to them today and tomorrow. It would be helpful, when I announce your appointment late tomorrow, if they'll notify the press they think you're the best officer for the post. Then the amateur admirals will put up no opposition."

Dewey wanted the assignment, but didn't trust Theodore's unorthodox methods. "Secretary Long may not give his consent—"

"You'll be well on your way to the Far East before he comes back to Washington."

"President McKinley—" The Commodore broke off abruptly.

"The appointment doesn't need presidential approval. As a courtesy, I'll send him a note just before I release the news to the press tomorrow. Just leave the details to me, Commodore Dewey, and concentrate on the Spanish fleet." Theodore was unruffled by the realization that he was making decisions of the utmost importance without consulting higher authority. Convinced he was making the right moves in a growing crisis, he saw no need to seek the approval of the President or the Secretary of the Navy.

Daily headlines printed in red ink on yellow paper in William Randolph Hearst's New York *Journal* and Joseph Pulitzer's New York *World* proclaimed the imminence of an American war with Spain during the closing months of 1897. Scores of other newspapers followed their example, and although the more conservative press deplored the sensationalism of the so-called "yellow journals," it seemed increasingly probable that there would, indeed, be war.

The reasons for the dispute were vague, and both governments were anxious to avoid a conflict. Spain's attitude was conciliatory, and her diplomats were ordered to find a prompt and peaceful way out. President McKinley, equally eager to prevent an outbreak of hostilities, instructed the principal officials of his Administration to work for the preservation of peace.

At the Navy Department a quiet but fierce tug-of-war was waged by the Secretary and Assistant Secretary. "We must do nothing," John Long said, "inconsistent with the President's desire to keep the peace."

"War is sure to come, no matter what the President or anyone else may want," Theodore insisted. "We've got to be ready, which means redeploying every American ship."

"Then Spain would have a right to accuse us of belligerent acts."

"That's a chance we'll have to take, Mr. Secretary," Theodore declared. "If our squadrons aren't ready for combat when the war starts, we might suffer some frightful humiliations, particularly in the Orient, where the Spanish fleet is stronger than our Far Eastern squadron. We've got to keep her ships bottled up at Manila."

"Are you suggesting that we deliberately disobey the President, Roosevelt?"

Theodore's jaw jutted forward. "Preparing for trouble in no way contravenes presidential directives, Mr. Secretary. If war is avoided, we lose nothing. But we'll be ready if it comes. If we don't redeploy we'll be forced to spend the first three or four most important weeks not in striking, but in making the preparations for strikes that should be made right now."

"The President meant his orders literally, and that's how I take them," Secretary Long said, closing the subject.

Events proved otherwise. On February 15, 1898, the U.S.S. *Maine* blew up in Havana harbor, and although it was never established, then or later, that Spanish saboteurs were responsible, most Americans echoed the cry of the yellow press, "Remember the *Maine!*"

Theodore's mood and that of the general public were identical. "I would give anything," he told his family the morning after the tragedy, "if President McKinley ordered the home squadron to Havana at once."

The President was still determined to preserve peace, if he could, and refused to take any steps that Spain might regard as threatening until he received a report from the commission investigating the cause of the sinking. Theodore, supported by the highest-ranking officers on the Navy Department staff, begged in vain for permission to alert the nation's squadrons. Long remained adamant, however, and the frustrated Theodore told Henry Adams, "McKinley has no more backbone than a chocolate eclair."

Then, unexpectedly, the Assistant Secretary was given the opportunity to influence national policy in the manner he deemed appropriate. John Long, exhausted by ten days of unceasing argument with his assistant and the staff officers on duty at the Department, remained at home on February 25. Theodore was Acting Secretary for the day.

Informing his receptionist that he wanted to be disturbed by no one, Theodore retired behind the closed door of his office to ponder. His duty to Secretary Long required him to observe his superior's policies, but the longer he mulled the problem, the more he became convinced that he owed a greater obligation to the American people.

Coldly, without emotion, he analyzed the situation, and knew public feeling had risen too high to subside. Therefore, no matter how much the President might want peace, war with Spain was as inevitable as the Hearst and Pulitzer newspapers were claiming. His friend, Justice Oliver Wendell Holmes, Jr., of the Massachusetts Supreme Court, had written him a few days earlier, saying there were occasions in a nation's history when even unnecessary wars could not be avoided, and this was such a time.

No matter what the personal consequences or the difficulty of defending himself against charges of disloyalty to Secretary Long, his course of action was clear. In fact, believing as he did, he had no real alternative.

Reaching for a pad of yellow paper and a pencil, Theodore scribbled a telegram, fully aware that what he was writing would become a historic document: DEWEY, HONG KONG: ORDER THE SQUADRON, EXCEPT THE

MONOCACY, TO HONG KONG. KEEP FULL OF COAL. IN THE EVENT OF DECLARA-
TION OF WAR SPAIN, YOUR DUTY WILL BE TO SEE THAT THE SPANISH SQUAD-
RON DOES NOT LEAVE THE ASIATIC COAST; AND THEN OFFENSIVE OPERATIONS
IN PHILIPPINE ISLANDS. KEEP OLYMPIA UNTIL FURTHER ORDERS. ROOSEVELT.

Commodore Dewey, he knew, needed no additional instructions to prepare for an invasion of the Philippines and trap the Spanish Far Eastern fleet in Manila Bay.

Manufacturers and the owners of retail establishments often commented that William McKinley looked more like a moderately prosperous businessman than President of the United States. And that, Mark Hanna said, was one of his strengths. Portly and conservatively dressed, he sat behind a modest desk in an office that, aside from an American flag and another bearing the Great Seal of the United States draped on standards behind him, resembled that of a merchant, too. Modest drapes stood at the sides of the windows overlooking the White House lawn, the rug was plain and the furniture, chosen by the President himself, was inconspicuous.

But a disturbed McKinley, shifting in his padded leather chair, did not resemble a successful businessman as he glared at his visitor. Scarcely able to control his temper, he found it difficult to speak civilly. "Your reasons for alerting Commodore Dewey are justified by your standards, Roosevelt, but they place this Administration in an embarrassing position."

"It would be far more embarrassing, Mr. President," Theodore replied energetically, "if Dewey did nothing until war was declared. I hate to think of the damage the Spaniards' Far Eastern fleet could do to our shipping if it slipped out of Manila. I wonder if you realize, sir, that enemy ships could sneak up on our major coastal cities and bombard them."

"I don't think in those melodramatic terms."

"As a lifelong student of war, I can't help but think in terms of them."

"You've created an awkward situation for Secretary Long and me," McKinley said, refusing to discuss the possibilities of surprise bombardments. "If we rescind your orders, we'll be opening ourselves to charges that we deliberately placed the Navy in a state of unpreparedness."

Theodore had realized when he had written his telegram to Commo-

dore Dewey that the President and Long would be vulnerable to attack if they canceled his directive, but he saw nothing to be gained by
openly admitting the fact. "I'd be pained if you were embarrassed,
Mr. President," he said.

McKinley sighed. "I can't see why you keep insisting we're going to
have war. Spain wants peace. I want peace—"

"It's too late for peace, sir." Even if no one else in the Administration spoke boldly to the President, Theodore refused to conceal the
truth behind a discreet façade. "American sympathy for the oppressed
people of Cuba has become a tidal wave of feeling!" He disliked speaking in clichés, but believed the situation required a strong expression
of sentiment in simple terms.

"Only because people like you and the yellow press keep the public
stirred up, Roosevelt." The President spoke in measured tones.

"I disagree, sir. It's a spontaneous feeling." Theodore was candid
rather than defensive. "The fact that I share the people's attitude is
irrelevant. The reason I spoke in terms of a tidal wave just now is
because there's literally no way of reversing that feeling!"

McKinley, afraid he was right, sighed.

"Every time an American businessman or tourist is arrested by the
Spanish authorities in Cuba, the demand for war mounts higher. To
the best of my knowledge, there are eleven Americans in jail there
right now, and that's intolerable, sir!"

"There are fourteen, not eleven. The press doesn't know about three
cases, and the less that's said, the easier it will be to effect their release.
The State Department is in daily touch with the Spanish Embassy
here on the problem."

Theodore removed his glasses and cleaned them, deliberately in-
dulging in the gesture to slow his reply. He could not let himself forget
that he was speaking to the President, whom he was serving in a responsible post. "I contend, sir, that in today's world we deal with situations that can't be resolved in clear blacks and whites. Madrid may not
want war. The Governor-General and his staff in Havana may not want
war. But tensions become self-generating, and the arrest of Americans
in Cuba proves my point. When men become nervous, they behave
foolishly."

"That's no reason for us to indulge in the supreme folly of going to
war."

"I also contend we no longer have a choice, Mr. President." Some
members of the Administration accuse me of being a jingoist, and if

my belief that the *Maine* was sunk by a Spanish torpedo makes me one, then I am. Without apologies. But the point I'm trying to make to you, sir, is that it doesn't really matter whether the Spaniards blew up the ship or whether there was an unfortunate accident in her boiler room."

"I can express no opinion until the investigation of the tragedy has been completed."

Theodore forgot his caution and shook a forefinger, pointing it at McKinley. "Even if you yourself were to issue a statement saying the explosion was accidental, the people wouldn't believe you. And I don't mean that as a slur on your integrity, Mr. President. Seventy-five million Americans are convinced that the Spaniards sank an American battleship. Right or wrong, fair or unfair, that's where they stand. And under such circumstances, only war is compatible with our national honor."

"If I were to listen to you," the President replied, "I'd be forced to conclude that we'll go to war."

"So we will, sir. There will come a point where Spain will have to make a stand, too. *Her* national honor will demand it. She'll realize she can't back off any farther without being branded as a coward in the international community."

"What you're telling me," McKinley replied, looking weary, "is that all of you young romantics want war. You aren't old enough to remember the horrors of the Civil War—"

"I abhor unjust war, sir." Theodore's voice became shrill. "I should never advocate war unless it were the only alternative to dishonor."

"I have no inclination to debate your definition of national honor, Roosevelt. All I know is that circumstances force me to support your order to Commodore Dewey, even though I'm chagrined that you sent it."

"Perhaps, sir," Theodore said stiffly, "you'd like me to submit my resignation."

"And make you a martyr, while I become a villain? Certainly not! If you leave now, before this issue is resolved, I'll guarantee you'll never hold another Republican office!"

It was galling to be threatened, but Theodore knew he had to submit. "I'm at your disposal, Mr. President." For the present he would keep his post, but a long-range plan that had been forming in his mind since the sinking of the *Maine* would alter his status. At the moment,

however, he had no intention of revealing it to the President or anyone
else.

On March 21, 1898, the court of inquiry investigating the sinking of
the *Maine* reported to President McKinley that the battleship had
been destroyed by an exploding submarine mine. The court also admitted, rather sheepishly, that it had been "unable to obtain evidence
fixing the responsibility." This point was ignored by Congress and the
general public as a new frenzy swept across the United States, and no
one bothered to think that the court itself, made up exclusively of
Americans and specifically excluding Spaniards, might be biased.

The people demanded war, and McKinley, no longer able to resist,
prepared a formal declaration to Congress on April 24. The few voices
in the Senate and House urging caution were drowned by the martial,
approving roars of the vast majority.

A few days later, Senator Henry Cabot Lodge arrived at the rented
house of the Roosevelts in response to an urgent summons from Edith.
Never had he seen her so upset, but before she could confide in him,
Theodore joined them, bounding into the parlor and exuding an air
of joyous excitement.

Lodge extricated himself from his friend's bear hug, and looked at
the couple in bewilderment.

"Apparently you haven't heard his bully news," Edith said bitterly.
"Tell him, Theodore."

"I'm resigning from the Navy Department and accepting a commission as a lieutenant colonel in the Army. I'll be second in command and
executive officer of a new regiment of volunteer cavalry."

Lodge sat down in the nearest chair.

"Uncle James and Douglas Robinson came down from New York
yesterday and spent hours trying to make him see reason, but he
wouldn't listen to them any more than he will to me." Edith, beyond
tears, was unable to conceal her frustrated anger.

"And I won't listen to Cabot, either," the beaming Theodore declared. "In just about anything else I'll accept the advice that you two
give me, but in this I intend to have my own way."

Lodge hid his own consternation. "Suppose you tell me precisely
what's been happening."

"I've been exchanging telegrams with the Adjutant General of New
York for the past couple of weeks on the subject of taking a commission in the National Guard, but it's obvious that this is going to be a

short war, so short that it'll be over before the Guard can see active service in Cuba. I've been worried, but night before last I was in great luck."

Edith muttered under her breath.

"I saw a copy of a War Department order authorizing the raising of three regiments of volunteer cavalry," Theodore continued. "Naturally, I went straight to the Secretary of War—"

"Naturally," Edith said.

"Russ Alger is a grand fellow, and offered me the command of one of the regiments. Well, contrary to what Edith and Uncle James and Douglas and the rest of the family may think, I'm not impetuously leaping into something, and I'll prove it to you. Alger offered to make me a full colonel and give me command of the regiment, but I refused!" Theodore was triumphant.

Lodge inclined his head and waited to hear the rest of the account.

"Although I've had some military training, and—as you know, Cabot—I've been a student of military affairs all my life, I'm not really a professional soldier. I might need as long as a month to master the science of modern warfare."

The Senator from Massachusetts raised a hand to his mouth so his friend wouldn't see his smile.

"By then, you see," Theodore went on earnestly, "the war well might be over. So I can't afford to wait."

Lodge's smile vanished.

"I've persuaded Captain Leonard Wood to take command. You remember Leonard?"

It was impossible for Lodge to distinguish one of Theodore's many friends from another.

"He's a physician." Theodore was slightly irritated, but brightened as he added, "He was graduated from Harvard Medical School before he joined the Army."

Wood's credentials for the command of a cavalry regiment were less than impressive, but Lodge kept his opinion to himself.

"He knows how to deal with higher authority, all that sort of thing. And I'll train the men. We're going to band together the finest fellows in the country. I'm sending out an appeal today in a public statement. I want men of character and athletic ability from Harvard. Yale and Princeton and Penn, too, of course. And I'll undoubtedly enlist some of the cowhands I knew in Dakota. Yes, and I'm sure there will be a strong response from the polo clubs in Oyster Bay!" Theodore began to pace up and down the parlor, narrowly avoiding tables and chairs as his excitement grew. "Oh, we'll have a dandy time!"

Edith looked pained.

Lodge coughed delicately. "Do you believe your regiment will make a significant contribution to victory?"

"I give you my flat guarantee, Cabot, we'll be in the thick of the fight!" Theodore's voice rose a half-octave. "If there's glory to be won, you can bet your last dollar we'll win it!"

"That isn't what I asked," the sober-faced former instructor said.

"I neglected to mention that I'm also sending telegrams to the Territorial Governors of Oklahoma, New Mexico, and Arizona. I'm sure they'll supply me with men who are young, good riders and good shots. And who have high personal standards!"

Lodge glanced at Edith.

"He can think of nothing except fighting in Cuba," she said wearily.

"Mark my words," Theodore declared, "we'll make our reputations in this war!"

"It seems to me," the Senator from Massachusetts replied, choosing his words with care, "that you've already acquired a very solid reputation, Theodore. As Assistant Secretary of the Navy you hold an exceptionally important post, particularly in time of war. You're a member of the sub-Cabinet—"

"My work at the Navy Department is finished. I can't do a blessed thing there now. It's up to the Admirals and Commodores to dispose of the Spaniards on the high seas. I must admit," Theodore added with an apologetic laugh, "that I hope I haven't done my job at the Navy too well. If Admiral Sampson takes the Spaniards' New World fleet, that will be the end of Cuba. She'll fall to us without a shot being fired." The prospect plunged him into momentary gloom.

"If we're as close to winning this war as you think—"

"Oh, we are, Cabot! In ninety days, at the most, it'll be ended!"

"Then I see no need for amateur soldiers and sailors joining the colors."

Theodore looked as though he had been struck across the face. "Leonard Wood is a professional. And I hardly call myself an amateur, sir!"

"He's already ordered several sets of uniforms from Brooks Brothers in New York," Edith said sourly.

"In the blue of the Regulars," Theodore declared, his good humor returning. "I'll have no need for more than one dress uniform, but I'm getting three for field use. It may be a little sticky for us in the Cuban jungles. I'm also ordering a dozen or more pairs of my eyeglasses. I'll carry some in my luggage, and I'll never be without at least two pairs of spares in my pockets. I'm trying to think of every possible contingency."

"Except the welfare of your family and your own future." Lodge, tired of subtlety, lashed out at him.

"Now you sound like the family." Theodore was aggrieved. "I can look after myself, you know. I think my stay in Dakota proved I'm no weakling!"

"You deliberately misunderstand me!"

"Oh, I know. Enemy bullets don't respect individuals. But my investments are sound, so Edith and the children would never starve if I were killed."

"Has it occurred to you that you might be maimed for life, which would create all sorts of problems?"

Theodore unconsciously struck a pose. "A soldier must take chances in battle. Warfare has become more scientific since the use of high explosives has become widespread, but the individual must still take his personal risks."

"He's been giving me the same answers." Edith was exasperated. "If he stops behaving like an actor strutting up and down a stage, perhaps he might listen to you, Cabot." She stalked out of the room and slammed the double doors.

Her husband shook his head. "Edith is the finest woman on earth, but war is a man's business, so I really can't expect her to understand or sympathize."

"Most men you know will find it very hard to sympathize with you, Theodore."

"Why do you disapprove, Cabot?"

"For the past year you've been a champion of preparedness. The whole country has heard of Theodore Roosevelt, and the coming of war has proved that you were right and your critics were wrong. Keep your post in the Navy Department, and cash in on your investment. If we win a quick victory, as you seem to think, you'll be in a position to claim your share of the credit. A man in public life who wants the support of the people can't afford to make quixotic gestures."

"Unless," Theodore said, "he wins even greater renown as a military hero than he could have achieved as a civilian."

"You're daydreaming. Think of the odds against you."

"I'll take my chances, and I'll be satisfied if we see some hot action in Cuba."

Lodge lost patience with him. "Stay here, and you can win a seat in the Senate, force the President to put you in his Cabinet, or get anything else you might want. *Anything*," he repeated, emphasizing the word.

Theodore returned his stare, saying nothing. Cabot knew him even better than he had imagined.

"Go off to Cuba, and you'll be walking in quicksand. I'm not denying all you've learned as a student of warfare, but experienced, professional soldiers have been known to ruin themselves overnight by making mistakes in battle that can't be corrected."

"I have confidence in myself and in the men I'll command."

"Damn you, Theodore, stop making speeches and talk sensibly. What do you want?"

"The chance to serve my country honorably."

"That's something you could do from your desk at the Navy Department. What do you really want?"

"If Edith is right, and I won't say she's wrong, I'm an adolescent who wants the thrill of battle. Uncle James says I'm an incurable romantic, and maybe I am. Douglas thinks I'm an actor seeking applause, but he has a low opinion of everyone in public life. You've hinted that I may have deep, ulterior motives, and, strictly between us, I'm willing to admit the possibility. I'm so involved I can't analyze my feelings, Cabot. All I know is that I can't and won't allow anyone to deprive me of this adventure!"

The American press, searching for potential war heroes, found the 1st Volunteer Cavalry irresistibly colorful. The men, proud of the newspaper-inspired nickname of the Rough Riders, quickly adopted it for themselves. And Lieutenant Colonel Theodore Roosevelt, leading his troopers on wild training charges across the Texas countryside near San Antonio, always made himself available for interviews.

Certainly the regiment was unique, making up in spirit what it lacked in discipline. In the few weeks of training time available in May and early June, Colonel Wood tried to form the unit into the Regular Army mold, but soon discovered that, instead, the men preferred the informality of his second-in-command.

Wood also learned that Theodore was incorrigible. One afternoon, after spending a long, hot afternoon cantering across the hills, he led the regiment into San Antonio, and treated the dust-covered men to all the beer they could drink. Colonel Wood rebuked him, reminding him that he was breaking Army Regulations, and the press, learning of Theodore's reply, gleefully reprinted it. "Sir," he said, "I'm the damnedest ass within ten miles of this camp."

The whole country chuckled and applauded him, and the approval became greater, a few days later, when he again disregarded the Army Regulation prohibiting the fraternization of officers and enlisted men by appearing in a restaurant with several of his sergeants, whom he was taking to dinner. The War Department began to wonder whether Secretary Russell A. Alger had erred when he had granted Lieutenant Colonel Roosevelt a commission.

Early in May word was received that Commodore George Dewey had destroyed the Spanish Far Eastern fleet in Manila Bay without the loss of a ship and only seven minor casualties. The United States had genuine cause to celebrate, and Dewey, in his first press interview a few days later, insisted on sharing the credit with the former Assistant Secretary of the Navy. "The foresight and long-range planning were Roosevelt's," he declared. "He made the victory possible, and gave me the ships and men, when I needed them, to win it."

The Rough Riders left Texas at the end of May, traveling by train to Tampa, the principal port of embarkation for Cuba. Thousands of men were being assembled there, supplies were short, and the overworked Navy failed to provide enough transports. The Rough Riders, like all the rest, were forced to wait.

On June 7 the regiment received orders to board the U.S.S. *Yucatan*, a troop carrier, the following day, but Colonel Wood and his deputy were dismayed when they learned there would be no space for them on the vessel. Two other units, the 2nd and 71st Infantry, had received prior orders to sail on the ship.

Theodore, still afraid the war in Cuba might end before he saw combat duty, decided to take matters into his own hands. He made a visit to Navy headquarters in Tampa, and there learned that the *Yucatan* was scheduled to arrive at seven o'clock the following morning. The Rough Riders reached the docks at six, and the mounted men picked their way through the vast throngs of foot soldiers awaiting embarkation.

The moment the *Yucatan* steamed into her berth, members of the 1st Volunteer Cavalry put up a gangway they had made during the night, and immediately swarmed onto the transport. Leading the "charge" was Lieutenant Colonel Roosevelt, who made certain that every Rough Rider boarded the ship. Bringing up the rear in a manner befitting the dignity of the Regulars was Colonel Wood, and as soon as he reached the deck, the gangplank was removed.

The infantrymen of the 2nd and 71st discovered too late that they had been outsmarted, and the Rough Riders, derisively waving their broad-brimmed hats as they lined the rails, suggested that the foot soldiers swim to Cuba. Severe rioting would have broken out had the infantrymen been able to board the vessel.

The commanders of the 2nd and 71st pushed their way forward to protest, and were permitted on board for a conference. Colonel Wood imperturbably showed them his unit's orders—and refused to take his men ashore.

The Rough Riders had won their first victory, but it proved hollow. The *Yucatan* remained in Tampa for a week, and living conditions were almost unbearable. A sewage stream flowed past the anchorage, and the stench, combined with the extreme heat, made many of the men ill. No ice was available, and the supply officer could obtain neither fresh meat nor vegetables. The Rough Riders lived on beans and salt pork, but no one had the temerity to complain aloud after Lieutenant Colonel Roosevelt declared, "This regiment glories in adversity. No matter how unpleasant the living conditions, we rise above them."

The torment ended on June 13, when the transport put out to sea, and the troops, streaming up to the decks to enjoy the sea breezes, saw their second-in-command, elated at the prospect of going into action, doing an Indian war dance on the aft deck. His enthusiasm was contagious, and even the sick looked forward to the start of the great adventure.

Other transports joined the *Yucatan*, forming a convoy, and on June 22 the Rough Riders had the dubious honor of being the first to wade ashore, near the village of Daquiri, in surf so savage that two men were drowned. Major General Joseph Wheeler, a gallant veteran of the Confederate Army, was in over-all command of the cavalry, and the 1st Volunteers were assigned to the brigade of Brigadier General S. B. M. Young, a crisp professional soldier who tolerated no nonsense from subordinates.

His first order did not make him popular with the regiment. There was a shortage of horses, so the Rough Riders lost their mounts to

the officers of other units. Not only were they compelled to march inland as foot soldiers, but had no recourse when the men of the 2nd
and 71st, who arrived at approximately the same time, jeered at them.

The Spanish defenders were entrenched outside the city of Santiago, more than a week's march away, and General Young's brigade led
the advance inland, the Rough Riders in the forefront of the right wing.
Waves of stultifying summer heat rolled down into the jungles from
the green Cuban hills, the foliage was so dense that men had to hack
a path for themselves with their bayonets, and swarms of ants, mos-
quitos and flies added to the torment. Men thought of survival, not
adventure, but Theodore remained cheerful, and rode up and down
the long line whenever the unit was on the march, encouraging his
men.

On June 24 the regiment saw its first action when troops of a Spanish reconnaissance patrol killed two members of the Rough Riders'
vanguard and wounded several others. The Spaniards suffered a
number of casualties, too, and the correspondents accompanying the
1st Volunteer Cavalry telegraphed their newspapers a brief statement
by Lieutenant Colonel Roosevelt: WE WANTED THE FIRST WHACK AT THE
ENEMY, AND WE GOT IT.

The regiment continued to push inland, but was forced to move at
a crawl because it was not receiving food supplies from the landing
area, where conditions were chaotic. Major General William R.
Shafter, the commander-in-chief of the expedition, had not yet come
ashore from his transport; sixty-three years old and weighing more
than three hundred pounds, he was suffering from a chronic case of
gout as well as the heat, and was unable to take personal charge of
the situation. A number of supply vessels had sailed to the wrong destination, and the food shortage became increasingly acute.

Meanwhile General Young had fallen ill, and Leonard Wood was
promoted to brigadier general, replacing him. Theodore Roosevelt,
promoted to full colonel, became the commander of the Rough Riders.

Infuriated by the lack of provisions, Theodore sent foraging parties
to the coast to buy supplies, giving them three hundred dollars out of
his own pocket for the purpose, all the cash he carried with him, and
borrowing an additional one hundred as well from members of his
staff. Members of the regiment later boasted that they were the only
men in the expedition who did not go hungry.

On the night of June 30 the Rough Riders could see the lights of
Santiago on the heights in the distance, and the Americans halted

within range of the entrenched batteries of Spanish artillery. A major action was certain to be fought the following day.

Theodore attended a council of war that night, and learned the simple strategy of the high command. Directly ahead of the American position on the right was a village called El Caney, while on the left were a series of fortified heights, the largest of which was known as San Juan Hill. A brigade of Regulars was ordered to attack El Caney, with General Wood's brigade acting as a supporting reserve. El Caney would fall, General Wheeler said, and the Spanish line would be turned.

The attack began at dawn, but the Spaniards at El Caney, supported by their heavy artillery, repulsed a series of assaults, and Wood's brigade was ordered forward. The Rough Riders, in the vanguard, moved into a small jungle valley, and the Spaniards on the heights opened fire on them with a deadly artillery barrage.

The regiment took cover, the men scattering, and Theodore rode back a short distance to Wood's command position for a conference. "Sir," he said, "we've got to blast the enemy out of the hills!"

Wood, who was watching the artillery fire through his binoculars, continued to study the situation before replying. "They have guns on two hills up there, and it will take days to bring up our own artillery. Even then the enemy will still hold the advantage."

"If we wait for artillery support, General, we'll be shredded." Theodore removed his hat to wipe his forehead with a blue polka-dot handkerchief, then thoughtfully tied the square of cloth to his hatband. "I request permission for the 1st Volunteer Cavalry to charge up the heights and drive the enemy out."

Leonard Wood lowered the binoculars and looked at his friend. "You're volunteering for a suicidal mission, Colonel."

"We'd rather die in an attack than be pounded in this infernal valley, General."

Wood hesitated.

"You know the regiment, sir. You know we can take our objective." Theodore spoke rapidly, shouting to make himself heard above the steady roar of enemy guns.

General Wood sucked in his breath. "All right," he said at last, and held out his hand. "Good luck!"

Theodore saluted, then rode forward again, grinning. "We'll attack. Now!" he told his battalion commanders, and the men assembled in battle formation, ignoring the gunfire that rained down on them.

Two troopers were reluctant to take their places in the ranks, and Theodore pointed his drawn sword at them. "Are you afraid to stand when I'm on horseback—and doubly conspicuous? Take your places!" Not waiting for them to reply, he rode forward through the underbrush and took his place at the head of his vanguard.

Several junior officers tried to persuade him to take a less prominent position, but he silenced them with a wave, then moved toward the ranks of the Regular infantry regiments ahead. "Let my men through!" he called repeatedly. "Let them through!"

Incredulous officers watched as the 1st Volunteer Cavalry headed toward the base of the hills from which the Spanish guns were firing.

Battalion commanders sent word forward that the regiment was prepared for the attack.

Theodore signaled his bugler to sound the advance, and pointing his sword toward the crest of the height adjacent to San Juan Hill, started up the slope.

The Spaniards were astonished by the foolhardy audacity of their foes, but recovered quickly, and directed a heavy cannon and rifle fire at the Americans struggling up the exposed slope of the hill.

Men dropped, but the regiment continued to advance, while Theodore, shouting at the top of his voice, called encouragement to his troops above the din. Miraculously, he himself escaped unscathed, and enough men reached the crest to open fire at the Spanish troops who were holding positions behind low breastworks of stone.

The American riflemen were more accurate, and the defenders, after a brief struggle, abandoned their guns and fled down the far slope toward Santiago. An American flag was planted at the crest of what came to be known as Kettle Hill because several kettles used for boiling sugar were found near the Spanish cannon. Theodore, still mounted, continued to wave his hat and shout exuberantly as his men occupied the abandoned positions and watched the Spaniards retreat from adjacent San Juan Hill, which the capture of Kettle Hill had made untenable. But his victory had been purchased at a high cost, and the troopers who sprawled on the rough ground of the slope, staring up at the sky with vacant eyes, could not join in the celebration.

Colonel Roosevelt's Rough Riders, correspondent Richard Harding Davis wrote in a dispatch to the New York *Herald, have shown a reckless courage that has aroused the fighting spirit of the entire expeditionary corps. Although the Spaniards still hold Santiago and the*

American brigades are plagued by inexplicable shortages of food, am-
munition and medical supplies, the corps is convinced that a great
victory is near at hand.

The losses suffered by the Rough Riders in their assault on the
heights were staggering, one man in four being killed or wounded.
Colonel Roosevelt estimates that his percentage of loss has been seven
times that of the other volunteer regiments. What is remarkable is
that any Rough Rider survived.

Three days after Theodore's charge, the disheartened Spanish garrison at Santiago surrendered, and the campaign in Cuba came to an
end. The American cavalry, from General Wheeler to the newest volunteer recruit, gave the lion's share of credit to the Rough Riders' commander.

Other Regular Army officers, both in Cuba and in Washington, were
less generous. Some said his casualties had been inexcusably heavy,
and thought that his amateur's carelessness had been responsible.
Others, even blunter, declared he had sought glory at the expense of
his own men.

General Leonard Wood stoutly defended his subordinate and friend,
writing in his official report to the War Department that Colonel Roosevelt possessed every important virtue of a soldier: he was courageous,
solicitous of his troops' welfare and always available to those who
felt aggrieved. He was deservedly respected by both officers and men.
And no fault could be found with him as a strategist or tactician.

Had Theodore remained silent, the controversy might have subsided, but he could not. "Look at those damned Spanish dead," he
told a group of American civilian and military visitors to Kettle Hill,
and the callous remark, quoted by several newspaper correspondents,
offended the sensitive.

Soon after the fall of Santiago he made a second error, and boasted
of the Rough Riders' accomplishments to anyone who would listen
to him. *I do not want to be vain,* he wrote to Henry Cabot Lodge, *but*
I do not think anyone else could have handled this regiment quite as
I have. The Regulars, who cultivated a tradition of modesty, neither
forgot his words nor forgave them.

Although the fall of Santiago brought the brief campaign in Cuba to
an end, the corps was neither transferred to Puerto Rico, as Theodore
hoped, nor sent home. The brigades continued to languish in their
jungle bivouacs, underfed and miserable, the care of the wounded
and sick hampered by the lack of adequate medical supplies. Then, in

mid-July, the first cases of yellow fever broke out, and within a week hundreds were bedded by the disease.

By the end of the month the commanders of brigades were deeply concerned, and Theodore decided something had to be done. He suggested that the senior officers send a joint letter to the War Department setting forth the facts of the situation and requesting that the expedition be relieved. His colleagues, virtually all of them Regulars, were afraid they would jeopardize their careers, and, as he was an author, urged him to prepare the communication himself.

He did, and it was not accidental that Richard Harding Davis and the other correspondents learned of the document's existence. On August 4 they accompanied him to General Shafter's headquarters, and were present when the commander-in-chief refused to read or sanction the letter.

Theodore sent the communication to the War Department by telegraph, and members of the regimental staff thoughtfully provided the correspondents with copies. The blistering description of the suffering endured by the corps appeared in newspapers throughout the United States on August 5, simultaneously with the War Department's receipt of the letter.

Secretary Alger was bitterly angry. He attacked Theodore at a press conference, saying that the Rough Riders' commander was contemptuous of the National Guard. As to the claim that members of the Cuban expeditionary corps were victims of yellow fever, he suggested that, in all probability, they were suffering from homesickness.

But the indignation created throughout the country was more effective than the Secretary's counterattack. Members of Congress received thousands of protests, and they, in turn, demanded that something be done to improve the lot of the volunteers. Unable to resist the pressures, Secretary Alger ordered the regiments at Santiago to leave at once for home.

The 1st Volunteer Cavalry embarked on the transport *Miami,* and that evening Theodore strolled on the deck with Richard Harding Davis, who was accompanying the regiment. "When I see how many of my boys are under the weather," the colonel said, "I'm almost ashamed of myself. I feel disgracefully well."

"I begin to think you're indestructible."

Theodore grinned. "You shouldn't tell me things like that, or I'll begin to believe them myself." They walked in silence for a few moments, then he said more soberly: "I've started making some notes on my farewell speech to the regiment. I'll appreciate your opinion of them."

"Certainly."

"There's one matter in particular I want to bring out. I don't believe any newspaper account of the Battle of Kettle Hill mentioned that a regiment of Negro troops was fighting on our flank, and did fine work holding the enemy. I intend to pay them a tribute."

"I intended to ask your plans when you're mustered out of service, Theodore. Now I know."

The eyes behind the glasses became glacial. "I beg your pardon?"

"You intend to go back into politics, obviously."

"I'm sincere," Theodore said, "in wanting to praise the troops who helped us win a victory."

"I don't doubt that," David replied. "At the same time, though, you'll do yourself no political harm."

Theodore shrugged as he walked to the rail and stared out at the blue-black water, indicating that the political consequences were of no concern to him.

Davis joined him. "I have no business mentioning this to you if you don't already know it," he said, "but I wonder if you've heard that General Wood recommended you for a Congressional Medal of Honor."

Suddenly tense, Theodore turned to him and gripped his arm. "You're sure?"

"Quite."

"Leonard didn't say a word to me."

"That's natural. General Wheeler has added a warm endorsement of his own."

Obviously shaken, Theodore blinked as he averted his face and looked out at the sea again. "It's odd, but ever since I was a sickly little boy, I've dreamed of winning the Medal of Honor. That's a private confidence, Dick. I'd be very distressed if you published it."

"I'll keep my mouth shut, Theodore."

"It's too good to be true." Theodore removed his broad-brimmed hat and felt the warm sea breeze ruffle his hair. "Aside from the personal satisfaction, it wouldn't do me any harm politically to win the country's highest military award."

"Don't count on it," Davis warned him.

"I won't." Theodore was perfunctory.

"Unless I'm badly mistaken, you're the last man in the expeditionary corps who'd be given one."

"I hope you're joking." It was impossible for Theodore to conceal his sudden alarm.

"I don't believe you've realized the consequences of the letter you sent to Secretary Alger."

"Every word was the truth, and you know it. So do the troops who were stationed at Santiago. Their neglect by the government was a national disgrace!"

"True, and your protest won you support throughout the whole country. It's too early to tell how much, but the effect in certain quarters must be obvious to you. How do you suppose President McKinley felt? And do you think Secretary Alger enjoyed being forced to back down and order the regiments sent home?"

"I can't imagine Alger or anyone else denying me a medal I've won."

"Then your imagination is as limited as your understanding of human nature!" Davis was emphatic. "The recommendation will move through the usual War Department channels. Do you suppose the generals whose negligence you exposed will approve the recommendation? Hardly. And although Alger could overrule them when the papers reach his desk, I'll bet you a dinner at Delmonico's that he won't."

"They can't deny me my due!" Theodore said fiercely, but a forlorn note in his voice indicated that he was a better student of character than he had admitted, and knew he had made enemies who would deny him the Medal of Honor. "But if they try, I'll fight them. I'll get sworn affidavits from every officer and man in the regiment, and from all the other units that saw us in battle. I'll go to friends in the Senate and House—"

"Don't waste your effort and time, Theodore. You and George Dewey are the biggest heroes of the war, and there's no telling how far you can go."

Theodore had already learned, in a letter from Henry Cabot Lodge, that the newspapers of New York were calling him a "natural" candidate for Governor. But he thought it better to pretend ignorance, particularly because of the principle at stake. "If I've earned the Medal of Honor, I deserve to get it," he said stubbornly.

"You'll get so many other rewards," Davis said, "that you won't miss it."

It was a waste of breath to tell the correspondent he was wrong.

On August 15 the Rough Riders were rowed ashore to the sandy beaches of Long Island from the *Miami,* anchored off the town of Montauk. Massed bands of amateur musicians serenaded the warriors with a rousing rendition of "A Hot Time in the Old Town" that made up in gusto what it lacked in melody. Relatives and friends of the troopers were on hand, and even the usually phlegmatic Long Island fishermen cheered when the regimental commander waded ashore from the last boat and embraced his wife and children before marching his men off to a bleak camp set up in the sand dunes.

It was rumored that Secretary of War Alger, with the quiet support of Senators Hanna and Platt, and the possible knowledge of President McKinley, was punishing Colonel Roosevelt by denying him a hero's welcome in Manhattan. If the story was true, the Secretary of War failed.

Several groups of reform Republicans and independent leaders who advocated the election of a governor "free of political taint" were on hand, and a representative of New York City, aroused by the emotion of the occasion, asked the regiment to parade up Broadway. Colonel Roosevelt promptly accepted.

Chauncey Depew was present, ostensibly as an old friend of the colonel's family, and soon thereafter paid a visit to Senator Platt's residence-office at the Fifth Avenue Hotel. "You and I know," the wily lawyer said, "that Frank Black can't be re-elected Governor. Too many people will ask embarrassing questions about the fortune he spent repairing the Erie Canal. We need a candidate so honest that no one would dare ask him about the Canal steal."

The ascetic-looking Platt fidgeted in his chair. "You forget I've had experience with Teddy Roosevelt," he replied dryly. "That rampaging bull wouldn't leave one china dish in the closet unbroken."

"You've seen the newspapers?"

"Oh, yes. By now he's won the war singlehanded, Chauncey. Even the Democratic papers are praising him. Joe Pulitzer probably feels indebted to him for helping to get us into the war, and then getting us out again so quickly. And the others are enjoying his feud with McKinley's War Department."

"If you had seen the crowd at Montauk, you'd know that Roosevelt is a genuine hero to the ordinary citizen."

"He's so unpredictable that I'm afraid of him, Chauncey."

"Certainly you can reach an understanding with him," Depew said. "Roosevelt isn't an ogre."

"I'm not so sure."

"Do you know of any other candidate who can win?"

"I'll find someone," Platt said.

"I'm not thinking just in terms of the candidate's own appearances in the state—where Roosevelt would be an obvious asset. What worries me is what will happen at all the other party rallies and meetings. Someone will ask about the Canal steal. It's inevitable.

"And do you know what the chairman will do?" Depew stood and imitated a nervous, small-town politician. "He'll say, 'I'm mighty glad you asked that question. We have nominated for governor a man who has demonstrated that he is a fighter for the right. If he is elected every thief will be caught and punished.'

"Then, when the cheers die down, the chairman will follow Colonel Roosevelt leading his men up San Juan Hill and will ask the band to play 'The Star-Spangled Banner.'"

Platt's smile was bloodless. "I appreciate his potential, but I'm not forgetting he's a trouble-maker. I'll try to find someone else."

"There is no such person. We're seeing democracy at work, Tom. The people want Roosevelt, and won't be satisfied with anyone else."

Theodore rarely ventured beyond the confines of the Rough Rider camp at Montauk, and appeared deaf to the clamor of Republicans, independents and dissident Democrats that he seek the state's highest office. Newspaper reporters besieged him, and he repeatedly gave them the same answer. "I'm still a soldier," he said, "and it wouldn't be fitting for me to comment on civilian political matters. Besides, I'm spending all my time trying to find jobs for members of the regiment who'll starve if they aren't employed. Be a good fellow, will you? Print another appeal for my veterans!"

Senator Platt sent reporters from newspapers controlled by his friends to ask trick questions, hoping to obtain a disclaimer of interest in the forthcoming gubernatorial race. But Theodore refused to be trapped. As long as he remained a soldier, he declared, his men were his sole concern.

In spite of his alleged indifference, volunteers worked incessantly to make the Rough Rider parade a memorable event. Representatives of the War Department were conspicuously absent, but no one missed them. Six units of Civil War veterans took part, as did several of their bands. Two full infantry battalions of the New York National Guard appeared, although no one could find out who had ordered them to participate. Members of fraternal and benevolent societies rode on floats, and among the marchers were delegations of German-Americans, Italian-Americans and Bohemian-Americans, as well as Catholic priests, Jewish rabbis and a few Protestant clergymen. Representatives of the independent political organizations refused to be left out, and the labor unions sent hundreds of workers, who were given a holiday for the occasion. According to the more enthusiastic press estimates, more than fifty thousand marchers participated.

A crowd of a half-million persons, the largest throng ever to gather in New York City, lined Broadway to watch the parade, and the *Sun* commented that people blocks from the route knew from the frenzied cheering where the Rough Riders were to be found in the line at any given moment.

The regiment, mounted for the occasion on horses loaned by patriotic citizens of Oyster Bay and other Long Island communities, rode four abreast. Colonel Roosevelt, in a rumpled, sun-faded field uniform, led his vanguard; the people shouted until they were hoarse as, smiling broadly, he waved his broad-brimmed hat, to which he had tied his now-famous blue polka-dot handkerchief.

Never, said the *Tribune, has this city given such an ecstatic welcome to one of her illustrious sons.*

Refusing a score of banquet invitations, Theodore returned to Montauk with his men.

On September 4 the regiment was mustered out of active service, in the presence of seventy-five newspaper correspondents. The enlisted men presented their commander with a replica of Frederic Remington's bronze, *Bronco Buster,* and the colonel was overwhelmed.

His farewell, delivered in a voice hoarse with emotion, was brief and direct. "I am proud of this regiment beyond measure," he said. "It is an American regiment, and it is American because it is composed of all the races which have made America their country by adoption and those who have claimed it as their country by inheritance." Scarcely pausing for breath, he went on to praise the Negro troops who had fought with valor beside the Rough Riders.

His voice cracked when he reached his closing words. "We are knit closer together than any body of men I know of. I would honestly rather have my position as your colonel than any other position on earth."

Tears appeared in his eyes, and, to prevent himself from weeping, he added an unplanned postscript. "Don't think too much of yourselves, and don't pose as heroes," he roared in parade-ground wrath. "Don't go back and lie on your laurels. They'll wither."

Only a handful of the most cynical newspaper correspondents present saw political overtones in the remarks.

And no one doubted the Colonel's sincerity as his officers and men filed past him. He shook hands with each of them, and, like the majority, he wept openly, without shame. Even outsiders who thought him brash and sentimental were touched.

After the regiment had broken camp, Theodore recovered his aplomb in time for a last, brisk word for the press. "Thank you for your interest in the regiment, and goodbye," he said. "Since I'm a private citizen now, and will be going home to my wife and children, my activities won't be of news value. So I doubt whether we'll meet again."

Every reporter present swore he spoke sincerely, without a trace of humor in his voice or expression.

Theodore enjoyed his privacy for only a few days. Senator Platt, in spite of his misgivings, was a realist who had learned to live with the unavoidable. So it was not surprising that he sent a cryptic note to Oyster Bay suggesting a meeting at the Fifth Avenue Hotel in the immediate future.

Theodore faced a minor dilemma. The reform groups that had been urging him to run for governor despised Platt, and might repudiate their champion when they learned he had made a deal with New York's Republican boss. But there was no choice, Theodore knew; it was far better to lose the unorganized support of a few well-wishing citizens than to oppose, openly, the leader of a political machine able to deliver large blocs of votes.

I am seeing your colleague, T.P., tomorrow, he wrote in a note to Lodge, *and I am convinced I can and shall protect my honor.*

The meeting took place in the shabby parlor of the Senator's suite, and the two men, sipping fruit juice, exchanged cordial, inconsequential banter for a quarter of an hour. Theodore soon realized that Platt was waiting for him to bring up the subject that had brought them together, but was determined to put his host on the defensive. "You said in your letter that you wanted to see me, Tom."

Platt was equally bland. "Just as you've wanted to see me, Theodore," he replied.

When subtleties were ineffective, a more direct approach was necessary. "What's on your mind, Tom?"

"The same thing that's on yours." The Senator had no taste for sparring. "There's been talk, ever since you came home a month ago, about running you for governor."

"I've heard some of it."

Platt studied him, aware that he had matured and hardened since his frustrating years as Police Commissioner. "How does it strike you?"

"I'm flattered, naturally."

The Senator lost some of his poise. "Damn it, Theodore, do you or don't you want to be Governor?"

"I think any man interested in the welfare of our people and wanting to improve our industries would be pleased to serve."

"When you and I are alone, you needn't make campaign speeches."

"When you and I are alone," Theodore replied quickly, "I must say precisely what I think."

Platt's eyes narrowed, the only sign that he resented the rebuke. "Will you accept the support of the independent reformers?"

"If they'll work and vote for me. I'll accept the support of any organization or group that thinks as I do."

"Could you spell out your thinking?"

"I haven't developed a specific program, since I'm not yet a candidate. But I stand solidly, as you do, on the Republican platform."

"I hope," Platt said slowly, "that we're really in agreement. If we are, I see no reason you shouldn't become the party's candidate."

"It takes two to agree, Tom." Theodore spoke pleasantly, but was unyielding. "I'm no man's puppet, as you know."

"It didn't cross my mind that you were." The Senator's laugh was genuine, but hollow.

"Do you want me as the candidate?"

"Yes, if you'll remember that the essence of politics is compromise."

"Except where principle and honor are concerned."

"Of course," Platt said easily.

"You'd expect a hand in some state appointments, I assume."

"It's an old custom for the governor to consult his party chairman on appointments. When devoted men all over the state go out and work hard for a governor's election, they deserve to be rewarded. There aren't many of us rich enough to live on our income."

"When a man has a family as large as mine, he needs a salary." Theodore grinned, then gritted his teeth. "It's no secret to you that I'm devoted to the civil service. As governor I'd want to extend Grover Cleveland's reforms."

Platt winced. "You can't change the whole structure of any government overnight."

"Certainly not. That isn't the American way. But I'd expect to broaden the base of the state's civil service employment. Since I've come home from Cuba," Theodore added, "I've also become interested in the conservation of our natural resources—our forests, rivers, the heritage of our people."

The Senator knew nothing on the subject, which sounded like a harmless pet project of a man devoted to the outdoors. "I can't see myself fighting with you about a forest." He paused. "Or anything else, really. We're both sensible men who understand the business of politics."

"If *you'll* understand that the ultimate public interest, in my opinion, stands above political considerations, I think we can work together," Theodore said. "But I want to make it clear, Tom, that I can cooperate with you only to the extent that my conscience permits."

Platt didn't know how he defined matters of conscience, but had to accept the bargain. The public was demanding Roosevelt, so there was no choice, and he could only hope the stubborn idealist had become more practical. "It's a deal, Theodore," he said warily, and extended his hand.

Theodore's campaign was an exercise in patriotic ingenuity. American flags draped every auditorium in which he spoke, former Rough Riders always escorted him to the speaker's platform, and his addresses were inspiring, very personal and vague. The "Canal steal" of his predecessor was never mentioned. His Democratic opponent, Augustus Van Wyck of Brooklyn, brother of the Tammany Mayor of New York City, Robert A. Van Wyck, struggled in vain against impossible odds, and Theodore won by almost eighteen thousand votes, leading the Republican ticket.

In January 1899 the new governor took the oath of office, and the Roosevelt family moved into the old Executive Mansion in Albany, which was decorated in a style so stuffily elegant that Theodore likened it to "a really swell Chicago hotel." There were so many rooms in the house that Ted and Kermit converted one into a guinea pig farm, which they operated, throughout their entire stay in Albany, with their father's enthusiastic help and guidance.

Other pets appeared in large numbers, too, among them dogs, cats and goldfish, and visitors soon learned the need to walk with care through the corridors. The unwary frequently tripped over a small child or animal.

More often than not there were guests for dinner, and the press, dutifully trying to report all of the governor's activities, found the pace bewildering. The Governor-General of Canada was entertained, as was a young English newspaper war correspondent, a close relative of the Duke of Marlborough named Winston Churchill, who bickered amiably with Theodore on the facts of history. *Dining with Governor and Mrs. Roosevelt is an unusual experience,* wrote a reporter from the *Tribune,* himself a guest. *One never knows whether one will sit beside a member of the Legislature or a former Rough Rider, a cowboy by trade, who has come East to make his fortune—with the Governor's always available help. One meets the socially eminent, labor union men, bankers, authors, prominent officials from Washington, diplomats, farmers and pugilists with whom the Governor boxes in a gymnasium he has built on the top floor at his own expense. On one occasion, one sat directly across the table from the doorman of the State Office Building, a Nature enthusiast who frequently accompanies the Governor on hikes through the woods to the northwest of Albany.*

Theodore instinctively adopted a moderate line as governor, rejecting the extreme demands of the reformers and quietly sapping the power of the conservatives. He first clashed with Senator Platt on the issue of taxing the corporations engaged in providing the public with transportation, particularly the new companies that were building electric streetcar lines in the cities to replace horsecars.

The Governor insisted on taxing the corporations, while Platt insisted that such taxes stifled the American tradition of free enterprise. Theodore, proving himself far more cunning than the Senator had imagined, personally drew up a bill far more stringent than he actually wanted, and threatened to appeal to the people of the state over the heads of the Senate and Assembly. The legislators were alarmed, and the Governor eventually allowed himself to be persuaded to work out a "compromise"—a bill he considered fair. Platt, relieved that an attempt to push through the stronger measure would be dropped, agreed to the milder measure.

When possible, the two men worked together, and Theodore developed the habit of going to New York for a part of every weekend to meet Platt, who came up from Washington for the purpose. The Democrats jeered the Governor, claiming that his so-called sense of ethics was a sham, and Theodore, refusing to counterattack, mildly stated he held office for the purpose of accomplishing what he considered necessary for the welfare of the state, and that he found the Senator's "counsel" valuable.

He made no mention of the fact that he had won a moral victory of considerable significance. The meetings never took place now at the Fifth Avenue Hotel, but instead were held at the Robinson town house at 422 Madison Avenue, where Corinne was always a silent third party. "My sister is so interested in everything I do," Theodore ingenuously explained to the Senator, "that I've invited her to attend all of my conferences." There was no need for him to spell out to the shrewd Platt that Conie was a reliable witness whose mere presence made it impossible for him to suggest unsavory deals or tactics.

In his relations with labor the Governor was ambivalent; union leaders impolitely called him confused. He approved a bill providing an eight-hour workday for state employees, but vetoed a measure that would have reduced the exceptionally long workday of drug clerks. He bitterly fought a bill giving schoolteachers pay raises based on longevity; agreeing they were disgracefully underpaid, he demanded, but only partially succeeded in obtaining a law basing their salary increases on merit.

Somehow he found time to write a book on his experiences in the recent war, called *The Rough Riders,* and was amused when his friend, Peter Finley Dunne, the columnist creator of a popular character called Mr. Dooley, wrote that the book should have been entitled, *Alone in Cubia.* "I regret to state," Theodore told him in a note, "that my family and intimate friends are delighted with your review of my book."

To the dismay of professional politicians the Governor consulted college professors when he wanted expert opinions, advocated granting at least limited voting rights to women and, ignoring the time-honored practice of conducting the state's business in private, held two press conferences daily for the purpose of keeping the public informed. His resources of energy proving inexhaustible, he not only boxed and hiked daily, but started work on still another book, a biography of Oliver Cromwell.

Inevitably, Theodore and Platt clashed. Although they had managed to avoid a major confrontation by maneuvering delicately, they found themselves on opposite sides of the fence in the autumn of 1899. Theodore, who had been eliminating corrupt and inefficient office-holders whenever possible, decided not to reappoint the state's Superintendent of Insurance, Louis F. Payn, a former Albany lobbyist for financier Jay Gould, Platt's close friend.

Confiding only in a few associates, Theodore did not know whether he had the power to dislodge Payn, whose reappointment was being enthusiastically endorsed by the insurance companies, or whether he could find a man of integrity as a replacement acceptable to Platt's supporters in the insurance business.

A scandal that broke in the newspapers late in 1899 seemed to strengthen Theodore's hand. The press, in screaming headlines, revealed that the State Trust Company, a major bank, had loaned Payn $435,000, demanding no collateral, even though he earned a salary of only $7000 per year. It could not be accidental, the newspapers said, that a number of the bank's directors also served on the boards of insurance companies whose activities Payn supervised.

Determined to get rid of the Superintendent, Theodore sent a note to Platt, saying he had a matter of urgent importance to discuss that weekend. The senator, obviously aware that a showdown was at hand, replied that he would be spending only a short time in New York City, and therefore regretted he could not come to the house of Mrs. Robinson. Accepting the challenge, Theodore promptly agreed to a completely private meeting at the Fifth Avenue Hotel.

Neither man was affable when Theodore walked into the Senator's suite, and Platt almost forgot to offer the Governor the customary glass of fruit juice. They sat opposite each other, both of them tense, and Theodore held himself like a boxer ready to spring into action when the bell sounded.

"You know what I want to discuss, Tom," he said.

"I've been reading the newspapers, just as you have."

"I hope you agree that Payn will have to go. Obviously he's unfit for public office."

The Senator raised a veined hand. "Not so fast, Theodore. Ordinarily, when the press is howling for the blood of someone on Payn's level, I wouldn't dream of asking you to embarrass yourself by reappointing him. In fact, when I first read the stories, I assumed he'd take the graceful way out and resign."

"He should." Theodore ground his teeth.

"As it happens, I had a letter from him just a couple of days ago." Platt sounded very calm. "He insists the charges against him are ridiculous, and he insists he'll fight for his job."

"Under no circumstances," Theodore said, "will I reappoint him as Superintendent of Insurance. That's flat and final."

"I'm not arguing, but I wish you'd hear me out. Lou Payn has been a loyal and valuable supporter of the Republican party. If I desert him now, when the bloodhounds are snapping at his heels, everyone else will become frightened. The chairman of a political party can't hold an organization together unless he supports his subordinates."

"I'm not the chairman of anything. I'm the governor of the most heavily populated state in the Union, and I'm responsible to all the citizens of New York, not just the Republican regulars."

"Of course."

"So I can't and won't keep a criminal in office."

"To the best of my knowledge," Platt said, "Lou Payn hasn't been convicted of anything. The newspapers have been full of charges against him, that's all."

"He hasn't denied taking the money from the State Trust Company," Theodore said.

The Senator shrugged.

"Why should Payn want or need almost a half-million dollars? That's a fortune!"

"I suggest you ask him."

"I did. He admitted getting the money, but said he wasn't on trial, that I wasn't a judge and that his reasons were his own."

"That's fair enough. I don't know his reasons, either, and I wouldn't presume to ask for an explanation."

"Tom," Theodore said heavily, "the facts are plain. A man who earns a modest salary, and who has the power to prevent abuses by very large, wealthy insurance companies, has taken a huge sum from a bank closely associated with those companies. They haven't even asked him to put up his house as security. So it's very clear the bank doesn't expect to be repaid. Payn has accepted a bribe, not a loan!"

"That can be proved only if he fails to repay the money through the years."

"On his salary he couldn't repay a nickel of it!" Theodore's voice rose.

"That's conjecture, not fact." Platt returned the younger man's glare. "I saw an article in the *World* the other night that said you're never satisfied with less than victory. But this is one time when you've got to admit defeat."

"The people and I can't concede," Theodore declared, only his anger preventing his pomposity from making him appear ludicrous. "And we won't."

"What's your next move?"

"I'll find a man of integrity and talent, who knows insurance, and I'll appoint him to replace Payn. Elihu Root was the counsel for several of the big insurance companies before he went to Washington as Secretary of War, and I'm sure he'll help me."

"Most members of the Assembly sit for year after year." Platt smiled. "And I know from experience that when a governor is starting the second year of a two-year term, they're inclined to treat him with less dignity than he thinks he deserves. They'll still be going back to Albany long after he's been retired and forgotten. The Assembly won't confirm anyone you nominate."

"If they turn down one," Theodore said stubbornly, "I'll name another. And another. And another. Eventually—and it won't take long—the press and the public will blame the man who deserves censure."

"And what do you think the Democrats will be doing? You'll not only hand them my Senate seat, but they'll elect the next governor and control the Assembly."

Theodore appeared to brighten. "That would be a catastrophe of the worst sort, wouldn't it?"

"Yes." The Senator found his sudden change in attitude inexplicable. "If you're so all-fired concerned about reform, how can you even think of opening the door to the thieves of Tammany?"

"It's a real dilemma, isn't it?" In command of the situation at last, Theodore chuckled. "You'll be branded as a crook, and I'll be called a fool. Well, you've always said you'd like to spend a year or so being wheeled up and down the Boardwalk in Atlantic City in a roller chair, Tom, so you may achieve that ambition sooner than you imagined. As for me, I'll try to find a job as a professor of history somewhere, and I'll write some more books. I have enough ideas to keep me writing for years."

"You can't be serious." The shocked Platt thought him mad enough to make good his threat.

"Why not?"

"Because you're popular enough to win re-election, or go to Washington in the Cabinet—or—who knows how high you might climb? Provided you show some sense!"

"My conscience wouldn't let me be remembered as the governor who nominated Lou Payn for another term as Superintendent of Insurance," Theodore said cheerfully. "The reason I'm so competely op- posed to him is because his immorality is professional. For the sake of keeping the machinery of government operating I've closed my eyes and signed my name to your minor appointments, the little fish who don't influence policy. But I'd strip myself of honor if I accepted Payn."

"Then you'll destroy us all."

"I don't believe any political problem is insoluble, Tom. Suppose I found an honest, efficient man whose qualifications satisfied me and who happened to be somebody you trusted? I think you might be willing to abandon Payn for him."

"There is no such person," the Senator said gloomily.

Theodore stood and strolled to the dirt-streaked window. "I knew I was going to see you today, so I asked Frank Hendricks to come down from Syracuse for a chat last night."

Platt stiffened. Francis Hendricks had been his campaign manager when he had run for the Senate, and they had jointly purchased valu- able real estate holdings in Manhattan and upstate New York.

"Nobody is closer to you than Frank, and he's rich enough to look at the problem objectively. He's also a loyal Republican who wouldn't sleep nights if the Democrats won control of the state. Well, sir, we worked out a bully solution, Frank and I. He'd be willing to become Superintendent of Insurance himself. If he had your support."

"I'd support him for any job, in preference to any other man in politics. He knows it, and so do you!"

"It seems to me," Theodore said quietly, "that we've worked out a compromise satisfactory to everyone."

"Your reform friends will damn you, Theodore. They'll say you've sold your soul to the Platt machine."

"The longer I'm in politics, the more I realize that the majority of reformers don't understand this business. I'm convinced Hendricks is an honest man who won't tolerate any nonsense from the insurance companies, and that's good enough for me. Any of my friends who think I've let them down will learn, after a time, that they were wrong."

The tension eased, but it had taken its toll. Platt's hand trembled as he picked up a battered tin pitcher and refilled their glasses with fruit juice. "Theodore," he said, "I'm damned if I understand you."

"I can't blame you. There are times when I scarcely understand my- self."

"You knew when you walked in here that you were going to suggest Frank Hendricks—a perfect man from both your point of view and mine. Yet I'll be damned if you didn't fight me, and even threaten to destroy both of us! Why, Theodore?"

"I couldn't let you walk all over me, Tom. If I'd mentioned Hendricks at the outset, you'd have thought I was giving in to you. But now you know I won't budge for anyone when there's a principle at stake! You see, I've always been fond of an old West African proverb: 'Speak softly and carry a big stick, you will go far.'"

Few citizens of New York would have recognized the man clad in a shabby, canvas windbreaker, old trousers stuffed into mud-caked boots and a small, brimless fur hat who squatted in the snow, frying fish in an iron skillet over a small fire. He appeared to be in good physical condition, which was unusual for a hobo, and he handled the skillet with an ease indicating he took pride in his talents as a cook. Only the glasses he wore above a five-day growth of beard revealed his identity.

Theodore's companion, equally unkempt, was busily cleaning fish and slicing potatoes with a hunting knife, using a slab of granite as a chopping block. Anyone hearing him singing a complicated version of one of Gérard de Nerval's *Poésies*, in French, to a tune composed by Berlioz, would have thought him an unusual vagrant. Certainly it was true that Gifford Pinchot, Yale graduate who had become fond of Nerval's work while engaged in post-graduate studies at the Ecole Nationale Forestière in France, was no ordinary person. Chief Forester of the United States although still in his early thirties, he was recognized by the few people who cared about such matters as the nation's greatest expert on the conservation of natural resources, and was principally responsible for an ambitious plan, submitted to the Departments of the Interior and Agriculture, to set aside vast areas as public preserves.

Pinchot was adept, but Theodore, the perfectionist, was not satisfied. "Cut the potatoes a little thinner, Gifford," he said. "Then they'll cook faster and be ready when the fish is done."

"There's enough here for at least four." Pinchot handed him several mounds of potatoes.

"We'll manage." Theodore dropped the potatoes into the skillet, adding bacon fat which he scooped out of a can with a whittled stick. "I'm ravenous."

"So am I, and we should be. We've been hiking for almost ten hours."

"It's a bully life." Theodore was silent for a time, listening to the crackling of the fat in the pan and the hissing of the wood fire. "Smell these fish! It sickens me when I think that within a few years there will be so much industrial waste in the Hudson that the millions of fish out there will either die off or be inedible."

"I read your special message to the Assembly on the subject," Pinchot said. "It was good, but a trifle too moderate for my taste."

"Moderate?" Theodore laughed scornfully. "The *Times* and the *Sun* called me a radical visionary, and the *Post* said I should have been satisfied with the unanimous vote making this tract on the river a state preserve. And you should see the letters I get from the quarrying interests that were carving the sides out of the Palisades!"

"I can imagine." Pinchot laughed, and, finished with the knife, wiped it absently on the side of his trousers. "I've had a few myself from lumbering and power interests."

"We can consider ourselves on the side of the angels."

"We'll have to, Governor. No one else does. But I'll tell you one thing—long after you're gone, you'll be remembered for setting up this preserve."

"Provided the commission that administers it gives the people the opportunity to enjoy it. I insist that it be opened to the public." Theodore flipped over the fish and rustled the potatoes in the skillet. "Is there anyone you'd care to recommend for the chairmanship, Gifford?"

"I've heard a very able man was recommended to you."

"You mean George Perkins? I don't know him."

"Of course you do, Governor! Both of you attended the last dinner meeting of the Boone and Crockett Club."

"We took care to avoid each other," Theodore said, grinning, "due to circumstances not beyond our control. I haven't been very popular with the insurance crowd lately, and Perkins is a top man at New York Life."

"I can understand your reticence—and his. But I'll have to get you together privately. George would have enjoyed this outing with us. He's devoted to the cause of conservation."

"Why should he be?" Theodore challenged.

"Why shouldn't he? Why do you care about forests and rivers and mountains? Why does any honorable American who stops to think about our heritage?"

"You win!" Theodore raised a hand. "If you say he's a good man, I'll take your word for it." Pinchot, Theodore thought, was the only human being he had ever known who could silence him by talking more rapidly and with greater vehemence. "Bring the plates, will you?"

The Chief Forester produced two battered tin plates, and started to put a pot of coffee at one side of the fire.

"I'll do that!" Theodore took the pot, and, still clutching the skillet with his other hand, arranged it to his liking. "I hate burned coffee."

Pinchot smiled, but made no reply. Anyone who went camping with Governor Roosevelt had to take second place on the expedition. "I'm still going to get you together with Perkins. I wouldn't want you to appoint him on my word."

Theodore beamed at him as he shoveled food onto the plates. "I sometimes think I'm slightly insane because most people think my standards are so unusual. Then I meet someone like you, and I find my ideals aren't strange, after all. All right, I'll be delighted to meet Perkins. Now, let's eat."

They sat cross-legged on the frozen ground, and ate with their knives.

Theodore enjoyed himself, but it was impossible for him to relax for more than a few moments. "You know," he said, frowning, "I was proud of building up New York's forest preserves to one and a third million acres, but now I'm not so sure. If the trees keep dying out, as they have just this side of that bend in the river, I—or my successor— may be forced to give in to the commercial interests that are demanding the sale of valuable public land."

"There's no need to lose a single acre," Pinchot told him. "In fact, you can not only build up these forests, but you can make enough money out of them to buy still more acreage for the state."

Theodore peered at him, wondering whether he might be joking, but saw he was serious. "How?"

"Cut the timber when it grows too thick, and sell what you've cut. The forests that are left standing will grow healthier."

"That's a radical notion!"

"It can be proved. But the lumbering operations must be conducted according to scientific principles that are very strict and demanding. I can give you some books to read on the subject, Governor."

"When?"

The surprised Pinchot was unaccustomed to Governor Roosevelt's relentless energy. "Well, I happen to have them at the little apartment I've been keeping in New York City, and—"

"Bully. We can pick them up tomorrow, then, when we end the trip. I'll be staying overnight with my sister and brother-in-law, so I can return them to you the next day."

The Chief Forester suppressed a grin. "There are three volumes, Governor. And one is in German."

"If the language isn't too technical, I shouldn't have any difficulty. I'm starting to prepare my annual message to the Legislature tomorrow, and I'd like to include something on scientific forestry. The subject intrigues me."

Pinchot found it difficult to believe that a man who would be required to prepare a long and carefully worded document could crowd in the reading of three books on forestry during a single evening, but he was beginning to believe that Theodore Roosevelt was capable of achieving anything he decided he wanted to do.

"I'd like to tell you something that very few people know. Consider this confidential until I tell you otherwise. Only my family and a very few close friends know what I have in mind."

"Of course, Governor." Pinchot was flattered to be considered his friend.

"I've taken aim on a target bigger than the job I hold at present," Theodore said.

Pinchot opened his mouth to mention the obvious, but was silenced by a sharp gesture.

"I prefer not to mention it aloud. Not yet. I suppose I've always wanted it, but I never knew how much until I became Governor—and realized how much needs to be done. In a couple of weeks we're moving into a new century, Gifford, and this country needs to be led and pushed and cajoled and bullied into the modern world if she hopes to survive!"

The Governorship of New York made any man who held the post a potential candidate for the presidency of the United States, and the press, remembering how Grover Cleveland had used Albany as a steppingstone to Washington, cast new, searching glances at Theodore early in 1900, almost six months before the national political conventions were scheduled to meet for the purpose of selecting their candidates. Speculation first appeared in the New York City newspapers, then spread to other parts of the country, and political leaders reacted sharply.

President McKinley said nothing, but Senator Mark Hanna, his closest associate, was less discreet. "Roosevelt," he told colleagues in the Senate, "is a fine governor, but he's too ambitious."

The West felt otherwise. North and South Dakota were enthusiastic over the political potential of someone they considered a native son, and Theodore's love for the West was reciprocated from the Rocky Mountains to Texas. The six hundred veterans of the Rough Riders considered themselves self-appointed advocates of Theodore's cause, and wrote letters to newspapers, praising their former commander and urging that he be nominated. Even such seasoned political veterans as Senator Edward Oliver Wolcott, who dominated the Republican party in Colorado, allowed himself to be quoted as a strong admirer of Governor Roosevelt, "who, in my opinion, is qualified for any office the people of this nation care to bestow on him."

George Dewey, the hero of Manila Bay, now an admiral, temporarily abandoned the politically neutral position taken by Navy and Army officers, and commented, "We would not have won the war had it not been for Theodore Roosevelt's foresight. A man of his caliber deserves the highest reward the citizens of this nation can bestow on him."

Newspapers in the East, however, refused to consider Theodore's possible candidacy seriously. The New York *Times* jokingly observed that President McKinley could not be worried, since the Governor was busily occupied with the affairs of his seven million constituents in New York, and that if he was allowing his thoughts to wander, he was doing his own state a disservice. The press in Boston and Hartford, Baltimore and Philadelphia praised Theodore, but indicated they believed any talk of his running for the presidency was premature. *Let him continue to gain experience in New York and administer her business wisely,* the Baltimore *Sun* said, *and other, higher posts will come to him in the years ahead.*

Theodore himself remained realistic. "If McKinley wants another term," he told Edith, "no one can take the nomination from him."

"Do you think he wants to be President again?" she wanted to know.

"Of course! Who wouldn't? I'm in a devilish position. I can't let him think I have such a swollen head that I could even contemplate fighting him for the nomination."

At a press conference, late in January 1900, Governor Roosevelt casually declared that he was grateful for the high opinion of him held by his many friends throughout the country, but that under no circumstances would he allow them to nominate him. "I served under President McKinley," he said, "and I've been his admirer for a long time. I intend to work hard for his re-election."

Tension in the White House and its environs lessened appreciably. But the President and Senator Hanna, remembering the problems Theodore had created as Assistant Secretary of the Navy and the embarrassment he had caused with his demand from Cuba that the volunteer regiments be sent home, did not revise their opinion of him as an impulsive troublemaker.

In March 1900, out of nowhere, men began to speak of Theodore as the ideal candidate for Vice-President, and New York City's newspapers quickly endorsed the idea. Theodore himself suspected that Senator Tom Platt was responsible; it seemed logical to him that Platt wanted to be rid of him, and thought the most convenient way would be to send him to Washington in a harmless post virtually devoid of power.

Henry Cabot Lodge stopped off in New York on a journey from Boston to Washington, and Theodore held an urgent meeting with him at the Robinson house on Madison Avenue. "This talk of the vice-presidency makes me very uneasy."

"It shouldn't," the Senator from Massachusetts said. "You're getting national attention—a great deal of it. And my private canvass indicates that you can probably win the nomination."

"I don't want it!"

Lodge raised an eyebrow. "Surely you're interested in the presidency? You've been driving toward it!"

"As you know, Cabot, I've had hopes—but not for this year, obviously. I'm thinking more in terms of 1904, when I might have a chance."

"Then the vice-presidency is the perfect spot for the next four years."

"I disagree," Theodore said, nervously tugging at his mustache. "The Vice-President is a nonentity who does nothing, is rarely in the news and has no influence in affairs of state. Think how few men who have held the job have ever been elected President. As Edith was saying when we talked about it the other evening, it's a dead-end road."

"With all due respect to Edith," Lodge replied dryly, "I think I know more about politics than she does. What's more, I can't imagine you being a nonentity in any position." He laughed. "If you had learned many years ago to keep your mouth shut and behave inconspicuously, it might be different. But you're incapable of hiding quietly in dark shadows."

"I'd go insane with nothing to do but preside over the Senate," Theodore said, sulking. "In fact, I'm not even sure I could do it. I'm not temperamentally inclined to the handling of a job that would require me to be impartial in all things at all times."

"I must agree with that much. You aren't."

"I'd very much prefer another term as governor."

"Will Platt let you have it?"

"He'd discredit himself if he tried to stop me!" Theodore became belligerent.

"Platt could use any one of a dozen techniques, none of them overt."

"And every last one will fail if I announce that I want to serve a second term. He'll have to support me, Cabot, and his people will have to work for me. His own standing as the party leader will drop if he can't re-elect a governor. Not just an ordinary governor, either. I honestly don't believe New York has seen better in modern times. Neither Cleveland nor Tilden accomplished as much!"

"I hope," Lodge said emphatically, "you aren't planning to make statements like that to the press! If you do, the voters will turn against you."

"You're wrong. The electorate judges a candidate for office by his character. New Yorkers know I'm honest and always say what I think."

"Sometimes," his friend declared, "I believe you have a yearning to be a martyr."

"That's preferable to being a cipher as Vice-President."

"Let's assume you could be re-elected governor—"

"A very reasonable assumption." Theodore's good humor returned.

"The situation you'd face would still be less than ideal."

"I know. My two-year term would end in 1902, and I couldn't ask the people to send me back to Albany again. So I'd have no power base, no influence and I'd be out of the limelight for two solid years until the next convention. I'm not fooling myself, Cabot. I'm popular right now because I was lucky."

"I haven't heard you speak that modestly in years."

"I mean it. I was lucky to go off to war, lucky to find myself in a situation down in Cuba that gave me a chance to win a victory and headlines. I was lucky to be discharged from the Army just in time to run for governor, and I've been especially lucky to have escaped major crises since I've been in Albany. I've been able to concentrate on building a good record—and what I've done as governor hasn't been luck."

"It must have been very difficult for you when you were Leonard Wood's deputy."

Theodore bristled, but suddenly softened and chuckled. "I guess," he said, "I'm the type who must command his own regiment."

Lodge smoothed a slight wrinkle in his neatly pressed trousers. "That's why you prefer Albany to Washington."

"I'm a realist, Cabot! I could take orders from McKinley—"

"Then why didn't you when you were in the Navy Department?"

"That was different. The situation with Spain was intolerable, and it was our obligation to set the people of Cuba free!"

The senator stood, shaking his head. "Theodore, you're the most exasperatingly contradictory man I've ever encountered. You swing like a pendulum from the practical to the impossible, and I can never predict when you'll start believing your own rhetoric."

"I wouldn't listen to that sort of criticism if it came from anyone but you!" Color rose to Theodore's face.

"But you'll accept it from me because it's the truth. You face a dilemma right now, and your decision is important to your future. Of course, if you say and do nothing—which, knowing you, is unlikely— Tom Platt's attempt to dump you in President McKinley's lap may die out. In that case your course will be clear, and you can run for re-election as governor, letting the two-year wait for the next convention work itself out in some way."

"Only a coward lets circumstances or the will of others determine his future."

"Only Theodore Roosevelt insists on drawing a precise blueprint and following it! You had your heart set on an appointment as Secretary of War—"

"Until McKinley gave the job to Elihu Root, yes. That would have been a perfect base of operations until 1904."

"It must have crossed your mind that Mark Hanna would have stepped in to prevent your appointment, even if the President had forgotten the headaches you caused him and had wanted to give you the job!"

Theodore removed his glasses and slowly polished them with a clean handkerchief, a sure sign he was pondering. "Do you suppose," he asked suddenly, "that Hanna wants the presidency himself in '04?"

"The only man I know who is more ambitious is named Roosevelt."

"Then he'd block my appointment to a Cabinet post, or some other important position, when my second term as governor expires."

"I think you can safely bank on Hanna doing everything he can to emasculate you. And the same applies to scores of others, Theodore, many of them men you don't even know. You've risen so high, so fast, that you're a threat to the ambitions of men in every part of the country."

Theodore squared his shoulders and thrust his jaw forward. "Then I'll have to take the initiative!"

"Not yet!" Even when Lodge was exasperated he spoke coolly. "At the moment it looks as though the vice-presidency might be your best bet. But don't move in any direction until the situation becomes clearer. Don't let yourself forget, not for an instant, that you're playing for the highest stakes in the United States, and that one false step can ruin you for life!"

Theodore's dilemma became increasingly intense as the winter of 1900 gave way to spring. Senator Platt maintained a steady pressure to force the nomination for Vice-President on him, but he refused to be influenced one way or the other.

"The reason Platt is hounding me," he told Edith one morning as they ate their usual light breakfast together in the master bedroom suite of the Executive Mansion, "is because so many big corporations are putting pressure on him to be rid of me. They're upset because I've insisted on putting through legislation taxing them, and they're afraid I'll increase their tax load."

"Will you?"

"If the cost of state expenditures goes up, they'll have to bear their fair share. But I have no intention of becoming vindictive." He paused. "If I can help it."

Edith smiled and refilled his coffee cup.

"Frankly, I don't care what Platt and his friends want. I've been analyzing—"

"Again, Theodore?"

"I can't stop myself, I'm afraid." He picked up a piece of toast, then put it down. "There was talk when I left the Police Commissionership.

I've heard from a number of sources that I was accused of being a coward."

"But that was an impossible situation. You couldn't push your program through the Police Board, and Mayor Strong wouldn't take a position for or against you."

"True enough, but when a man has political enemies, they'll take any opportunity, legitimate or not, to smear him. And I wouldn't want to be called a coward again. If I spend two more years here, I'll solidify my program for New York, and it'll be very hard for any successor to turn back the clock."

"Then you've decided to seek re-election as governor." Edith made a flat statement, and appeared pleased.

"Yes, I think so. I want to leave a record that will last. It's important that the children be proud of me after I'm gone."

"They will be, no matter what you decide." She refrained from saying that it would be a mistake to rationalize and use the opinion of their children as an excuse for his decision.

"When I went down to Washington last week, President McKinley and Senator Hanna were very pleased at the prospect of my staying here. I assured them I don't want to be a cipher—and the Vice-President can't be anything more than that."

"Have you told Senator Platt their reaction?"

"Oh, yes. I had a chat with him in the Senate cloakroom as soon as I left the White House. He just smiled. There are times," Theodore added, suddenly angry, "when I could throttle Tom."

"There isn't much he can do if you're determined not to become the candidate for Vice-President."

"But he can! That's what makes me so vulnerable. He controls the New York delegation to the convention, and can put my name in nomination, whether I want it or not." He sipped the hot coffee, which steamed his glasses. "Of course I could take a very firm stand and announce that under no circumstances would I accept. But I don't want to alienate my friends in the West. If they think I'm high-hatting them, they may be so hurt they wouldn't support me for the presidency in 1904."

"I'll admit I don't understand the intricacies of these things, but I don't see how you can look that far ahead."

"I must!" he said fiercely.

"Everyone we know says that sooner or later you'll be the Republican candidate for President."

"Only if I handle this year's question in the right way. If I muff it, I can kill myself for all time. That's why this decision is so crucial!"

The West, indifferent to the machinations of Senator Platt and to Theodore's own wishes, continued to give him enthusiastic and unqualified support for the vice-presidential nomination. The Kansas City *Star*, probably the most influential newspaper in the Great Plains and Rocky Mountains areas, spoke for the entire region when it said editorially: *Beneath Roosevelt's chivalry and the picturesque style which has aroused the enthusiasm of the nation, there is an intense sense of duty and a moral courage that is invincible. The record of Roosevelt is a quite sufficient plea upon which to go before the people. It is of a character to make plain his enmity toward corruption and his devotion to public morality.*

The more Theodore was maneuvered toward the vice-presidency, the harder he fought for the right to run for a second term as governor. Some of his friends were amused by his problem, and Secretary of War Elihu Root, after listening to a long, impassioned declaration listing all the reasons against the vice-presidency, replied with a straight face, "Don't worry, Theodore. You really aren't fit for the job, and soon the whole country will realize it."

For once Theodore was speechless.

As June approached, and the convention loomed ahead, Platt won important reinforcements. Senator Joseph B. Foraker of Ohio, long jealous of the influence exerted on President McKinley by his colleague, Mark Hanna, announced that he and the delegates to the convention friendly to him would support Theodore Roosevelt for the second place on the slate. The dismayed Theodore protested in vain that he was being used by others for purposes of their own.

His naïve reaction earned him no sympathy from professional politicians, and he was even more upset when Platt gained still another ally. Matthew Quay, leader of the Republican party in Pennsylvania, had been fighting the influence of Mark Hanna in vain, and chose to register his feelings by holding a joint press conference with his deputy, Senator Boies Penrose. Both men declared they would, of course, support the renomination of President McKinley, and then added, with even greater enthusiasm, that Theodore Roosevelt would be their candidate for Vice-President.

Aware that he would not be able to halt the tide unless he acted quickly, Theodore went to New York for a grim confrontation with

Senator Platt. Only two weeks remained before the convention would meet in Philadelphia, on June 19, and Theodore was afraid he was losing control of his own future.

"Tom," he said, wasting no words, "I wish you'd let me make my own decisions!"

Platt's serenity was maddening. "Men who hold high public office," he replied, "sometimes find the public making their decisions for them."

"That's sententious drivel, and you know it!" Theodore was thoroughly aroused. "You've been working behind the scenes for months to send me off to Washington. I won't have it!"

The Senator smiled, but his eyes were cold. "You might as well stand under Niagara Falls and try to spit water back as to stop your nomination by the convention."

"I want another term as governor!"

Platt shrugged.

"You think you've won." Theodore ground his teeth, and his face grew flushed.

"I've neither won nor lost. I'm not a candidate for office this year."

"And I don't appreciate your sense of humor." Theodore cast aside the discretion that had always marked his relationship with Platt. "You know as well as I do that the vice-presidency is a graveyard. If I should be elected, it would be the end of me."

"I'm sure that a great many men would consider it a high honor to be elected to the second highest post in the United States."

"Well, I'm not one of them. And the job sounds far more important than it is."

"What do you want me to do?" Platt asked, gesturing with mock resignation.

"Stop campaigning for me!"

"Nature is taking her course, Theodore."

"My work as governor isn't finished! I won't let you turn me out!"

"I'm not conspiring against you, Theodore. And I don't have even a fraction of the power you think I have. If I were to go off to Atlantic City today, and stay there until after the convention, seeing no one, speaking to no one and corresponding with no one, you'd still be nominated."

"You're very clever, Tom. But I hold the last trump. I can announce that I won't accept the nomination, and if the convention doesn't take me at my word, I can refuse it after I've been nominated!"

Platt hunched his thin shoulders. "If you do, I give you my word that I won't permit the party to renominate you for governor. Your friends and some of the newspapers may damn me for a few days, but I'm accustomed to abuse."

"You wouldn't dare—"

"You underestimate me, Theodore. It would be remarkably easy. The line the party regulars will use is self-evident. A man who refuses to accept the nomination for the second highest position the citizens of the United States can bestow on anyone doesn't deserve to be Governor of New York. Maybe the argument wouldn't stand up under close examination. But voters don't really think. They accept generalities, and if we repeat the line often enough—which we will—they'll agree."

"You ought to know me well enough," Theodore said shrilly, "to know that I won't surrender to threats!"

"When you've entered a game for high stakes, you've got to play according to the rules. You can't walk out because nobody else will accept your rules."

"If there's to be war, then we'll fight. That's all there is to it!" Theodore bowed stiffly, turned and stalked out of the room, his frustration so great he forgot he was a gentleman and slammed the door behind him.

Accept what only you would call "defeat," Henry Cabot Lodge wrote. *I still believe this fate, against which you struggle, offers the most direct and certain route to your ultimate goal. If you have recovered your sense of humor, it will amuse you to learn that, although most Washingtonians think you will be nominated, you have staunch allies in the highest places. The President doesn't want you as his running-mate, and Hanna will fight to keep you off the ballot. Charles Dudley Warner was wiser than he knew when he wrote, "True it is that politics makes strange bedfellows."*

Theodore refused to be consoled by his friend's advice and continued to struggle, but there appeared to be no escape from the tightly woven net that Senator Platt had cast. And it disturbed him when even Edith appeared to resign herself to the seemingly inevitable.

"Perhaps it will all be for the best," she said. "I'm sure you could do things with the vice-presidency that no one else has ever done."

"I'd find the job insufferable," Theodore said.

"Only because you can't stand being controlled by someone else, and Senator Platt has won the battle."

"Not yet! He hasn't!"

"Only a few weeks ago you weren't certain which way to move. Now, because Mr. Platt is trying to force you in one direction, you insist on going the opposite way."

"That isn't my reason!"

She knew it was useless to reason with him.

"I just hope," he said gloomily, "that the President and Hanna hold firm against me."

Unwilling to rely exclusively on others to fight his battles for him, Theodore searched desperately for allies who would help him win a nomination for a second term as governor in the event he rejected the offer to become the vice-presidential candidate. One of those from whom he asked counsel was the state's most respected Democrat, Chief Justice Alton B. Parker of the Court of Appeals. A handsome, gray-haired man who resembled an actor playing the part of a distinguished jurist, Parker listened quietly through a long dinner at the Executive Mansion in Albany as his host explained the miseries of his situation.

Not until he had eaten the last of his apple crumb cake did Judge Parker speak. "I realize your pride is at stake, and as you know it, too, we won't dwell on the point. What other reasons make you prefer staying here to moving to Washington?"

"After the President, the Governor of New York holds the most important political office in the country," Theodore said.

"Possibly, although the point is debatable." Parker stirred his coffee.

"I'm afraid that Platt will undo all I've accomplished here. That sticks in my throat." Theodore looked and sounded as unhappy as he felt.

"You've achieved more than you know," the state's Chief Justice told him. "I'm not claiming that Platt's people will refuse bribes, any more than the boys at Tammany would take their hands out of other people's pockets. But you've changed the moral atmosphere of New York politics, Theodore. Thieves will have to be more circumspect hereafter, and no one will be able to survive politically if he flaunts basic morality."

"That's good to hear, but I have an uncomfortable feeling you're trying to tell me I won't be needed in this job."

"You won't." Parker smiled fleetingly at Edith, who had been listening in silence to the conversation. "Your successor—and it won't matter whether he's a Republican or Democrat—will be committed to reform, corporation taxes, conservation, all the major policies you've instituted that have won approval throughout the whole state."

Theodore was dour as he spooned sugar into his coffee. "I can't admit you're right, Alton, but if you are, it gives me a helpless feeling to know I'm not wanted."

Parker laughed.

So did Edith, who hastened to explain when her husband looked hurt. "That's an odd comment, dear, from a man who is being inundated with demands from all over the country that he take the vice-presidential nomination."

"The vice-presidency doesn't mean a thing!" Theodore sounded waspish. "If I were elected I'd have so little to do that I'd probably enroll in law school, just to keep myself occupied."

Edith and the Chief Justice exchanged quick glances. It was apparent to both that, although Theodore wouldn't admit it, he was beginning to reconcile himself to the possibility of being unable to evade the nomination, and was taking the election of a McKinley-Roosevelt ticket for granted.

"I feel as I did in Tampa, when my regiment was waiting to sail. I was afraid the war in Cuba would be ended before I could get there, but my hands and feet were tied, and there was nothing I could do about it. Unless I defy Tom Platt and do something drastic, my future depends on the President and Senator Hanna holding firm against me. I think I ought to go to Philadelphia. I've even been wondering if I can have a frank talk with Mark Hanna."

Judge Parker shook his head, then turned to his hostess. "Do you plan to go, too, Edith?"

"No, I keep out of politics."

"The ridiculous spectacle of a national political convention is something that every American should see at least once. And if Theodore is serious about going to Philadelphia—"

"Why shouldn't I be serious?"

"Your husband's strength," Justice Parker said, continuing to address Edith, "lies in his extraordinary combination of political naïveté and cunning. He breaks all the rules, but he does it with a sixth sense that's unfailing. Shall I tell you what will happen if he goes to the convention?"

"I'll try my best to outwit Tom Platt and avoid the nomination," Theodore said.

Parker ignored him. "He'll arrive late. Just a little late, after everyone else is seated. Then bedlam will break loose, and he'll receive an ovation that'll make it obvious to everyone that he's the most popular man there."

Theodore tried to interrupt.

But the Chief Justice raised an imperious hand to silence him. "Being a devoted wife, Edith, you'll be very proud and happy. Then, two or three days later, you'll see your husband unanimously nominated for Vice-President of the United States."

"Not if I can help it," Theodore said, but the others were laughing, and apparently did not hear him.

On the eve of the Republican convention of 1900 President McKinley barred the doors of the White House to reporters and went into seclusion. But he was the only member of his party who failed to hold a press conference.

Senator Platt was exceptionally jovial as he talked to newsmen before leaving New York. "I've heard it rumored that I intend to push Governor Roosevelt into second place on the ticket against his will. Such stories are absurd. For one thing, I can't imagine any man turning down such an honor. But if Governor Roosevelt should be reluctant to accept, and I have no way of knowing his feelings in the matter, there are other candidates equally appealing. In fact, we have someone right here in our own delegation who would be eminently suitable, Benjamin B. Odell."

Senator Mark Hanna, the party's national chairman, took care to mention no names when reporters met his train as he reached Philadelphia from Washington. "Unusual interest is centered on the vice-presidential choice this year, which is fitting and proper," he said. "I think it quite possible that the man we nominate for the place might be our presidential candidate four years from now. In any case, at this convention, if ever, the vice-presidential nomination should be made a serious question. A man should be chosen who would give the country an Administration equally as good as that of President McKinley if he should, by any mishap, ascend to the first place."

Senator Nelson W. Aldrich of Rhode Island, a rugged conservative who had held his seat for nineteen years and ruled his colleagues as Majority Leader, would not discuss personalities, either. "The convention, I feel sure," he said, "will make its choice wisely, and will select a candidate as the President's running mate who feels, as President McKinley does, that the future of this nation depends upon the continuing free expansion of the industries that are making us strong and prosperous."

A reporter from the New York *Herald* asked him whether Governor Roosevelt's policy of taxing corporations made him ineligible.

"I am not in a position to rule any man eligible or ineligible," Senator Aldrich replied. "I have only one vote."

"Would you cast it for Governor Roosevelt?" the reporter persisted.

"The Rhode Island delegation will hold a caucus after nominations for the vice-presidency have been made, and will vote together for that candidate whom the majority favor." Aldrich was unsmiling as he entered a carriage and was driven to his hotel, which led the press to speculate that Governor Roosevelt was too liberal for his taste.

Chairman Matthew Quay of the Pennsylvania delegation was coy when questioned. "You boys and I have heard the same rumors, I guess. Everybody tells me I've made a deal with this one or that one. Let's take this convention one step at a time, shall we? First we'll nominate President McKinley. Then we'll get to the vice-presidency, and all I can say for sure is that Pennsylvania will vote for the best man."

The Southern delegations, all of them indebted to Senator Hanna, maintained a tight-lipped silence. Diligent reporters were unable to find one Southerner willing to discuss the vice-presidency, even when reminded that Governor Roosevelt's mother had come from Georgia.

At noon on June 18, only twenty-four hours before the convention was scheduled to begin, Theodore told members of the Albany press corps that he had not yet decided whether he would take a seat as a member of the New York delegation. Reporters who had known him for years thought him strained when he said, speaking with unusual care, "I appreciate to the full the friendly support I am being given for the vice-presidential nomination. I understand the high honor and dignity of the office, an office so high and so honorable that it is well worthy of the ambition of any man in the United States. I honestly believe, however, that my best usefulness to the public and to the Republican party lies in my renomination to the post I now hold. I sincerely hope that every friend of mine in the convention will respect my wish and judgment in this matter."

His friends from the West totally ignored his wish and judgment. That night dozens of delegates from North and South Dakota, Wyoming, Montana, Utah, Colorado, and Texas, as well as some from other Western states, paraded up and down the hotel corridor outside Senator Hanna's suite, chanting, "We want Teddy."

edly, "we've got to look out for ourselves. Now, we know that nobody likes to have a fist waved under his nose—"

"I won't tolerate it," Theodore said, interrupting in an attempt to assert himself and salvage his pride.

"But we have no choice, you see? Work with us, and we'll be in your corner from now on. You can count on our support for any job in 1904. *Any* job." Quay, chewing on his cigar, sounded affable, but all at once his manner changed. "But if you turn us down, you'd better start looking for a job in Wall Street with some of your rich friends. Because you'll be finished in politics. We give you our flat word that you won't be nominated for another term as Governor of New York, and you'd never be elected to any other office in the United States."

"By uniting against you, and we'd do it," Penrose added, "we could even stop the President from putting you in his Cabinet or making you an ambassador. You'd be out of politics for life."

Theodore bristled, but Lodge's urgent, silent appeal to keep his mouth shut was effective, and he subsided, overwhelmed by a feeling of impotent disgrace.

"Don't give us an answer tonight," Quay said. "We hear you're having talks later this evening with Senator Aldrich and some others. So hear what they have to say, too, before you make up your mind. Get some sleep, and by morning you'll know what you want to do. Then you and I can have a quiet breakfast together. How does that sound?" Not waiting for a reply he stood, indicating that, having served his ultimatum, the meeting had come to an end.

Nelson Aldrich offered his guest a choice of whiskey or sherry, and was obviously pleased when Theodore indicated that he preferred either fruit juice or coffee. The Senator rang for a waiter, and, while waiting for the refreshments to arrive, chatted about mutual acquaintances who spent their summers in Newport.

Finally, however, he abruptly came to the point of the visit. "Governor," he said, "some of my friends say you're a radical. Are you?"

Theodore was amused by the blunt approach. "Name-calling has become popular of late, Senator," he said. "When you don't know a man, don't trust him and can't figure out what he may do next, you pin a nasty tag on him. I've been a Republican all my life, and I'll die one, but I've heard myself called a Socialist, a Populist and a Communist. The only thing I haven't been accused of being is a William Jennings Bryan Democrat who waves a cross of silver to win votes."

Aldrich's appreciation of his humor was mild. "It's been my own opinion that you're fairly sound, Governor. I understand that your own fortune is invested in securities, most of it stock in steel and railroads. So I've thought it unlikely that you'd try to destroy the economic system that supports you."

"For the sake of clarification," Theodore said, "I wouldn't call my modest inheritance a fortune."

"Let's just say you aren't starving."

"Not at the moment, Senator. As for my investments, I don't know much about them. My brother-in-law handles these things for me." Theodore paused for a moment. "However, I wouldn't permit my own investments to stand in the way of what I believe right."

"I'd very much like to know what you do believe, Governor."

"I make no secret of my position. I've seen the tentative draft of the platform, and I certainly agree that the free development of business and industry will make the United States stronger and more prosperous."

Aldrich relaxed as he sipped his coffee.

"If the platform were mine and not President McKinley's, I'd want to include something to the effect that business owes an obligation to the community at large, and must contribute to the welfare of the community."

"Can you spell that out?"

"Not specifically. It depends on circumstances. You're familiar with my corporation tax program."

"Yes, and my friends and I don't like it."

"If I could, I'd expand that program onto the national level." Theodore knew he was antagonizing his conservative host, but wanted no misunderstanding. "I don't believe in crippling business, but if we're to play a larger role in the world, which we must if the United States intends to become great as well as wealthy, it's going to cost money. Business, which will benefit, must carry a portion of the government's increased burden."

"You have a tax program in mind?"

Theodore grinned. "I'm not much of an economist, Governor, as Chauncey Depew and Elihu Root can tell you. I've usually leaned on Root for advice in these matters."

"He's as sound as they come." Aldrich's tension dissipated somewhat. "What's your attitude toward labor?"

"I refuse to mollycoddle the working man! He deserves to be treated honorably and fairly, though, and should be paid the wages he earns. I do insist that he earn his way, mind you! He has a right to expect decent working conditions, and since he's becoming stronger and more articulate, I believe that any employer who tries to take advantage of him is asking for trouble. But I say he's got to sweat for his money, like all the rest of us."

The senator drained his coffee. "I can see no reason why I'd withhold my support from your candidacy, Governor."

Theodore wanted to say he was sorry to hear it, but forced himself to refrain. Quay and the other political bosses had meant their threat, and he knew his future was at stake.

"Some of my friends have wondered whether they could contribute to the President's campaign fund if you were his running mate. I believe I can recommend that they make their usual generous contributions to the party."

Theodore could hold back no longer. "I hope you realize, Senator, that I'd run for Governor of New York again if I had my own way in this matter."

"Impossible, Governor Roosevelt!" Aldrich was emphatic. "I've tried to make the President and Senator Hanna see that you're essential to the ticket, and I still have hopes they can be persuaded to accept you!"

"For the life of me," Theodore said miserably, "I can't see why I'm needed."

"Then you're not much of a politician. McKinley might or might not take the East. With you in second place, organized labor would be certain to support him, since you've earned a reputation as the friend of the working man."

"But I'd have no voice in the Administration's policymaking!" Theodore was anguished. "I'd be getting votes under false pretenses."

"We're speaking in terms of winning the election, Governor!" Aldrich said sharply. "And without you, we're sure to lose the West, too. There's been talk that the Democrats might nominate Admiral Dewey, but they won't—"

"I certainly hope not! He's a war hero, not an administrator!"

Aldrich saw he was not only sincere, but had made the observation in all innocence, not relating Dewey's situation to his own. The Senator coughed behind his hand. "Quite so. The Democrats will name Bryan, and his promises of a silver-lined heaven will capture the West, unless you run with the President."

Theodore was clinging to a last, forlorn hope. "If my friends in the

Western delegations learn how I feel, they'll withdraw their support and won't insist that I run."

"You can't undermine the party, Governor!" Aldrich was shocked. "You'd not only lose us the election, but you'd be known as the man who destroyed the Republican party. You'd ruin yourself."

The last door had been slammed, and Theodore knew there was no escape.

Late in the morning of the convention's second day Matthew Quay arose to propose an amendment to the rules. Each delegation, he said, should be given a vote based on the record of the Republican electoral strength in the last national election. The clerk read the amendment in full, and the startled Southern leaders were on their feet, protesting and demanding the floor.

Similar motions had been made for years, but no one of consequence had paid any attention to them for a simple reason: such an amendment would emasculate the Southern delegations, since the Republican vote in the South was small, and the amendment would drive most of the Southern Negro leaders home, thereby denying the party the right to proclaim that it was living up to the traditions of Abraham Lincoln.

When the clerk completed his reading, Quay was on his feet again, suggesting that a discussion and vote on the amendment be postponed until the delegates had an opportunity to study the matter.

A perplexed Mark Hanna entertained a motion for adjournment. He knew that he, not the Southern delegations indebted to him, was the primary object of Quay's attack, and he watched apprehensively from the platform as the Pennsylvania chairman walked out of the hall with several of the Southern leaders.

Meanwhile speculation that Governor Roosevelt would accept the second-place nomination became more intense. Mrs. Roosevelt, the press learned, had just arrived, and would sit in the front row of the Distinguished Visitors Gallery that afternoon.

Nicholas Murray Butler, founder and editor of *The Educational Review* and soon to become president of Columbia University, had a brief chat with his friend, Governor Roosevelt, and confided to his intimates, "Theodore's tail feathers are all down. The fight has gone out of him, and he has changed his former tune to, 'I cannot disappoint my Western friends if they insist on nominating me. I cannot seem to be bigger than the party.'"

Henry Cabot Lodge, as always, was self-controlled. "Sixteen years ago," he told the reporters who crowded around him, "Governor Roosevelt and I sat on the losing side at the Blaine convention, and were discredited. I'm sure you'll agree that the scales have tipped in the opposite direction." Pressed for a more explicit statement, he declined, saying he was meeting Mrs. Roosevelt and her sister-in-law, Corinne Robinson, for lunch.

Governor Roosevelt, the primary target of the press, had vanished. No one knew he had retired to his own hotel suite, and feeling both queasy and depressed, tried to lose himself in a reading of *The Jewish Antiquities,* by Flavius Josephus, an ancient historian, in the original Latin. "Everyone in Palestine and Rome wanted to preserve law and order after the great rebellion of 66 A.D.," he told a surprised Senator Aldrich that afternoon, "but no one knew how to work out a compromise."

Senator Hanna also retired to the privacy of his own quarters, intending to call the President at the White House and tell him the latest developments. The lines, as usual, were in disrepair, and while he waited for frantic telephone officials to put through his connection, the leaders of the Southern delegations came to his suite.

Chairman Quay of Pennsylvania, they told him, would withdraw his amendment if they would support Governor Roosevelt for the vice-presidency. Reconciled to the deal, they started to enumerate Roosevelt's virtues.

The Senator from Ohio lost his temper. "Don't any of you realize," he shouted, "there would be only one life between that madman and the White House?"

Still unable to complete his telephone call, he sent the President a telegram summarizing the day's frenzied activities.

The convention reconvened that afternoon in an atmosphere of excitement overlaid with uncertainty. Most delegates believed Governor Roosevelt would win the second place on the slate, but the President would make the final decision. Senator Hanna allowed no delegation leader to forget that the most powerful voice in the nation was in Washington, not Philadelphia.

The President was duly renominated that afternoon, and one of those who made a brief seconding speech was Governor Roosevelt. When he appeared on the platform the delegates, abetted by the galleries, began another demonstration, but he silenced everyone in the hall by scowling and waving his arms for silence.

The unanimous renomination of the President gave the delegates their opportunity to parade up and down the aisles. Meanwhile the state chairmen and other leaders gathered in small, anxious groups at the sides and rear of the platform to confer. The next order of business on the agenda was the vice-presidential nomination, but nothing definitive could be done until word was received from the President.

Necessity forced the various factions to work together, and it was decided that the nomination of favorite son candidates by individual states, with no time limit imposed on the speakers, would be the most effective method of delay. Nominations began as soon as the marching delegates returned to their seats. They, like the crowd in the galleries, had no idea what was taking place, and grew increasingly restless.

Candidates were nominated and seconded in a series of endless speeches, and although the talks were boring, the tension was so great that no one left the hall. A stir ran through the throng when a telegram was delivered to Senator Hanna, who opened the envelope and read the message in stony-faced silence.

Everyone present watched him as he rose and said a word to Lafayette Young, chairman of the Iowa delegation, who was about to make a brief seconding speech.

Young took the telegram and walked to the rostrum.

The murmurs died away, and delegates who had been wandering around the hall quickly returned to their own seats.

"Mr. Chairman and fellow delegates," Young said, "it was my intention to second the nomination of my distinguished friend and fellow Iowan, Jonathan Dolliver. Instead, I withdraw his name."

A fresh, excited undertone swept through the chamber.

Young gestured for silence. "I have been granted the privilege of reading a telegram to you. It is addressed to the Honorable Mark Hanna, National Chairman of the Republican party. It reads: IF THE CONVENTION SO WISHES, I WILL NOT OPPOSE THE NOMINATION, FOR THE VICE-PRESIDENCY, OF GOVERNOR ROOSEVELT. It is signed, WILLIAM MCKINLEY."

A roar began to swell up and fill the hall.

Young had to shout to make himself heard. "Mr. Chairman, I place in nomination for the vice-presidency of the United States the name of the Honorable Theodore Roosevelt of New York."

The Massachusetts state standard, carried by an exuberant and remarkably spry Senator Henry Cabot Lodge, was the first to move into the aisle and led the parade. Virtually every delegate was on his feet, and in a moment the aisles were filled with cheering, perspiring politicians. The galleries were equally unrestrained, and the band struck up "A Hot Time in the Old Town," playing it so loudly that conversation was impossible, even in the farthest reaches of the hall.

Edith Roosevelt played the part expected of her, smiled until her face ached and returned the waves of those who called to her. Corinne Robinson, sitting beside her sister-in-law, appeared to be enjoying herself enormously. *Mrs. Robinson,* the New York *Post* reported the next day, *showed the animation for which the Roosevelt family is becoming famous.*

Only one man remained unmoving. Governor Roosevelt sat in his aisle seat, his face wooden as he accepted the congratulations of the delegates who streamed past him. The deafening noise made it unnecessary for him to reply to those who addressed him.

Order was restored after a wild seventy-five minutes, and Henry C. Payne of Wisconsin, making the first seconding speech, set off another demonstration when he said, "Theodore Roosevelt is not New York's son, but the nation's son."

At last the balloting took place, and Senator Lodge was given the honor of announcing what everyone already knew. "Governor Roosevelt has won the unanimous vote of this convention, and will be the Republican candidate for Vice-President."

The cheer that followed was the convention's longest and loudest.

Not until it subsided did the press and others notice that, in the excitement, Governor Roosevelt had slipped out of the hall.

Theodore's appearance at the end of the hotel corridor started a stampede, and in a few moments he was surrounded by reporters, all of them shouting questions. "I might have known you boys would be lying in ambush for me," he said, and gently but insistently pushed his way through the throng.

Members of the press, still calling their questions, saw that his smile was genuine, although he looked tired.

"Later this evening," he said, "Mrs. Roosevelt and I will be serving sandwiches in our suite. Join us there, and I'll try to tell you anything you want to know. Fair enough?"

Most agreed, but a half-dozen still persisted.

"I don't believe in corridor interviews," Theodore said, "and right now I've got to attend to some business."

A correspondent for Pulitzer's newspapers cupped his hands and shouted, "You can't make any statements until you get your orders. Is that right, Governor?"

Theodore stopped short, and those closest to him thought for a moment that he would charge through the throng and attack the reporter. But he controlled himself, wheeled and resumed his march down the corridor.

Obviously he was expected; as he drew near the door it opened, and the members of the press caught a glimpse of Senator Hanna in the living room of the suite before the door closed again.

Mark Hanna forced a smile as he extended his hand.

Theodore grinned at him. "Senator," he said, "I believe you and I are the only men in the party who didn't want this to happen."

His candor caused the startled Hanna to laugh.

"We're stuck with each other," Theodore said, "so we'll have to work together."

The Senator eyed him shrewdly. "Governor, I never thought I'd hear myself saying I admire you, but I do. By God, you have courage."

"So does any animal that's been backed into a corner. But the one thing I can't do is feel sorry for myself."

They moved together to an overstuffed couch, and Hanna, knowing his visitor did not smoke, took a cigar from a humidor for himself. "How soon can you go to work?"

"I'm available right now."

"Good. The President will be telephoning you here very shortly, and will invite you to Washington for a conference. Meanwhile you and I can settle some details."

"You'll be in charge of the campaign?"

"The heaviest burden will fall on you. The President will be busy in Washington, where he'll make no statements, and at the most he'll hold one or two rallies and press conferences when he goes out to Ohio. Are you willing to carry the load?"

"Of course. I'm as strong as a bull moose."

"You'll need to be."

"My voice might give out if I talk too much," Theodore said thoughtfully. "That's what happened in my campaign for governor. But I'll have to take the risk."

"Where do you stand on the issues of the day?"

"With the President, naturally," Theodore said firmly. "I favor the gold standard, high tariffs, and the unrestricted right of business and industry to develop."

Hanna made no secret of his surprise.

"This is President McKinley's campaign, not mine. He commands the regiment."

"What about your own views, Governor? The people will see through you if you do nothing but speak the President's sentiments."

"I'll only speak out on my own with the President's permission. I imagine he knows how I feel on government reform—"

"Certainly, and he approves. Everyone does."

Theodore refrained from replying that no one ever opposed the cause of reform, on the surface, but that it would be difficult to make anyone believe Mark Hanna, the ardent practitioner of the spoils system, was in favor of civil service extension. "I also believe the United States should stop isolating herself from the world. We're strong and powerful, and it's time we make our influence felt."

"You've made that position clear in some of your speeches, Governor. The President doesn't feel one way or the other, but if Bryan is the Democratic candidate, and we're assuming he will be, he'll be attacking us as imperialists, so it can do no harm for you to counterattack."

"I'd rather storm the enemy without waiting until he strikes first."

Hanna smiled. "That's reasonable. And you've reminded me of something I hadn't intended to mention quite so soon. But we're both being frank, so we might settle it now. William Jennings Bryan is a colorful man, and attracts voters. So we can check him by taking advantage of your—ah—natural flair when you appear before crowds."

Theodore stiffened. "I'm not an actor, and I won't go whooping around the country like a second-class Bryan."

"No, of course not," the Senator said hurriedly.

"What did you have in mind?" Theodore had become cautiously alert.

"An informal campaign committee met here earlier tonight to draw up some of the broad outlines of the campaign. And we thought it would be a tremendous attraction to organize Rough Riders' marching units in every state—"

"I won't permit it," Theodore said.

Hanna was surprised. "Think of the votes we'll attract—"

"Rather than stoop to such techniques, I'd prefer to lose the election."

"You confuse me, Governor. In your New York campaign—"

"I went straight from the Army into that campaign, and I stupidly let myself be maneuvered into behaving like an idiot. Responsible people criticized me for taking advantage of my military successes, and they were right."

"I can't help thinking of the hat you wore when you came to the convention."

Theodore's smile was chilly. "There's a difference between suggestion and overt exploitation, Senator. No, sir—I'll stand on my record as Governor of New York, but I won't use my regiment as a campaign device. The presidency and vice-presidency are too dignified for that!"

The lines at the corners of Hanna's mouth tightened as the full import of Theodore's thinking became clear to him. One campaigned for a governorship on a far less formal level than for the presidency of the United States, and it was plain that Roosevelt was looking ahead to 1904. "We must think only in terms of winning this year's election," the Senator said. "If we need color, even touches of flamboyance, to beat Bryan, we should use them."

"I'll travel anywhere you and the committee want to send me," Theodore replied. "If you wish, I'll go into every state, and aside from the time I'm obligated to spend in Albany, I'll live in hotels and trains between now and the election. I'll make as many speeches as you arrange for me, and I'll gladly talk until my voice gives out. But I won't go before the American people as a military hero, a circus performer, or a freak."

Hanna became irritated, too. "I don't believe in conducting a campaign—any campaign—in a carnival atmosphere, either. On the other hand, I do think it's imperative that we fight the Democrats' fire with fire of our own."

"I've told you my limitations, Senator," Theodore said frigidly. "If President McKinley decides to take a more active part in the campaign, that's his prerogative."

Hanna's expression indicated that he was shocked. The President had already outlined the limitations he intended to place on the role he would play in the months ahead. In addition, his personal nature was such that he was constitutionally incapable of matching William Jennings Bryan's gaudy platform style.

"Although I'm very much the junior partner, I'll do ninety percent of the work. Even one hundred percent, if that's what President McKinley wants. But I'll have to do it in my own way."

"You're thinking of far more than this year's election, Governor." Hanna saw no reason to evade or ignore the self-evident, and sounded accusing.

Theodore was equally open. "If I am, sir, can you blame me? I neither sought nor wanted the vice-presidency, and this nomination was thrust on me by my friends and my enemies. I'll do my best now, during the campaign, and later, if the President and I are elected, although there will be little enough for me to do in Washington. I'm realistic enough to know I'm being put onto a shelf, and I'll accept my place there with good grace. But I don't intend to stay there longer than four years, and I have no intention of retiring to my house on Long Island in 1904 to write books—unless I have no choice."

"The President wants—"

"I'll do everything he expects of me, and more. I'll do what no other candidate for President has ever done, and although I'm not a betting man, I'll put up five dollars to your nickel on the proposition that I'll make more newspaper headlines—favorable headlines—than Bryan and his running-mate can produce, combined."

Hanna was alarmed by his vehemence, and wondered whether his visitor was going to strike him.

Theodore brandished a clenched fist only a few inches from the Senator's face. "But I won't do anything, now or ever, to hurt my own interests!" Carried away by emotion, he was shouting, and his voice had become ugly. "I've learned one lesson in the past few months, and I have no intention of forgetting it! If I don't look after Theodore Roosevelt's best interests, nobody else is going to do it for me! I'm willing to serve as Vice-President, because I've been given no practical choice. But I'll retire from politics permanently before I'll become a clown for the purpose of insuring William McKinley another term in the White House!"

ROOSEVELT TAKES COLORADO BY STORM; THOUSANDS GREET TEDDY AT HUGE DENVER RALLY

ROOSEVELT ROUSES BUTTE!

LARGEST CROWD IN CHEYENNE HISTORY PARADES FOR TEDDY ROOSEVELT

RANCHER ROOSEVELT COMES HOME
TO DAKOTAS; HOME FOLKS
PROMISE HIM SUPPORT

GOVERNOR ROOSEVELT BACKS GOLD
STANDARD, URGES U.S. EXPANSION
IN WORLD, LARGER NAVY & ARMY
Republican V.-P. Candidate Attacks
Bryan in Chicago's Biggest Turnout
of Presidential Campaign and Draws
Enthusiastic Audience of Thousands

The tireless candidate appeared everywhere. After attending a Rough Rider reunion in the Oklahoma Territory, his determination not to capitalize on his military background temporarily cast aside, Theodore set out on a series of tours that took him back and forth across the United States. He made extensive visits to the Rocky Mountain states and the Middle West, a rapid but thorough trip to the Pacific states, and even invaded the Democratic strongholds in the South, where he reminded his audiences that his mother had come from Georgia and that two of his uncles had fought for the Confederacy. He toured New England, too, and visited every major population center on the Atlantic seaboard, and had there been more time, he would have repeated his exhausting itinerary.

Everywhere the reaction was the same. Voters by the thousands and tens of thousands came to see him, often bringing their wives and children with them. Citizens cheered his speeches in halls and churches, open fields and auditoriums, and, when he was rushed, listened to his pungent addresses from the observation car of his train.

And everywhere Theodore's theme was unvarying as he attacked Democratic presidential candidate William Jennings Bryan and, to a lesser extent, his running mate, Adlai E. Stevenson of Illinois. A Republican defeat would be a disaster, and would plunge the nation into miseries from which it might never recover. A Republican victory would insure continued prosperity, the retention of the gold standard, widespread governmental reform and a vast increase of American influence in Europe, the Far East, and the Latin nations to the south.

Politicians, ordinary people and, above all, the weary newspaper correspondents who accompanied him on his tours were stunned by Theodore's energy. No member of his entourage could maintain his sizzling pace. He awakened at dawn, delivered as many as six to ten speeches in a day, shook the hands of thousands, and, in an astonishing spectacle that the members of his party could not understand or explain, never forgot a name. He rarely went to sleep before the early hours of the morning, spending his late evenings in hotel suites or on board his special train reading the next day's itinerary and glancing through the lists of those he was scheduled to meet in the following twenty-four hours.

His fear that he might lose his voice proved unfounded. Occasionally he became hoarse, but a long address, delivered in booming tones, seemed to have a beneficial effect on his vocal cords. He set aside at least an hour each day for physical exercise, neither gained nor lost weight and returned home for a final rally at Madison Square Garden in radiant good health.

He was attacked, of course, for neglecting the affairs of New York, but confounded his critics. Constant exchanges of telegrams and letters, and, when possible, visits from aides enabled him to fulfill his major duties as governor, and his opponents could find him vulnerable on no single issue. *He may be a show-off*, the Baltimore *Sun* declared, *and there may be many who find his dramatic exuberance grating, but there has never been anyone like him in American public life. We sometimes forget that McKinley, not Roosevelt, is Bryan's opponent for the Presidency.*

Statistics accumulated by the awe-stricken New York *Times* at the end of the campaign dazed the nation. Theodore had traveled 21,209 miles, and had spoken before audiences in excess of three million persons, the largest number ever to have heard and seen any one man within a limited period. In all, he spent more than two months in travel, made major visits to twenty-four states and stopped in five hundred and sixty-seven cities and towns, where he made a total of six hundred and seventy-three speeches. The *Times* did not include the small communities at which his train halted briefly, nor the number of times he commented to crowds at these places from his train.

Finley Peter Dunne's Mr. Dooley accurately summarized the country's reaction when he said, " 'Tis Teddy alone that's runnin', and he ain't runnin', he's gallopin'."

Even the industrialists and Wall Street financiers who mistrusted Theodore were grateful to him for his herculean efforts. Bryan, the impassioned, silver-tongued orator was roaming the country, too, and might have dented the popularity of President McKinley, whose "front-porch" campaign consisted of two short, uninspired speeches made in his home town, Canton, Ohio. Senator Hanna found it necessary to say repeatedly, "The President feels it is inconsistent with the dignity of his high office for him to take a more active part in the campaign."

In spite of the fears expressed by J. P. Morgan, railroad magnate Edward H. Harriman, and others who poured money into the Republican campaign chest, the outcome of the election was never in doubt, and most of the seventy-six million Americans accepted with equanimity the predictions of the press that the results would be one-sided.

Voters across the nation went to the polls on November 6, 1900, and the McKinley-Roosevelt ticket emerged triumphant, winning 7,219,530 votes to 6,358,071 for Bryan and Stevenson, the largest plurality amassed by either party since the election of 1872. The Electoral College gave McKinley 292 votes to Bryan's 155.

Theodore, saying he was too busy to celebrate, went to Albany to clean up his desk. He took his successor as governor, Benjamin B. Odell, Jr., with him for purposes of indoctrination and the insurance of a smooth transition in January. Odell, who had never seen him at work, told friends that "TR's pace makes me dizzy."

There were campaign debts to be paid, too, and the incoming Vice-President had no need of the reminders that McKinley and Hanna sent him. Recognizing the need to carry his share of the burden, he gave a series of small dinner parties at Delmonico's for the most generous contributors to the Republican cause.

Less than a month after the election he demonstrated that his election to higher office had not gone to his head and that his self-mocking sense of humor was intact. In a hastily scribbled letter to Secretary of War Elihu Root he wrote: *I hope you can come to my dinner to J. Pierpont Morgan. You see, it represents an effort on my part to become a conservative man in touch with the influential classes, and I think I deserve encouragement. Hitherto I have given dinners only to professional politicians or more or less wild-eyed radicals. Now I am at work endeavoring to assume the vice-presidential pose.*

His depression of many months having been dissipated by the reception he had received while barnstorming as well as by the credit the press gave him for McKinley's smashing victory, Theodore was able to contemplate his future with a newly acquired calm. "I had a bully time on my tour," he said at a family gathering. "I never knew I had so many friends. And now that I'm going to be Vice-President, with almost nothing to do, I can romp with my children and may be able to help them become literate. Alice won't listen to me any more, but I can't complain, I suppose, since she appears to be as headstrong as her father and is deaf to everyone else, too. What really pleases me is that I'll be able to spend some time with Quentin. He's only three, and I've seen so little of him that he must wonder whether his father is a myth."

After vanishing from the headlines after the election, Theodore returned to the front pages of newspapers throughout the country when it was revealed, late in the year, that he intended to take a vacation, that few would envy, in the deep winter snows of the Colorado Rockies. Under the guidance of a professional hunter, he and a small party planned to hunt wildcat and lynx, riding cow ponies and accompanied by a pack of half-domesticated dogs.

"To make the sport more exciting," Theodore told reporters, "we'll dismount, whenever possible, as we move in on our quarry."

The newspapermen, usually callous, were impressed by the recklessness of the venture, and wanted to know why Theodore was setting up such obstacles.

"In March," he said, "I'll start presiding over the Senate, and will be dealing with some real wildcats. So I need the practice."

Members of the Senate read the comment, and were not amused. The incoming Vice-President, it appeared, would encounter deeper snow and colder weather in Washington than he would find in the Rocky Mountains.

IV

1901–1905

My view was that every executive officer, and above all every executive officer in high position, was a steward of the people bound actively and affirmatively to do all he could for the people, and not to content himself with the negative merit of keeping his talents undamaged in a napkin.

N0 ONE ENJOYS being a cipher," Henry Adams said, "and the vice-presidency is a long row of ciphers. I pity Edith."

Theodore confounded everyone, including the cynical Adams, by enjoying himself thoroughly. After renting a house large enough for his family's needs, he realized that the Vice-President, although granted few responsibilities, was regarded as an eminent citizen by the public. His daily mail included numerous requests that he appear as a speaker, and he accepted every engagement that looked interesting.

"I've steeled myself to official anonymity," he told his wife, "and I refuse to become annoyed when the President and the Cabinet forget I'm a member of the Administration. I'd go mad if I were idle, so I'll travel. I always enjoy seeing new places and visiting old friends."

The Constitutional duties of the Vice-President were no barrier to Theodore's travel plans. Congress convened on March 5 and remained in session only until March 9, its principal business being that of approving presidential appointments. Reporters in the press galleries wrote that the new Presiding Officer of the Senate looked somewhat apprehensive on the podium when he called the upper chamber to order, but Theodore conducted himself soberly, quietly accepted the advice of parliamentarians and made no mistakes.

On March 11, after Congress adjourned, he went to Pittsburgh to make an address. Three days later he was in West Virginia, the following week he appeared in Hartford, and organizations in Louisville, Peoria, and Kansas City (Kansas) announced that he had accepted invitations to address them.

Political observers immediately concluded that the Vice-President was beginning his campaign for the presidency, and several prominent newspapers drew the same conclusion. They were right. Theodore privately arranged with Governor Henry T. Gage of California to make an extended tour of that state the following year. He disapproved of the excess patronage demands that Quay of Pennsylvania was making on the White House, and confided to Cabot Lodge that he was relieved that McKinley, not he, had to grapple with the avaricious Quay.

Friends throughout the country were quietly rallying to the "Roosevelt in '04" banner, among them the liberal, humanitarian Kansas editor, William Allen White. He and Theodore spent an evening together in Kansas City, and both were unusually candid. Money was an essential ingredient of every campaign, and White offered to "pass the hat."

Theodore, accepting, assured the editor that his position was solid in almost every section of the country. Charles G. Dawes of Chicago had not only assured him of his strength in Illinois, but, after voluntarily undertaking a tour of the Southwest on his behalf, assured him that he was the most popular of all Americans there. Lodge was working with silent efficiency to obtain the unanimous backing of New England. Quay was going out of his way to demonstrate the warmth of his regard for the Vice-President.

"Even Mark Hanna," Theodore said, "has stopped calling me a bull in a china shop. We're on very friendly terms now."

"Perhaps," White replied, "but don't forget that Hanna has presidential ambitions himself."

"There's no need to worry about him. He's a king-maker, not a king."

White wondered how Theodore could speak so positively in his assessment of someone else's character, but did not pursue the point. Some men had a seemingly instinctive ability to evaluate and judge others, and the Vice-President appeared to be developing this talent. "What about Tom Platt?"

Theodore's teeth clicked. "He's in an uncomfortable spot, Bill. He'll find it difficult to repudiate a fellow New Yorker when there's a demand for my candidacy elsewhere. In fact, he gave himself away just before I came out here. He was furious with me because Mrs. Roosevelt and I entertained Dr. Washington of Tuskegee Institute at lunch recently."

"Booker Washington?" White seemed as surprised as he was pleased. "I read nothing about such a lunch."

"It was a private, social affair. But let me assure you I have no reason to keep my friendship with Dr. Washington a secret. He's a great scientist, a man of high character and a bully fellow besides!"

"I needn't tell you the reason Platt is upset is that your lunch meeting with Dr. Washington could be used against you if it became known. You'd lose the support of every voter in the country who dislikes the Negro."

"Good! I don't want the support of bigots! The color of a friend's skin means nothing to me!"

"I'm not arguing with you, Theodore," White said. "I feel as you do."

"What's more," Theodore said more quietly, "the anti-Negro vote is concentrated in the Southern states the Democrats control. Dr. Washington is hoping to organize some Republican clubs in Alabama and Georgia, and although I can't put much faith in his plans, there's nothing to lose."

Everywhere Theodore went during his first six months as Vice-President his theme was the same. He appreciated the enthusiasm being shown for his future candidacy, but his private life was his own, and he refused to give up any personal associations in return for political support. Among his friends were Catholics and Jews, minority groups that were being subjected to increasing discrimination now that so many immigrants from Ireland, Russia and Poland were coming to the United States. But he would rather be retired to private life, he insisted, than turn away from a single friend.

His declarations of principle were reported to Senator Platt, but the Republican chieftain remained surprisingly unruffled. Every Catholic and Jew in New York would cast his ballot for TR, Platt said, and the Roosevelt landslide there would be the biggest in history. For the first time, the senator added, he could appreciate the advantages of the vice-presidency when an ambitious man held the post. Free of obligations and a heavy work load, he could devote virtually all of his efforts to his own future advancement.

Theodore found his lack of responsibility gave him other, more precious benefits. Whenever he was in Washington, or, during the summer months, in Oyster Bay, he spent every available moment with his children, sailing, swimming, and romping with them. He rode with Alice, boxed with Ted and Kermit, and insisted that everyone, even little Quentin, accompany him on hikes through Washington's Rock

Creek Park, an unspoiled little wilderness preserve that delighted him. He invented games, acted as referee in competitions, taught his sons the use of firearms and read stories to the younger children before bedtime.

There were pets underfoot everywhere. Only Theodore and the children themselves could remember how many dogs and cats they owned, there were horses and ponies in the stable, and the wildlife was varied. Ethel had a duck, which sometimes slept in her bedroom, a delegation of Maine Republicans presented Archie with a raccoon, and Quentin was the proud proprietor of three chicks, which he insisted on keeping in the house instead of the stables.

Rejoice that you aren't in Washington these days, Henry Adams wrote to Cecil Spring-Rice. *When I go to the Roosevelts' I'm convinced I'm visiting a zoo.*

Early in September Theodore took his family on a hiking trip in the Adirondack Mountains of northeastern New York state. On September 6 he interrupted his holiday to deliver an address on conservation before a group dedicated to the preservation of natural resources, the Fish and Game League, of which he was a member. While he talked to the men assembled in a rustic lodge of pine logs on the Isle La Motte in Lake Champlain, President McKinley was making a far more formal speech at the other end of the state in his first appearance at the highly publicized Pan-American Exposition in Buffalo.

After Theodore concluded his remarks he adjourned with the other fishermen and hunters to the home of former Governor Nelson W. Fisk on the island for a barbecue. There, during the height of the festivities, he received a telephone call informing him that the President had been shot and severely wounded by a maniac named Leon Czolgosz.

Leaving at once, Theodore crossed the lake and hurried to Burlington, Vermont, where a special train awaited him. He reached Buffalo the following afternoon, and there, in the private home to which the President had been carried, he and the Cabinet members who were also arriving on the scene were given good news. McKinley, who had a strong constitution, had rallied, and his physicians believed he would recover.

Theodore spent three nights in Buffalo, and by September 10 the President seemed to be completely out of danger.

"There's no need for you to stay here any longer, TR," Senator Hanna said.

"If the rest of you stay, so should I."

Secretary of War Elihu Root demurred. "You're wrong, Theodore. It will be a sign of reassurance to the whole country if you go back to the Adirondacks for the rest of your vacation."

Other Cabinet members, including the venerable and distinguished Secretary of State, John Hay, agreed with Root, so Theodore left Buffalo to join Edith and the children at a private club near Mount Tahamus, deep in the mountains. Edith, in a letter to Bamie, said that her husband felt greatly relieved.

His vitality restored, Theodore plunged into a new round of holiday activities. On the afternoon of the 12th he swam and fished with all the children, and that night he was captain of one team and Ted of another in a pillow fight that threatened to destroy the club's serenity until Edith intervened.

On the morning of the 13th the entire family went for a hike through the woods, and, after a picnic lunch, Theodore still felt so ebullient that he decided to work off excess energy by climbing nearby Mount Marcy. None of the children could keep pace with him, so he went alone.

He enjoyed himself thoroughly, and late in the afternoon, started his descent. He made his way down through thickening clouds, and, as he reached the shores of Lake Tear, saw someone hurrying toward him on the slope.

The man had been running; he waved frantically, but was too breathless to speak.

Theodore took a telegram from him and tore open the envelope. The message was succinct, but its significance was so great that he had to read it twice before it made complete sense to him: THE PRESIDENT APPEARS TO BE DYING AND MEMBERS OF THE CABINET IN BUFFALO THINK YOU SHOULD LOSE NO TIME IN COMING. ROOT.

It was dark by the time Theodore reached the clubhouse at the base of the mountain. The children raced out to greet him, and his reaction bewildered them. He kissed each of them, even though he had last seen the family at noon, and, not speaking a word, he went into the building.

The expression in his eyes told Edith what had happened before he handed her the telegram. She read it, then raised her face for a brief, tender kiss. Quickly composing herself, she asked, "What can I do?"

"Get me a buckboard and driver while I pack."

When she rejoined him in their bedroom he was hurling clothes into two valises. Edith quietly took charge, and began to repack his belongings. "The buckboard will be here in a few minutes. And I've asked the cook to make you some sandwiches."

"I'd forgotten about food. Thank you, dear." He glanced at his thick pocket watch. "They'll come in handy. It's going to be a long night."

"What are your plans?"

"I'll drive to North Creek, and if I know Bill Loeb, he'll have a special train waiting there for me." He often boasted that Loeb, his secretary, could read his mind.

Edith looked out of the window at the dark, starless sky, and frowned. "It's fifty miles to North Creek, and you'll be taking frightful risks driving there on mountain trails through the forests. It would be bad enough on a clear night."

"It's the nearest railroad station, and Bill will be expecting me there." He spoke without emotion.

But his jaw was set, and Edith, knowing he had made up his mind, did not pursue the subject. "Give me those shirts and your razor," she said. "There. Your valises are packed."

Theodore closed the bags and carried them to the door. "Unless you hear from me that Mr. McKinley has rallied," he said awkwardly, "you'd better go back to Oyster Bay and start closing up the house."

"Are you sure you don't want us to meet you in Washington?"

He swallowed painfully. "There's no rush, Edith. I imagine I'll be very busy—"

"That isn't your real reason."

"No. We'll want to be fair to Mrs. McKinley, and give her all the time she'll need to move out of the White House."

Edith nodded, tears in her eyes, and quickly turned away.

"This is what I've wanted for a long time." Theodore's voice was almost inaudible. "But, God knows, I haven't wanted it this way."

"I'll get the sandwiches."

He carried the valises to the front door of the club, and recognized his waiting driver, Henry Jenkins, whom he knew to be competent but cautious. "Lash my luggage to the seat, will you, Henry? My son will help you." He beckoned Ted.

"Don't need help," the man said.

Edith appeared, carrying a neatly wrapped parcel. "The sandwiches in white paper are chicken, and those in brown paper are roast beef. There are enough for the driver, too."

Theodore thanked her with a quick grin.

The other guests at the club, about a dozen adults in all, as well as various children who were playing tag on the lawn, had gathered in front of the building. Theodore saw that several of his own children were involved in the game, and, wanting to maintain as casual an appearance as he could, did not summon them to bid them farewell. He kissed Alice, and, rather than embarrass Ted in the presence of strangers, shook the hand of his eldest son.

The kiss he and Edith exchanged was light, but he gripped her shoulder for a moment, and the pressure was a barometer of his tension.

Then, kicking aside a stone with the toe of a mountain-climbing boot, Theodore climbed onto the hard wooden seat of the rickety buckboard. The horse, he was relieved to see, was a strong gelding. Waving as though he was starting out on an ordinary trip, he spoke to the driver in a low tone.

"Take me to North Creek, Henry. As fast as you can get me there."

"Tonight, Mr. Roosevelt?" Jenkins flapped the reins and they started off. "Can't be done."

"But you'll do it."

"We'll be lucky if we get there by noon. I've been driving on these roads for twenty-three years—"

"I've got to be at the railroad station by daybreak at the latest, earlier if possible."

Jenkins made no reply.

Theodore remained silent, too, for about a quarter of an hour. "That's a sure-footed animal, Henry. He can go faster."

"It's too dangerous, Mr. Roosevelt! You can't see more than a few feet ahead—"

"We'll stop, Henry, and I'll drive."

With Theodore at the reins the buckboard careened down the dirt roads, and Jenkins, sometimes perspiring, sometimes shivering, closed his eyes on sharp turns. Late in the evening they stopped at a farmhouse to change horses, and Theodore, realizing he was hungry, opened the parcel of sandwiches and offered the food to the driver.

"I'm not hungry, but I'd better eat something. The way you drive, Mr. Roosevelt, it may be my last chance."

They made a second stop for a change of horses at two o'clock in the morning, and a third about an hour before dawn at a small mountain inn whose proprietor kept a stable. Day was breaking over the mountains to the east as the fresh horse cantered through the quiet streets of North Creek. A train consisting of an engine, coal car and two passenger cars was waiting at the little station, and a dark, slender young man in city attire emerged from the shadows of the little one-room station as the carriage pulled to a halt.

"I knew you'd be here, Bill," Theodore said.

William Loeb removed his hat as he stepped forward to shake hands. "Good morning, Mr. President," he said.

Although Theodore had known what was ahead, the salutation stunned him. "When did it happen?"

"About three and a half hours ago. At two o'clock."

Theodore straightened. "How soon will the train be ready to leave?"

"The moment you step aboard, Mr. President. The stationmaster didn't think you could get here before late morning, but he doesn't know you."

Jenkins had untied the valises, and Theodore reached for them, but the man refused to relinquish them. "If I'd known what was afoot, I wouldn't have been so scared. It'll give me no pleasure to tell my children that the President of the United States drove me fifty miles through the mountains when I was afraid to do it myself, and the least I can do is put your luggage on the train, Mr. Roosevelt." He moved ahead.

"Before we pull out, Bill," Theodore said, "I wish you'd ask the stationmaster to wire ahead for the right of way."

"You already have it."

"Good boy." Theodore looked at the train as they approached it. "Why two cars, Bill? I don't want to start my Administration by costing the taxpayers unnecessary money."

"The one up front is a diner, sir."

Theodore sniffed appreciatively as he looked at the dining car. "Now that you mention it, I won't refuse a pot or two of coffee."

The stationmaster, standing with the conductor beside the train, stood stiffly at attention.

"What was your regiment?" Theodore asked him.

"7th Infantry, sir!"

"I always know a soldier when I see one."

Loeb quietly marveled at his superior's ability to slip into his public role no matter what the circumstances.

Theodore thanked the man for his efforts, told the conductor to lose no time and then shook hands with the waiting Jenkins. "What do I owe you, Henry?"

"Not a penny, Mr. Roosevelt!"

Searching in vain for his wallet in the shirt and trouser pockets of his mountain-climbing clothes, Theodore chuckled ruefully. "I left in such a hurry that I forgot to bring my money. Settle with him, Bill."

"Not a penny, sir!" Jenkins was adamant.

"I'm grateful to you, Henry." Theodore shook hands with him, then climbed onto the train. "Bill," he said quietly, "send his family one hundred dollars worth of meat and flour and potatoes. Use my personal funds, not the government drawing account."

The private car was luxurious. It was divided into four sections consisting of a living room, two bedrooms and a bathroom with a full-sized porcelain tub. "I can use a bath." Theodore looked at his filthy clothes and rubbed the stubble on his chin. "This is an elegant car, Bill."

"It's the private car of James J. Hill, the head of the Great Northern Railway. It was in the yards in New York City, and Hill insisted on sending it up to you when he heard that Mr. McKinley was failing."

There was a hint of wry amusement in Theodore's eyes as he removed his spectacles. Going to the washbasin, he filled it with hot water and began to scrub himself. "I imagine some of his friends on Wall Street have told him I'm not partial to the big railroad trusts. I'll use his car, but I can't be bought, and Hill ought to know it."

It was far too soon to ask Theodore's intentions toward the magnates who controlled a large proportion of American business and industry. He would need time, Loeb knew, to formulate the policies he intended to pursue, and his accession to the presidency was so sudden that he himself couldn't yet know what he wanted to do.

"I'll shave and soak myself in that fancy tub after breakfast, Bill. Right now I'm ravenous. We can start getting work organized while we're eating, and that will save us time later in the morning."

The secretary saw no way to express himself diplomatically. "You have some difficult days ahead, Mr. President, and you had no sleep last night. You need at least a few hours of rest."

Theodore, vigorously drying himself, lowered the towel from his face and stared at the younger man as though he had gone mad. "How could I possibly go to bed this morning? I'll make a statement to the Cabinet, and I want to memorize it, so it won't look as though it had been prepared in advance. I'll have to work out answers to the obvious questions the newspaper crowd will be sure to ask me—"

"You're under no obligation to hold a press conference today."

"It's essential," Theodore said flatly. "The public is uneasy, and the financial community will need to be soothed."

"Then let me prepare rough drafts for you while you sleep, sir."

"I'll expect you to help me, as always." Theodore reached for his spectacles. "But I can't let someone else, not even you, write my speeches for me. It's the duty of a President to express his thoughts in his own words."

He was setting himself an impossible goal, and the demands on a President's time were so great that every Chief Executive since James K. Polk had assigned the writing of speech drafts to others, although reserving the right, of course, to create their own major policy statements when they saw fit. But Loeb thought it likely that no previous President had been endowed with the energy of his forty-two-year-old superior, and, if challenged, Theodore undoubtedly would try to write every address and statement he made. One of his secretary's principal tasks, it was apparent, would be that of conserving his time without his knowledge.

They went forward to the dining car, and Theodore braced himself for the most important day of his life by eating two kinds of melon and a dish of blueberries, a grilled fresh fish, poached eggs and bacon, and, as an afterthought, an order of buckwheat cakes and Vermont maple syrup. Then, after bathing and dressing in a dark suit, he sat down with Loeb for a morning of work, and at no time did he show the effects of his sleepless night. Writing rapidly, he soon completed his initial statements, and dictated letters to Speaker Joe Cannon of the House of Representatives and other Congressional leaders of both parties asking them to call on him as soon as he reached Washington. Soup and sandwiches were served at noon while he worked in the living room of the private car, and by the time the speeding train reached Buffalo in the early afternoon he had completed the better part of the draft of a special message to Congress intended to calm the nation.

When the train finally arrived in Buffalo, six husky young men, all of them carrying pistols, came on board, and the chief of the detail immediately went to Theodore, who was packing away papers before disembarking. "Edward Wilson of the Secret Service, Mr. President," the man said, showing his credentials. "The Secretary of the Treasury has assigned us to guard you."

"I appreciate your concern." Theodore tried to curb his temper. "But I need no guard. I'll thank Lyman Gage when I see him this afternoon, but I can take care of myself."

"Mr. Gage is in Washington, sir." The Secret Service man was embarrassed. "We were taken off counterfeiting details and assigned to you. A permanent guard will be established after you reach Washington."

"I refuse to let anyone infringe on my privacy. I mean no personal offense, Wilson, but I'm sure you can understand how I feel."

"I do, sir, but I have no choice. Secretary Gage told us not to obey you if you tried to send us away, and the members of the Cabinet who are here support him unanimously."

No President of the United States had ever been subjected to such confining treatment, and Theodore's irritation increased. "This is outrageous!"

Loeb felt it necessary to intervene. "Ever since President McKinley was shot, there's been a demand all over the country that the President be given personal protection. A great many members of both Houses have announced they intend to introduce or support bills expanding the function of the Secret Service, Mr. President. This is something the people very much want."

Theodore checked himself and became thoughtful. "I can't blame them," he said at last. "McKinley is the third President killed by an assassin." Sighing, he turned back to the Secret Service man. "I'll try to accept your help, Wilson. If both of us are tolerant, maybe we can get along."

"I'm sure we can, Mr. President." Wilson's tone belied his words.

"If some of your men can box, I'll have enough sparring partners." Theodore's grin flashed for a moment, then he sobered. "Let's be on our way."

He followed the others, bareheaded, a slouch hat in his hand. The members of the Secret Service detail formed a cordon around him as they started down the platform toward the station, but their progress was slowed when a group of thirty or forty men and a few women hurried toward them.

Theodore recognized several newspaper reporters with whom he had become friendly in Albany, and a number of others from Washington bureaus. There was a clamor as they came within earshot, but the Secret Service men started to push through the crowd, ignoring the newsmen.

"Hold on," Theodore said, and halted.

"Do you have a statement, Mr. President?" someone shouted.

"Sir, Mr. Hearst wants to know—"

"How does it feel to be President?"

Theodore raised a hand. "Ladies and gentlemen, I'll be pleased to meet with you later this afternoon, and at that time I'll issue a statement. I'll also answer any questions that are reasonable and seemly. Right now I'll be otherwise occupied. I want to pay my respects to Mrs. McKinley, and for her sake I'll be grateful for privacy. Then I want to meet the Cabinet. Phil," he added to a correspondent from the New York *Sun* in the front of the crowd, "I wonder if you'll do me a favor. Tell the members of the Cabinet I'd like to see them in about an hour, if that's convenient. At the home of my friend, Ansley Wilcox, where I stayed when I was here last week. Thanks, ladies and gentlemen, and please remember I've made a deal with you. Don't pester me now, and I'll give you all the time you'll need as soon as I can get to you."

He nodded to Wilson, and his escort started forward again, leaving the newspaper correspondents who did not know him startled and bemused. Never had a President dealt so informally with the press.

Two hours later Theodore and his entourage finally drove up to the Wilcox house in two carriages, and the reporters, waiting at the gate, thought the new President looked haggard. He had found his ordeal with Mrs. McKinley unsettling, and had been unexpectedly affected when he had stood in silence for a long time at the open coffin of his murdered predecessor.

Wilcox came to the door, and apologized for the condition of the house. "My family is still off on vacation, and there hasn't been time to take the muslin dust covers off the furniture—"

"Your hospitality was more than good for me last week, Ansley. I don't believe I've changed that much in a few days." Theodore tried to smile, but the strain was too great.

He walked toward the front parlor, squaring his shoulders.

The entire Cabinet with the exception of Secretaries Hay and Gage awaited him, and everyone stood as he came into the room.

"This frightful thing has left a permanent mark on all of us," he said, then fell silent again as he shook hands with each Cabinet officer in turn.

"Mr. President," Elihu Root told him, "we believe you should take the oath of office without delay."

"Of course." Theodore polished his glasses and cleared his throat nervously as he turned to Attorney General Philander C. Knox of Pennsylvania, who was holding a Bible. But his nervousness vanished as he repeated the oath. Then, unaware of the redundancy, he concluded by adding firmly, "And so I swear."

Secretary of the Interior Ethan A. Hitchcock of Missouri sighed, but the tension was unrelieved.

Theodore turned and bowed with unaccustomed stiffness. "I wish to say," he declared in a high-pitched, almost tinny voice, "that it shall be my aim to continue, absolutely unbroken, the policy of President McKinley for the peace, the prosperity and the honor of our beloved country."

No one present knew he had spent more than an hour writing and revising the simple declaration.

"It is my hope," he continued, "that all members of the Cabinet will remain in office. The country needs you, and so do I."

One by one the officers assented, some bowing, some inclining their heads.

"I'm not well acquainted with some of you, but we'll soon remedy the deficiency. As soon as we return to Washington I want to spend as much time with each of you as you feel necessary. I'd also like concise reports on the state of each department. I'm particularly interested in your problems, and if any are urgent, we can discuss them today, before I see the press."

The conservative Postmaster General, Charles E. Smith of Pennsylvania, looked disturbed. "You're going to see those newspapermen waiting outside, Mr. President?"

"I am."

"Shouldn't you wait until you become familiar with the government's affairs? I can't help wondering if it's wise—"

"In my opinion," Theodore said, "I owe it to the people to speak candidly to the press. Today."

Smith and several others were disconcerted. They had known that the new President was pugnacious, but hadn't expected him to demonstrate truculence only a few moments after being sworn in.

"I'm finding it very warm in here, and I'd like some fresh air. I hope you'll wait for me. Elihu, will you come out into the garden with me?"

Secretary Root accompanied his old friend, and they headed toward the flower beds at the rear of the house, where they couldn't be seen by the reporters.

"This has come three and a half years earlier than I had imagined it could, Elihu, and I still find it difficult to believe I'm President. Do you and Hay have any advice for me?"

"That depends on your plans."

"For the present," Theodore said, speaking rapidly, "I want to do nothing and say nothing that will upset any individual, faction or group. I want to convey the definite impression, both here and abroad, that there will be no changes in McKinley's policies."

"Isn't that misleading?"

"You've often accused me of being impetuous, and so I am." Theodore grinned, but continued to speak soberly. "Sooner or later I'll begin to develop my own ideas, and undoubtedly will want people I know and can trust in executive positions to carry them out. It goes without saying that I'll want your help as long as I hold office."

"I'll try to be worthy of your faith in me, Mr. President."

It occurred to Theodore that, henceforth, only the members of his family would address him in any other way. "I know from past experience that you can sit on me when I need squashing." He bent down to examine a bed of unfamiliar flowers. "Keep a tight hold on the reins, Elihu. Ever since I was elected Vice-President my brain has been seething with changes I'd like to make in 1904. Shock has pushed them into the back of my mind, but in a week or two they'll start popping into the open."

The temperamentally cautious Root was alarmed. "A week or two! You'd destroy the very stability you've got to achieve!"

"You begin to see the trouble you'll have. With Cabot still in Europe, I don't know of anyone else who can clamp a lid on me when I start behaving like a jack-in-the-box." There was no humor in Theodore's grimace. "John Hay is a splendid old gentleman, a real trump, and I've respected him for many years. But he isn't an initiator, and I'm afraid he won't fight me. So, until Cabot comes home, you'll have to carry the burden alone."

"Surely you realize that no one, in or out of the government, can control the man who holds your office."

"Precisely. That's why I'm asking you in advance to be strong."

"You sound," the Secretary of War said, "as though you're afraid of the presidency."

Theodore halted and leaned against the trunk of a giant elm. "I suppose I am, although I hadn't quite thought of it that way. I believe it was Edmund Burke who wrote, 'The greater the power, the more dangerous the abuse.' To be honest with you, Elihu, I'm afraid of myself."

"Nonsense! You're dedicated to our kind of government, you're an honorable man—"

"Don't tell me all the things I'd say to you if our situations were reversed. I'm vain, I'm tactless, and I become very angry when I don't get what I want." Theodore straightened when he saw a carriage pulling to a halt, and his curiosity impelled him to move to the side lawn, where he could see it more clearly.

The waiting newspapermen moved aside grudgingly, then converged on the carriage, making it difficult for its occupant to emerge. Obviously a dignitary of importance had arrived at the Wilcox house.

Theodore stiffened when Mark Hanna stepped to the ground. The Senator from Ohio had not only been William McKinley's mentor and closest friend, but had nurtured presidential ambitions for himself, hoping that McKinley's support would win him the Republican nomination in 1904, so his loss was political as well as personal. Certainly he was still the most powerful member of his party in the Senate, enjoying not only the trust of his colleagues but of the nation's leading financiers and industrialists.

Casting aside the dignity of his high office, Theodore sprinted across the lawn, slowing to a walk only when he approached the gate. His smile of welcome was genuine, and he extended both hands to his visitor.

Hanna was not only impressed by the warmth of the greeting, but was conscious that the press was watching the unusual gesture. "Mr. President," he said, removing his hat, "I wish you success and a prosperous administration. I trust that you will command me if I can be of any service."

Elihu Root, standing on the side lawn, couldn't help smiling. Theodore had struck the note best calculated to win the support of the proud Hanna. It was absurd to think that the new President lacked a sense of diplomacy, in spite of his protests to the contrary. And Root couldn't help wondering whether, consciously or otherwise, he had made his plea for help because he had enjoyed the drama of the moment. Theodore Roosevelt had a greater control of himself and a more highly developed talent for commanding others that anyone the wise, seasoned Root had ever known.

The new President, after writing to Senator Lodge that he refused to be morbid about the way he been catapulted into office, went to Washington on the McKinley funeral train. On September 22, while Edith was still busy closing Sagamore Hill, he moved into the White House.

That night his sisters and their husbands were his only dinner guests, and Theodore seemed to be lacking his usual buoyancy. He dominated the conversation, to be sure, but spoke so quietly that Douglas Robinson couldn't help wondering, briefly, whether the responsibility of his office had already changed him.

Finally, at the end of the meal, Theodore expressed the thoughts that were uppermost in his mind. Looking first at Bamie, then at Conie, he said, "Do you realize this is our father's birthday?"

Anna nodded, and Corinne blinked away sudden tears.

"None of us is superstitious," Theodore continued, "but I can't help feeling it's a good omen that I begin my duties in this house on this day. I feel as if my father's hand were on my shoulder, as if there were a special blessing on the life I'm to lead here."

It occurred to Corinne that she had not heard him mention their father in a long time.

The butler appeared with a small tray of flowers, continuing the long-standing custom of giving each gentleman a boutonniere. He went first to the President, and, with a slight bow, handed him a small yellow rose.

Theodore flushed, but remained silent until the servants left the room. Then, showing the rose to his sisters, he said in a strained voice, "Isn't this strange? This was father's favorite flower—and every time I've ever seen one, I've thought of him."

Go slow, Mark Hanna said in a letter to the President a few days after the McKinley funeral. *You'll be deluged with opinions. Hear them all patiently, but reserve decision.*

Theodore replied immediately: *It would not be possible to get wiser advice, and I shall act exactly upon it. I shall go slow.*

Robert Bacon and George Perkins, both partners in J. P. Morgan's enterprises, came to Washington from New York to find out whether the new President intended to halt, if he could, the rapid expansion and consolidation of major financial and industrial interests throughout the United States. "Bob," Theodore said to his Harvard classmate, "you can assure Mr. Morgan that I don't plan—as of now, anyway—to attack anyone. There will be no innovations, no changes. You might remind him that I'm a Republican!"

The financial community was reassured, but Henry Adams remained skeptical. "They don't know Theodore," he said. "He'll be quiet—for him, that is—until the pressure becomes too great. In the meantime the country is going to watch the rare spectacle of a never-ending circus performance at the White House."

The press had easy, unprecedented access to the President, and the country soon learned details of his life that people found astonishing. "I don't know why there should be so much talk about the way we live," he told Edith. "Our household is very normal."

"Is it?" she replied, and laughed.

Certainly the American public was fascinated. The President, Washington correspondents wrote, awakened at six o'clock every morning, no matter how late he retired. Three-quarters of an hour later he had bathed, shaved, dressed and, over a cup of coffee, read the morning newspapers. Then, no matter what his schedule, he enjoyed a thirty-minute romp with his children, visiting nephews and nieces, and, of course, the household pets.

Promptly at 7:15 A.M. he—and sometimes Edith—went downstairs from the family quarters for breakfast with Senators, Congressmen, Cabinet members, and other government officials. Few men in Washington were accustomed to arising at dawn, but a new era had begun, and those who were requested to appear at a White House breakfast presented themselves on time.

At 8:30 the President went to his office, and spent the entire morning at his desk before entertaining other official visitors at lunch, then plunging into work again. Not until late afternoon did he take his only real break of the day. Sometimes he hiked in Rock Creek Park, and soon was taking advantage of the privacy the surroundings afforded him to invite one or more members of the diplomatic corps to accompany him. *Ambitious foreign service men in European nations,* the Baltimore *Sun* declared, *are hereby notified that the first and foremost requirement for assignment to a post in Washington is a pair of strong legs and tireless feet.*

At least two afternoons a week Theodore went off on solitary horseback rides, however, and the public sympathized with him when it was revealed that, irked by the presence of hovering Secret Service agents, he frequently tried to elude them. The Philadelphia *Evening Bulletin* reported that he invariably failed, which he denied, but at the urgent request of the Secret Service itself he gave the press no details of his successful attempts to break away from his guards.

The Chicago *Tribune* was the first newspaper to learn that the President was having a gymnasium installed in the White House at his own expense. Theodore refused to talk about boxing with the correspondents he saw almost daily, however, believing such discussions would be harmful to the dignity of his office. He did reveal to representatives of the Los Angeles *Times* and Minneapolis *Tribune* that, "I'm going to curb my desire for hunting. I don't want the people to get the idea that they have a sporting President." But in spite of his good intentions he could not keep his pledge. The lure of the field proved too great for him, and he made several hunting trips each year throughout his presidency, usually combining them with political visits to various parts of the country.

Theodore's work day rarely ended at the dinner hour. After another romp with the children, followed by the reading of stories to the youngsters, he and Edith usually entertained large numbers of dinner guests including diplomats, Supreme Court Justices, visiting political dignitaries and a wide assortment of people who interested the insatiably curious President, among them many university professors, alumni of the Rough Riders and Dakota ranchers, authors, professional prize fighters and baseball players, ladies and gentlemen prominent in high society and an assortment of labor leaders.

The nation was enthralled by these presidential dinners, but the press scolded Theodore editorially when it was learned that he read daily Cabinet reports for at least an hour before going to bed. *Mr. Roosevelt will ruin his health unless he relaxes his blistering pace of living, which no man can maintain,* the *Rocky Mountain News* said. Refusing to change his habits, he ignored the advice.

On the other hand, he kept his promise to make no innovations of consequence in affairs of state. An exception was a memorandum to the Cabinet, instructing the State Department to explore the possibilities of opening a canal linking the Atlantic and Pacific. Other departments were directed to cooperate, but Theodore made no specific suggestions, confining himself to the observation that the expansion of American international trade, military might and growth as a world power made the building of such a canal imperative.

He quickly demonstrated, nevertheless, that even with the best of intentions he could not escape controversy. Early in October he appointed Thomas G. Jones of Alabama, a Democrat, as a judge of the United States District Court. Democrats everywhere, particularly in the South, were elated, but Republicans in and out of Congress protested. Theodore cut them short. "I'm sorry he voted for Bryan," he said, "but I had to appoint him. He was the man in the district best qualified for the job, and I refuse to let politics take precedence over ability."

His honeymoon with the South was short-lived. Less than a week after the new President moved into the White House he conferred privately with Dr. Booker T. Washington, discussing not only the problems of the Negro but of the South in general. On October 16 Dr. Washington returned to Washington and was entertained by Theodore and Edith at a White House dinner.

White men of the South, how do you like it? the New Orleans *Times-Democrat* demanded. *When Mr. Roosevelt sits down to dinner with a Negro, he declares that the Negro is the social equal of the white man.* The Richmond *Times* said it wouldn't be surprised if the President favored racial intermarriage, and the Memphis *Scimitar*, almost inarticulate in its anger, declared, *Roosevelt is responsible for the most damnable outrage ever!*

"What I've done speaks for itself," Theodore told Elihu Root, "and I refuse to get into a name-calling contest with bigots. Dr. Washington is my friend, and one of the most brilliant men in the country. I'll invite him to dinner with me whenever I wish, and I refuse to worry about the political effect."

His sense of humor intact, he added a brief postscript to a dinner invitation he sent to Finley Peter Dunne: *You need NOT black your face.*

The era of mutual good will with Theodore's fellow Republicans lasted a little longer. But, by late autumn, he became restless when he learned that, only a month after he had taken office, J. P. Morgan had initiated the formation of the most powerful financial holding company in the history of the United States. In November the Northern Securities Company was incorporated, with a capital of $400,-000,000, for the purpose of merging two large railroads, E. H. Harriman's Union Pacific and James J. Hill's Great Northern.

"I wonder if you realize," Theodore said to Senator Lodge, "that this new company will have a complete monopoly of railroads in the Northwest."

"Is that necessarily bad?"

"Not in theory, perhaps, but I shudder to think of what will happen in practice. Freight rates will go up. And up. With no competition to hold them down."

"You can't be sure—"

"I'm positive, Cabot! I saw what happened when I was living in Dakota and the railroads worked together to fix rates."

"I hope you'll do nothing hasty, Mr. President. Remember that J. P. Morgan is a very powerful man, and he has influential friends."

Theodore's eyes became cold. "Surely you aren't trying to tell me he's more powerful than the President of the United States!"

Lodge immediately recognized his tactical error. "Of course not. I was merely—"

"It's my duty to protect all the people."

"I know. I—"

"And I want your help. I wish you'd reconsider my offer of a place in the Cabinet, Cabot."

"If you're going to start a fight with J. P. Morgan," Lodge said ruefully, "I can do you more good in the Senate. You'll need friends there."

The first hints of an impending battle came when Theodore started to prepare his annual message to Congress. Rumors reached Wall Street in November that the President planned to attack giant financial trusts, and Morgan's associates appealed to Mark Hanna for help.

The Senator from Ohio was unsympathetic. "I warned Morgan last summer that McKinley might have to take action if he formed Northern Securities, and I don't see how Roosevelt can do less than a far more cautious President would have done."

Robert Bacon and George Perkins made another trip to the White House, and attempted to soften Theodore's approach. Giving them neither assurances regarding his long-range plans nor any inkling of specific action he might take, he said, "I intend to be most conservative, but in the interests of the big corporations themselves, and above all in the interests of the country, I intend to pursue, cautiously but steadily, the course to which I have been publicly committed again and again, and which I am certain is the right course."

Unable to persuade him to amplify his remarks, they returned to New York, still unable to divine his plans.

The President's message, which he sent to Congress on December 3, was a long document which, in the main, soothed the business community. An occasional phrase or sentence indicated that he believed there was a need to curb abuses harmful to the public interest, but only Lodge and a few others who knew him well guessed that he might be planning to assault the corporate interests that were threaten-

ing to absorb the nation's principal commercial and industrial enterprises.

Only one man knew the Chief Executive's mind. "Northern
Securities and all the other trusts that will be formed in its image en-
able a few very rich men to become wealthier at the expense of everyone else," Theodore told Attorney General Knox. "They abuse our
system and must be destroyed. Find a way to do it."

Knox, after an intensive, private study, decided to use the hitherto
neglected Sherman Anti-Trust Act of 1890 as his weapon. On February 19, 1902, war was declared when the Attorney General announced
that the Federal Government would seek, through the courts, the dissolution of the Northern Securities Company.

The stock market slumped on February 20, and three days later
Morgan himself, escorted by Senators Hanna and Depew, hurried
to Washington and called on the President. "If we have done anything
wrong, send your man," the banker said, pointing at the Attorney
General, "to my man, and they can fix it up."

"That's impossible," Theodore replied, aware that Morgan failed to
recognize the principle at stake.

Knox was less abrupt than his superior. "The purpose of the government's suit," he declared, "isn't to 'fix up' anything. We want to
halt illegal mergers that harm the public."

The crestfallen Morgan returned to New York. Still unwilling to
believe that a Republican President would prosecute the financial interests which had supported the party so generously, Morgan pushed
ahead with his private plans to form a steel trust far larger and more
powerful than the railroad merger the government was contesting.

Meanwhile, Theodore, more conscious than ever of the ultimate
authority exercised by the Federal judiciary, was conducting a careful
search for someone to fill a vacancy on the Supreme Court. Lodge
recommended Chief Justice Oliver Wendell Holmes of Massachusetts,
a distinguished son of a distinguished father, and a Civil War hero.
After a careful reading of Holmes' more important decisions on the
Massachusetts bench, Theodore called in Lodge for a final discussion
of the matter.

"I like your man," he said. "He's an aristocrat, and if he were in
private practice the big trusts would be his clients. But in decision
after decision he shows remarkable sympathy for the ordinary work-
ingman. He seems to understand instinctively that if the United States

is to become a great nation, it's the common citizen who'll make us great—provided he's protected. I'm going to appoint Holmes."

The appointment, which brought a great humanitarian to the Supreme Court, strongly indicated a significant change in Theodore's own feelings. Neither he nor anyone else quite understood how he had developed a deep love for America's little people. "I lived and worked with them in Dakota, I commanded them in the Rough Riders, and I've met them by the thousands in my political travels," he told a group of White House guests one evening. "And all I can say is that they and I think and feel alike."

His sympathies were put to the test in the first major disturbance of his Administration, the anthracite coal strike of 1902, and the situation was complicated by the fact that Theodore had already antagonized J. P. Morgan, who exerted great influence in the coal mining industry.

The miners of Pennsylvania led miserable lives. Badly underpaid, forced to work long hours under dangerous conditions, they lived in hovels provided for them by the coal mining companies. After living and dying in hopeless poverty for decades, the men had formed a union, the United Mine Workers of America, but the employers had refused to recognize the organization until an aggressive, ambitious young miner, John Mitchell, had become its president in 1899.

In the following year he had called a strike, which had won the union partial recognition and a token wage increase. Now, with the union larger and better disciplined, Mitchell called another strike in May 1902 after the employers had refused to grant the miners a fair pay raise, shorter hours and an elimination of the worst hazards of mining.

One hundred and forty thousand men quietly walked off the job, their principal target being the Philadelphia & Reading Coal & Iron Company. Mitchell and his supporters had been reluctant to call a strike, but George F. Baer, the president of Philadelphia & Reading Railway, had given them no choice, refusing to deal with the union, rejecting all demands and insisting that he would make no changes.

Archbishop John Ireland of St. Paul, the most renowned liberal Catholic prelate of the day, openly sympathized with the miners, but most Americans were unfamiliar with the issues in the dispute, and remained neutral, at least for the moment. Senator Hanna tried to work out a compromise, but had to abandon his efforts when Baer said to him, "The miners don't suffer. Why, most of them can't even speak English."

Hanna went to the President. "There will be hell to pay," he said, "when coal stockpiles disappear. Railroad trains won't be able to operate, food and other essentials won't be shipped, and when autumn comes, buildings won't be heated. This strike can become the worst catastrophe in our history."

Theodore summoned the Cabinet to a meeting, but his subordinates felt that, lacking a precedent, the Federal Government could not intervene unless one side or the other requested such a move. By June the situation showed no improvement, and Theodore, becoming increasingly restless, asked Attorney General Knox whether anti-trust proceedings could be initiated against the coal and railroad companies. Knox said that the companies, under the wording of the Sherman Act, did not constitute a trust, so the President dropped the idea.

In July, thanks to a priest, the Reverend J. J. Curran of Wilkes-Barre, the public began to sympathize with the strikers. A commercial photographer in Wilkes-Barre wrote to Baer, telling him it was his religious duty to end the strike, Father Curran called the attention of the entire country to Baer's arrogant reply: *The rights and interests of the laboring man will be protected and cared for—not by the labor agitators, but by the Christian men to whom God in His infinite wisdom has given the control of the property interests of this country.*

In August, Senator Lodge reported to the White House that the price of coal was rising rapidly throughout New England. Theodore, who was alarmed by the situation and by the potential political consequences in a Congressional election year, was temporarily incapacitated early in September when, on a brief political tour, the carriage in which he and Governor Murray Crane of Massachusetts were riding was struck by a trolley car near the town of Pittsfield. Theodore suffered a leg injury, which he tried to ignore as he extended his tour to the Middle West.

But his condition became worse, the physicians who were called in were afraid of blood poisoning, and he was taken to a hospital in Indianapolis for minor surgery. By the time he returned to Washington on September 24 his injury was healing, but, much to his annoyance, he was temporarily confined to a wheelchair.

Meanwhile the strike had become violent. Until September the miners had demonstrated patience and discipline, but attempts by several of the companies, among them the Philadelphia & Reading, to bring in outside workers caused riots in several Pennsylvania towns. Many moderates, disturbed by the beatings, burnings of company officials' homes and other acts of desperation, began to feel that the companies were right and the workers wrong. The president of Princeton University, Woodrow Wilson, declared, "The real issue is the union's drive to win more power."

Senator Lodge returned to Washington and went straight to the President. "You've got to do something, or the Republicans will lose the election."

Theodore's nerves were frayed, and he found his wheelchair galling. "What do you suggest?" he snapped. "I'm at my wits' end how to proceed."

His mood remained gloomy, and he called Matthew Quay to Washington for a conference that brought no positive results. *We have no earthly responsibility for it,* Theodore wrote to Mark Hanna, *but the public at large will visit upon our heads responsibility for the shortage of coal.*

In spite of his pessimism, Theodore was nagged by the feeling that something had to be done. "I can't see misery and death come to the great masses of the people in our large cities and sit by idly," he told his sister, Bamie, who paid him a brief visit.

The first ray of hope appeared on September 29. Hanna, acting on a suggestion made by Theodore, went to New York to see J. P. Morgan, his friend. To the Senator's surprise he found that Morgan, who controlled a number of coal companies, was distinctly in favor of a compromise.

Unable to tolerate inaction any longer, the President decided to call the coal operators and the union leaders to a meeting at which he would preside. Secretary Root, who had been a distinguished corporation lawyer, told him he had no authority to intervene and was wasting his time. Attorney General Knox was even more emphatic, and said the government would be acting illegally if the President interfered.

Theodore responded by sending telegrams of invitation to the coal company heads and union officials, asking them to join him in Washington on October 3. Realizing that Baer and some of his colleagues would be unwilling to attend, he released to the press the list of those he had invited, thereby exerting pressure on the operators.

On the morning of October 3 both groups began to convene at Blair House, directly across from the White House, where the President

was living and working while renovations were being made on the
Executive Mansion. The largest chamber available for the purpose
was a drawing room on the second floor, and the atmosphere became
increasingly strained as the participants arrived singly and in pairs, the
operators gathering at one end of the room and the miners' representatives at the other. No greetings were exchanged across the room, and
the members of both groups stood self-consciously, speaking in low
tones.

Promptly at 11:00 A.M. a pair of double doors opened, and Theodore
was wheeled into the room by a Secret Service agent, with William
Loeb following. Everyone turned, but the President gave no one else
the opportunity to speak. "Good morning, gentlemen," he said calmly.
"The American people and I thank you for coming here today." Nothing in his manner or delivery indicated that every word had been
carefully rehearsed. "I'm sure all of you realize that the government
and its employees—and I ask you to remember that I draw my pay
from the Treasury—has any right to intervene in your dispute. Let me
stress that it isn't the government's *duty* to intervene, either. There's
nothing in the Constitution that either permits or obliges me to see
you today.

"And there's nothing but your own consciences that has brought
you here." He wheeled himself to the center of the room, then
gestured broadly. "Sit down, gentlemen. We may be here for a few
hours."

The operators and union men, still holding themselves apart,
moved toward chairs and couches on opposite sides of the room.

"You're here," Theodore continued, his voice rising as he became
more emphatic, "because you share my urgent feeling that good will
is necessary on both sides in your fight if a great public tragedy is
to be averted. The terrible nature of the catastrophe that hangs over
this land, a winter fuel famine, has made it self-evident that you must
resolve your differences. Agreed?"

John Mitchell nodded, a quick smile illuminating his dark face, but
George Baer stared out of the nearest window, giving no sign that he
had heard the President.

"Permit me," Theodore said, his voice hardening a trifle, "to put this
meeting in its proper perspective. I have not called you here for a
discussion of your respective claims and positions. I have no intention
of acting as a judge in your conflict. I am not qualified to be your
referee, to determine the merits of your opposing arguments or to

suggest the terms of a settlement both parties might consider fair. I don't presume to know anything about the mining of coal or the management of mines."

William Loeb took a handkerchief from his pocket and pretended to mop his face with it, hiding a smile. The President's departure from his prepared remarks was both amusing and startling; he had read everything he could find on the subject of mining, and knew as much as any man in the room.

"Why, then, have I presumed to invite you to Washington?" Theodore paused and spoke very slowly. "With all the earnestness there is in me, I ask that there be an immediate resumption of operations in the coal mines in some such way as will—without a day's unnecessary delay—meet the crying needs of the American people. I appeal to your patriotism, to the spirit that sinks personal consideration and makes individual sacrifices for the common good."

He waited, but no one on either side of the room chose to reply.

"Gentlemen," Theodore said, "I ask you to submit your dispute to mediation, on mutually satisfactory terms that you can work out here, today."

Again there was a taut silence.

Theodore had been prepared for hostility from both camps, but found the stony attitude of his guests irritating. "Mr. Baer, perhaps you'd like to begin the discussion."

"I haven't agreed to your terms or any others, Mr. President, and my fellow operators and I came here only because you gave us no real choice. For the present I have nothing to say."

Theodore pretended to ignore the rebuff. "Mr. Mitchell?"

The union leader decided to utilize the forum, and rose to his feet. "I'm much pleased, Mr. President, with what you say." His manner was suave and his voice slightly musical; he showed none of the fire that characterized his union speeches, and obviously he was on his best behavior. "My organization, representing nearly 150,000 miners, is willing that you shall name a tribunal which shall determine the issues that have resulted in the strike. And if the gentlemen representing the operators will accept the award or decision of such a tribunal, the miners will willingly accept it, even if it be against our claims."

Theodore was pleased. "That's fair, Mr. Mitchell. And generous. I congratulate you."

George Baer jumped to his feet. "It makes me ill," he shouted, "when I hear the President of the United States complimenting a damned anarchist!"

Theodore tried in vain to let the challenge pass unanswered, but his own temper soared. "No one has asked how you vote, sir, and Mr. Mitchell deserves the same courtesy. I'm inclined to think he's either a Republican or a Democrat, but we have a secret ballot in this country, and his affiliations—if he has any—are irrelevant to this discussion."

"You're completely wrong, which is what I expected from a damned busybody!"

Everyone in the room, including the other operators, was shocked. No American, regardless of his feelings, attacked the President or called him names to his face.

Baer, however, was too angry to care. "The mines would be open and thousands upon thousands of men would be at work if it weren't for the intimidation, violence, and crime inaugurated by Mitchell and his anarchist union!"

Theodore gripped the arms of his wheelchair, and only Loeb knew the effort it cost him to speak calmly. "Nothing will be accomplished unless we confine ourselves to the broad issues I've outlined."

Baer pointed a finger at him, and was so enraged his hand trembled. "You're responsible for this—this travesty. Instead of ordering these swine jailed and deported, you've honored them by inviting them here. If you want to destroy the confidence of the American people in our government, I'm afraid I can't stop you. But I refuse to deal with a band of outlaws!"

Loeb stepped forward and put a detaining hand on the shoulder of the President, who was struggling to rise from his wheelchair.

Theodore, aware of his physical helplessness, was so angry he could not speak for a moment. "Baer," he finally shouted, "I can't stop you from throwing stones at union men who are showing a brand of patriotism far greater than yours. And I don't care what you think of me. But I demand—without qualification, right here and right now —that you show respect for the office of the presidency."

Baer held his ground. "You ought to be ashamed of yourself for negotiating with criminal anarchists who defy the law and have no respect for American institutions."

"I need no instruction from you," Theodore retorted in a voice that could be heard far down the outside corridor, "in the deportment required of the President! Your insolence, Mr. Baer, is beyond endurance!"

"We consider it insolent of the President," Baer declared, "for him to bring us here for the purpose of consorting with known criminals!"

Loeb caught hold of the wheelchair so the President could not propel himself across the room.

"We refuse to negotiate with the anarchist union," Baer said, "and we reject the attempt of the President to force us to deal with Mitchell and his sort. I want to place the opinion of the operators on the record. We believe the President is making a grandstand play!"

Theodore sat back in his chair. "There is no point in continuing this discussion at the present time. The meeting is adjourned, gentlemen, and I bid you good day."

Loeb signaled to the Secret Service man, who quickly wheeled the President out of the room, and the secretary followed them to the temporary Executive office at the end of the corridor.

Theodore slumped in his chair, his eyes closed, as the Secret Service man moved the wheelchair into place behind the desk.

The bewildered, angry agent left the room, and Loeb poured his superior a glass of water from a carafe.

"Thanks, Bill." Theodore was listless.

"Do you mind if I smoke, sir?" Ordinarily staff members refrained from using tobacco in the inner sanctum, knowing the President disliked its odor. But, not waiting for a reply, Loeb took a cigarette from a case and lighted it with a self-igniting match of a type invented by a man named Kreuger several years earlier in Sweden.

"I tried, Bill, but I didn't try hard enough. I failed." Theodore suddenly pounded a fist on the desk. "I couldn't have done worse if I'd deliberately wanted to make matters even more impossible than they were before I called the meeting!"

"You couldn't help it, Mr. President. Baer goaded you—"

"Ah, but that's the whole point, Bill. I could have controlled myself. I knew what was at stake, but I let Baer drag me down into the gutter with him. There might have been a chance to salvage at least the hope of mediation if I'd remained a gentleman. And instead of prattling about the dignity of the presidency, I should have demonstrated it!" He buried his face in his hands.

Loeb had never seen him so despondent, and was at a loss for words.

"When a lunatic curses me as I ride past him in my carriage," Theodore muttered, "I pretend not to hear him. Why couldn't I have done the same with Baer?" He sat upright, and when he removed his glasses to clean them his myopic eyes were stormy. "Bill, I swear to you that if I weren't suffering from this lame leg I'd have disgraced the presidency forever by punching him in the nose. As it was, you stopped me."

"He gave you provocation, sir."

"That's no excuse. The only man in the room who behaved like a thoroughbred and kept his sense of balance was Mitchell. Now the coal strike deadlock is worse than ever, and I don't know what I can do after this fiasco."

"You'll find some way, Mr. President."

Theodore donned his spectacles, and his voice became hard. "If I don't, I'll be sorry until the day I die that I didn't break some of George Baer's teeth!"

Public suffering increased as the autumn of 1902 wore on, and both sides in the dispute lost the last remnants of public sympathy. *The operators,* the New York *Post* declared, *are robber barons. They deserve no consideration, and the President should take immediate Federal action against them in the courts.*

There is no coal strike in Pennsylvania, the New York *Journal of Commerce* said. *It is an insurrection. The President should heed the request of the operators, call out Federal troops and put them to work mining coal.*

Theodore ignored the contradictory advice of the press, but could not remain inactive. Telling Cabot Lodge he would go mad if he did nothing and that he'd deserve being called "another President James Buchanan," he wrote to Mitchell, suggesting that the miners return to work pending a settlement. The head of the United Mine Workers politely declined, explaining that men like Baer would refuse even the mildest of compromises once the men were producing coal again.

Recognizing the validity of his argument, Theodore called the Attorney General and Secretary of War into an emergency conference. "I refuse to twiddle my thumbs," he told them, "and I have a double-barreled offensive in mind. Elihu, you and J. P. Morgan are old friends, and the coal operators may listen to him. After all, he has major investments in the coal companies and in the railroads that own some of them."

"I know he's worried about the strike," Secretary Root replied. "Our whole economy is upset, so I'm sure he'll do anything he can to help."

"I hope so. Ask him to go to the operators with the suggestion that an impartial commission be formed. He can tell them he'll have a voice—a major voice—in naming its members. Each of the coal companies would go before the commission, which would draw up a five-year agreement after hearing the miners separately. The operators wouldn't even have to sit down at the same table with the union. Doesn't that sound fair?"

"Very. How soon do you want me to go to New York?"

"As soon as you've performed another function for me. A highly confidential one. Find me the toughest, most efficient general officer in the Army—a man who isn't afraid of unions or wealthy financiers or politicians. Or public opinion."

Attorney General Knox stirred uncomfortably. "I hope you've read the opinion I submitted to you, Mr. President. In the opinion of the Justice Department, Federal intervention would be illegal."

"I read every word," Theodore replied, suddenly genial as he evaded the issue. "You and your lawyers prepared a very impressive document."

"I hope you noted in particular that we were in complete agreement on the subject of President Cleveland's intervention in the Pullman strike."

"I've been corresponding with him," Theodore said. "He's offered me any assistance he can give, and would be willing to sit as a member of the commission. Very generous of him."

Knox refused to drop the cardinal point at stake. "May I ask why you want to see a general, Mr. President?"

"I've had another chat with Senator Quay. Governor Stone of Pennsylvania is calling out the National Guard to protect any miners who want to return to work."

Both Cabinet officers were puzzled. "I don't see the connection," Root said.

"The operators claim the men are afraid to go back to their jobs. Mitchell says they'll stay on strike, no matter what else happens, unless there's a settlement. The mobilization of the Pennsylvania Guard will call the bluff of both sides."

Knox and Root exchanged blank glances.

"If my guess is right," Theodore continued, "the deadlock will continue. And I refuse to let the American people suffer, regardless of whether the Federal Government has the right to intervene. I hope Elihu will be able to get negotiations started through J. P. Morgan.

If not, I'm prepared to take drastic action. I prefer not to discuss details, even with you, until later. I'm in no mood for protests."

Root fingered the heavy gold watch fob that dangled from a vest pocket. "I'm sure there's no need for me to remind you that the whole question of Federal action is delicate, Mr. President."

"Unless this strike is settled very quickly, more Americans will die this winter than in any year since the Civil War. There's nothing delicate about mass slaughter, Elihu!"

"That isn't what I meant, Mr. President." The Secretary of War sounded aggrieved.

"I won't conceal more from either of you than I think is necessary." Theodore became soothing. "And I see no reason to conceal one step in my strategy. If the miners won't go back to work, Governor Stone will send me a telegram—which both of us will publicize—asking me to take action."

"Federal intervention," the Attorney General said firmly, "is illegal even when requested by the principal executive officer of a state."

"I refuse to have my foolproof plan marred by any taint of legality," Theodore said.

Knox's sense of humor was limited when questions of the law were involved. "Obviously, Mr. President, you intend to take possession of the mines in some way."

"Obviously," Theodore replied, "I must."

"The Constitution doesn't permit it, Mr. President. Private property can't be seized for public purposes without due process of law."

Theodore's patience snapped. "The Constitution was made for the people, not the people for the Constitution!" he declared, raising his voice. "And that's how the Federal Government will operate as long as I hold this office. Chisel it on my epitaph!" He wheeled himself around the desk, crossed the room and opened the door, terminating the interview.

In the next few days the misgiving of the Cabinet members increased, and Theodore's pessimistic estimate of the efficacy of the mobilization of the Pennsylvania National Guard proved accurate. Governor William A. Stone sent his troops to the mining towns and the fields outside them, but only a few miners accepted the invitation of the operators to go back to work. And people everywhere learned that George Baer's insistent claim that the rank-and-file wanted to return to the mines was vastly exaggerated.

A growing sense of panic gripped the nation. The New York *Sun* summed up the country's feeling when it declared, *Pennsylvania is in a state of anarchy beyond the power of her entire Guard to control.* Like scores of other newspapers, it begged the President to take immediate, drastic action.

Theodore kept his own counsel and took the unprecedented step of barring his office to reporters, who insisted on asking questions he preferred not to answer. Then, on October 11, while Elihu Root was meeting secretly with J. P. Morgan on board the financier's yacht, the *Corsair,* which rode at anchor near the mouth of the Hudson River, a high-ranking Army officer paid an equally private call on the President, entering Blair House by a rear entrance, where representatives of the press would not see him.

Major General John M. Schofield was a short, wiry man, with a weather-beaten, lined face and thick side whiskers. He saluted, then continued to stand at attention until invited to sit.

Theodore, who took pride in his judgments of character, liked what he saw. "General, do you know why you're here?"

"Because you wanted to see me, sir."

"I told Secretary Root to send me the most hard-boiled, uncompromising general officer in the Army. Did he pick the right man?"

Faint, grim humor appeared in Schofield's eyes for an instant. "There's only one way to find out, Mr. President. Try me, and then make your own decision."

Theodore was increasingly pleased. "Are you willing to undertake a mission that may harm your reputation?"

"I obey orders, sir."

"What's your opinion of the coal strike, General?"

"Professionally, Mr. President, I have no opinion. Personally I think it's damnable."

"There's never been a situation like it. The position of the operators, that the public has no rights in the case, is untenable. What I find particularly shocking is the refusal of George Baer and his colleagues to admit they have any responsibility to the poor people of this country. They can't look beyond the ends of their fat noses and realize they'll be responsible for great social disturbances if there should be a national catastrophe this winter."

"I have little use for the operators, sir."

"The miners have shown a more conciliatory attitude, and while I sympathize with their refusal to work, I can't help wishing they'd put the country's interests above their own."

"I'm not fond of the miners, either, sir."

Theodore was convinced that Root had sent him the right officer. "General, I'm giving you a tentative assignment here and now. There's a meeting taking place in New York today, and if it fails, the welfare of the country will depend on you and me. I'll want you to take Regular Army troops into the mines. Put them to work mining coal. Keep the operators and the union out."

Schofield showed no surprise, even though the directive was the most radical ever given by a President to an Army officer, and, as the general knew, was unprecedented. "How many troops will you give me, sir?"

"As many as you need."

"May I arm them?"

"That's up to you."

"Infantrymen will carry rifles into the mines with them. Officers will wear sidearms. And I'll want some artillery regiments, although I'll have no real use for cannon. The sight of a few howitzers at the mines will cool off hot tempers."

"The worst threat to your operation will come through the courts. The mine owners will be certain to petition for an injunction to prevent you from mining coal, and the union may do the same, although it has less cause."

"If there should be an injunction issued, what are my orders, sir?"

"Keep mining coal," Theodore said. "I'll insist the Justice Department appeal, and it will take time for the case to go up to the Supreme Court through the Appellate division. Some lawyers will argue, of course, that an injunction is binding unless the higher courts dismiss it, but you'll pay no attention to the courts. I'll take full responsibility, and by the time the dust settles in the Federal courtrooms, you should have enough coal mined to see the country through the winter."

"Yes, sir," Schofield said.

"You'll be subjected to tremendous pressure, General, but I'll want you to ignore it. You'll be acting in a purely military capacity, and reporting direct to me in my capacity as Commander-in-Chief. You'll heed no authority, judicial or otherwise, except mine."

"Yes, sir." Schofield's reply was crisp and impersonal, but his expression indicated admiration for a superior who not only knew what he wanted, but was willing to create a national furor for the sake of his convictions.

Theodore sensed his sympathy, and was tempted to divert their con-

out across Theodore's desk. In order to expedite the matter, the operators were gathered in Morgan's New York office, while Bacon and Perkins spoke to them by telephone from the President's Blair House study. The formation of the commission developed slowly but fairly smoothly until Theodore said, "Tell them the union's requests. And tell them I agree with Mitchell. Both sides should be represented."

The operators adamantly refused.

Bacon and Perkins spent the better part of the evening of October 15 on the telephone, arguing, cajoling, and pleading, but to no avail. The owners were holding firm.

"Tell them," Theodore said at last, "that Bishop John L. Spalding of Illinois is my choice, not Mitchell's. If they won't accept him, I'll make their rejection public, and they'll be branded as bigots by the whole country."

After long additional discussion, the operators finally accepted Bishop Spalding, but under no circumstances would agree to a representative of labor. Bacon and Perkins grew increasingly frenzied as midnight approached, and, taking turns on the telephone, talked themselves hoarse. The President was demonstrating remarkable patience, but Bacon, knowing him, realized he might lose his temper without warning.

Finally, when Perkins once again took the telephone from his colleague, Bacon slumped in his chair. "Theodore," he said, too weary to remember that the President was always addressed by his title, "I've read more literature than you've given me credit for reading. 'What's in a name? That which we call a rose by any other name would smell as sweet.' Ben Jonson."

"Shakespeare," Theodore replied, thinking Bacon was humoring him. "*Romeo and Juliet,* you ignoramus. But what a time to think of quotations from the classics. Unless those mules can be persuaded to compromise, Mitchell won't be able to hold his people in line. There'll be violence in the coal towns by dawn, and I wouldn't be surprised if a social war beyond the power of any President to control swept across the entire country."

"I wasn't quoting the line for its own sake." Bacon's hoarse, wry laugh sounded like a cough. "Something just occurred to me. The operators accepted the editor of the *Engineering and Mining Record,* Parker, without a murmur. He's basically a journalist, not a mining expert, although he does know something about mining, of course."

Theodore was silent, shutting out the sound of Perkins' voice on the telephone in the background. "If I understand you correctly, Bob, the mighty brains of those captains of industry sitting in Morgan's office would rather have anarchy than tweedledum, but if I used the word tweedledee instead, they'd hail it as meaning peace."

"I think so."

In spite of his own exhaustion, Theodore chuckled. "This is so absurd I feel foolish mentioning it. But I wonder if they'd accept my labor man if I called him an 'eminent sociologist.'"

"That's the point I'm trying to make. I believe they would." Bacon was laughing, too. "I realize the idea is ludicrous, but—"

"Try it!" Theodore commanded. "Get back on the wire and tell the operators I've found a sociologist who meets their qualifications. Mr. E. E. Clark."

"Who is he?"

"Between you and me, the Grand Chief of the Order of Railway Conductors, one of the most dedicated labor leaders of our time."

Bacon went back to the telephone, and, to Theodore's delight, Baer and his associates promptly accepted Clark, believing they had thwarted the United Mine Workers' request for a labor representative.

Theodore played out the farce to the end. The following morning, when he called in the press to announce the membership of the commission, he referred to Clark as a sociologist, and added solemnly, "Sociologist means a man who has thought and studied deeply on social questions and has practically applied his knowledge."

The coal strike immediately came to an end and the miners went back to work pending the commission's investigation and recommendations, which, five months later, would win the miners a substantial pay increase and improvement in working conditions.

Samuel Gompers, more than any other man, understood the significance of the role Theodore had played in the critical fight. *Had it not been for you, Mr. President,* he wrote, *the operators would have destroyed the union. It may be many years before they nominally recognize the United Mine Workers, but the truth of the matter is that you recognized the union in your negotiations, so the operators did the same, regardless of whether they will admit that fact.*

Accepting the congratulations of the country for settling the dispute, Theodore learned a lesson he would never forget. "These wealthy industrialists," he told Cabot Lodge, "aren't snarling, dangerous tigers.

It's amazing to discover that they're nothing but pampered house cats, and not very bright ones at that."

The strain of the protracted coal strike had tired Theodore, and in November, when his leg had healed, his physicians urged him to take a holiday. His desk was piled high with work, but he took the advice, going off to Mississippi for a brief camping trip. The real but unpublicized purpose of the expedition was to hunt bear, and several members of the press, who accompanied the party, agreed not to write about the subject until the President returned to Washington.

One morning a pair of zealous guides drove a young bear cub toward the camp just as Theodore was setting out for the day's hunt. He indignantly refused to shoot the animal, and, losing his temper with the guides, blistered them for endangering the life of a helpless little cub.

Clifford K. Berryman, the political cartoonist of the Washington *Post,* who was a member of the presidential party, witnessed the incident, and was inspired to create a cartoon which he called, "Drawing the Line in Mississippi." He portrayed a stalwart Theodore, rifle butt resting on the ground and his back resolutely turned toward the guide, refusing to assault a small, weeping cub.

The cartoon was printed by hundreds of newspapers and created a national sensation, winning Theodore greater popularity than he had ever achieved. As Gifford Pinchot said, "By that one act the cause of wild animal conservation was advanced immeasurably. President Roosevelt did more in minutes than others have accomplished in decades."

The Teddy bear became America's most popular vogue. Toy manufacturers could not keep up with the demand, children romped in Teddy bear suits, and no courtship was complete until a swain presented the girl of his dreams with a Teddy bear she could perch on her vanity table or bed.

Theodore, as yet unaware of the overnight reaction to Berryman's cartoon, spent the better part of his holiday in Mississippi thinking about the coal strike and its implications. And by the time he returned to Washington he had formulated a new policy which became a fundamental tenet of his Administration.

"American business," he told Cabot Lodge, "is responsible for our national growth and prosperity. We've developed a genius for manufacturing goods of every sort and for selling them to our own people and the world. But our system is abused when a few men, standing together, gain complete control of an industry. Monopoly is evil because the natural restraints imposed by competition are removed."

Lodge, aware of the Senate's conservatism, was uneasy. "What do you intend to do about it?"

"I'm instructing the Justice Department to launch a full-scale attack on the trusts."

"You'll have a fight on your hands in Congress."

Familiar with the powers of his office after fifteen months as President and conscious of his soaring popularity with the public, Theodore could afford to laugh. "Have you ever known me to avoid a good fight?" he demanded.

In his less exuberant moods, however, he admitted that the road ahead would be rough. Senators Aldrich and Hanna would do everything in their power to prevent his attempts to curtail the increasing centralization of industrial interests, as would many members of the Democratic minority. And the press, he knew, would subject him to a constant barrage of editorial criticism.

He realized that his success or failure would depend, in the main, on the approval or disapproval of the electorate, and the fascination of the people with his private life gave him renewed hope. Newspapers reported all they could learn about the guest lists at White House breakfasts, lunches, and dinners. The clothes worn by Edith and Alice to these functions were described in detail, but Theodore protested when his wife told him that she and her stepdaughter needed new wardrobes.

"We can't afford to spend a fortune for dresses," he told her.

"I wonder if you realize," she replied, "that Alice uses only five dresses, and I have no more than eight. We describe them in new ways to the press so people think we have far more clothes than we really own."

Theodore expressed unbounded admiration for her tactics.

"But we can't keep finding new ways of saying the same old things!"

"I have unlimited confidence in your imagination and ingenuity," he told her, and refused to provide the funds for new gowns.

The new pets acquired by Ethel, Archie, and Quentin were no strangers to the public in every state and territory, but one incident that threatened the harmony of the President's relations with the House of Representatives was kept out of print. Speaker "Uncle Joe" Cannon came to the White House for breakfast to discuss the legislative program. As he was leaving, a small kitten belonging to Quentin and Archie hurled itself at him, clawed his ankle, then rubbed against his legs, depositing white hair on the black wool, and, as a final, grand gesture, darted between his legs. Cannon, just starting down a flight of stairs, remained upright by hastily grasping the bannister, and departed red-faced, followed by the giggles of the children.

Prince Henry of Germany, son of Kaiser Wilhelm, was the first member of a European royal family to pay a visit to Washington, and was treated without pomp or ceremony at the White House. *The President and Mrs. Roosevelt served him a dinner of chopped beef and baked potatoes,* the Los Angeles *Times* reported. *What's good enough for plain Americans is good enough for foreign potentates. More power to the President and his lady!*

The simple fare did not prevent other European royalty from descending on Washington in ever-growing numbers. And, at the personal request of the Kaiser, Alice christened a new yacht built for him in an American shipyard.

Meanwhile the Teddy bear craze continued to soar, and the affection of the people for the President expanded accordingly. "I'm indebted to that stupid toy," Theodore told Edith, "but I can't tolerate the name. I wish they'd call it anything but Teddy."

"It's too late to change now, dear," she replied, "and be glad they didn't make you a laughingstock by calling it a Theodore bear."

Our days as an insular, inward-looking people are ended, although most of our citizens don't yet realize it, Theodore wrote to Cecil Spring-Rice soon after assuming the presidency. *I hope I shall have the opportunity to assist in the education of the nation.*

If I know you, his friend replied undiplomatically, *you'll create a great many opportunities.*

Spring-Rice was right. Almost immediately after taking office Theodore appointed dedicated public servants to administer the affairs of Puerto Rico and the Philippine Islands, dependencies acquired from Spain. Good health and improved education were the first requirements of any people, he declared, and, obtaining increased appropriations from Congress for medical assistance and schools, he promised the colonies self-government as soon as they could stand alone.

It was in his relations with the great powers of Europe, however, that he not only gave the American people a new understanding of their country's growing role in world affairs, but, even more important, enunciated a policy that, in time, would become known as the Roosevelt Corollary to the Monroe Doctrine.

"You're a great Secretary of State," he told John Hay, "and I have no intention of telling you how to conduct your business. I suppose all that circumlocutionary language you use in dealing with foreign governments is necessary. But my principle is very simple. The Monroe Doctrine tells Europe to stay out of the Western Hemisphere, but what happens if a South American country misbehaves in its relations with a European country? We can't afford to let Europe get a foothold in our backyard, so we'll have to act as policeman for the West."

His first chance to demonstrate this policy came in 1902, when the coal strike was occupying his attention. Venezuela was lax in its settlement of financial obligations, and Great Britain and Germany, believing they had exhausted normal diplomatic methods, sent warships to collect what was due them. Theodore found this situation intolerable, and expressed himself emphatically in walks through Rock Creek Park with the British and German ambassadors.

"If your gunboats aren't withdrawn from the coast of Venezuela immediately," he told them, "I'll send Admiral Dewey down there with a fleet to drive them away. And if they're blown out of the water, don't blame us! We'll see to it that Venezuela pays her debts to you, but we can't permit you to threaten force against an American nation!"

The British took him at his word and discreetly withdrew. The Kaiser, bolder and more stubborn, refused to budge, and the President set a deadline. The Germans ignored it.

"This is a final warning," a stern Theodore said to Ambassador Speck von Sternburg as they scrambled together over boulders. "I'm telling Secretary Hay to instruct our people in Bogotá to notify us if your gunboats are still there seventy-two hours from now. If they are, Dewey will sail with the largest fleet we can muster, and I think you know I believe in keeping our Navy up to full strength!"

"What will become of our claim against Venezuela?" the unhappy Baron von Sternburg wanted to know.

"Submit to arbitration. Trust us to look after your interests, and if your claims are fair, you won't lose."

Kaiser Wilhelm capitulated, and asked Theodore to act as the arbitrator in the dispute. The United States had established a new, bold policy, and her people, proud of the country's ability to force her will on established powers, cheered their President.

Theodore utilized the same principle when, after long negotiations, he reluctantly sent American officials to administer the affairs of the debt-ridden Dominican Republic in the Caribbean. But it was his handling of an argument with Canada and Great Britain over the Alaska-Canada boundary that convinced the world the President carried a very big stick, no matter how softly he spoke.

The dispute had been simmering ever since Alaska had been purchased from Russia in 1867, but Theodore displayed no interest in the problem until, in 1902, he learned there might be gold deposits in the disputed territory. Then, to the dismay of Secretary Hay, who had worked long and hard to maintain cordial relations with other English-speaking nations, he ordered the War Department to send troops to the region. Aware of the furor that publicity might cause, Theodore directed Secretary Root to transfer the regiments "as quietly and unostentatiously as possible, so as to be able promptly to prevent any possible disturbance." Neither Hay nor Root was told the identity of the persons or groups who might cause such a disturbance.

The Canadian Prime Minister, Sir Wilfrid Laurier, knew his country was no match for the neighboring giant suddenly flexing its muscles, and suggested arbitration.

Theodore accepted, even though the Senate showed no enthusiasm for the idea, but privately maintained his own concept of reaching a fair decision. The Canadian claim, he told Secretary Hay, "is an outrage, pure and simple. To pay them anything would be dangerously near blackmail."

Three American commissioners and three representing Canada and Great Britain met in London to fix the line of demarcation, and Theodore prepared for the worst. If a decision should be made that was detrimental to American interests, he told Root, he would break off negotiations and "run the boundary as we deem it should be run."

The Secretary of War found the directive ambiguous, and asked for a clarification. Theodore obliged. "If they play fast and loose with us," he declared, "we will station troops along the boundary of the territory we rightfully claim."

In October 1903 the commission awarded the disputed territory to the United States, and as a sop to British and Canadian feelings, the losers were given two small, uninhabited islands in the Pacific, off the coast of British Columbia. Theodore was pleased, and issued a public statement in which he said that the work of the arbitration commission "offers signal proof of the fairness and good will with which two friendly nations can approach and determine issues."

But this victory, like those in the Dominican Republic and the Venezuelan affair, which the world already called "Roosevelt's big stick diplomacy," were relatively minor triumphs. For years Theodore had believed that a canal linking the Atlantic and Pacific, built somewhere in Central America, was necessary for American security and economic development. And his elevation to the presidency gave him the opportunity to translate his conviction into action. The Cabinet, under Secretary Hay's direction, began an intensive study of the question only two weeks after Theodore took office.

For centuries dreamers had concentrated on one site for a proposed canal, the Isthmus of Panama, where the two oceans were separated by a neck of land only 40¼ miles wide. Great Britain, the world's foremost maritime nation, long had shared the interest of the United States in the construction of such a canal, and in 1850, more than a half-century before Theodore had become President, the two countries had signed the Clayton-Bulwer Treaty, which had provided for the joint building and management of an unfortified canal, open to all nations for peaceful commercial purposes.

The Americans and British did nothing concrete, however, and France was the first nation to take positive action. In 1879 a company was formed for the purpose of building a canal, and Vicomte Ferdinand de Lesseps, the genius who had constructed the Suez Canal, became its head. Investors, most of them French, bought $40,000,000 worth of stock in the enterprise, and prospects were bright.

But De Lesseps, after nine years of hard labor, was forced to admit defeat. He could not conquer the heat and deep tropical jungles of Panama; the swift-flowing rivers, rugged mountains and venomous snakes and insects of the region proved his undoing. Above all, the curse of yellow fever, its cause unknown, hovered over the Isthmus, and the ranks of surveyors and engineers were decimated. De Lesseps abandoned the struggle in 1888, and early the following year the company went bankrupt, leaving the investors holding $40,000,000 in worthless stock.

Interest in an Atlantic-Pacific canal languished until 1898, when, in the Spanish-American War, the U.S.S. *Oregon* was compelled to make the long journey around South America from the Pacific in order to reinforce the American fleet off the coast of Cuba. American demands for a canal were revived, and in 1900 the United States and Great Britain signed a new agreement, the first Hay-Pauncefote Treaty, which provided that the Americans would build and administer a canal, but

out an agreement, and initiated a personal correspondence with President José Manuel Marroquín, the Colombian dictator. The haughty Marroquín immediately demanded an indemnity of $20,000,000 and annual payments, in perpetuity, of $1,000,000 per year.

"The demands are outrageous," Theodore remarked to Hay, "but we'll whittle them down. In the end we'll get our way. I think the Colombians would change their constitution if we offered enough."

The situation became complicated overnight by the intervention of various Colombian political factions, each of which wanted a hand in the United States' purse, and soon Bogotá appeared at odds with its own legation in Washington. José Vicente Concha, the Colombian minister, cited one set of demands to Secretary Hay. President Marroquín made others in his letters to Theodore, while members of the Colombian Senate indicated in correspondence with Bunau-Varilla that discreet payments into their private bank accounts would reduce the over-all cost to the United States.

The confusion was at its worst at the time the coal strike was moving toward its climax, and Theodore was short-tempered when the French engineer-adventurer paid a private visit to Blair House, entering by a rear door. The President indicated he had neither the time nor the inclination to chat.

"I'm tired of Colombian haggling," he said, "and I'm tempted to send the fleet down there to teach Marroquín he can't mock the integrity of this country!"

Bunau-Varilla knew there would be an uproar in the major capitals of Europe if the United States resorted to naked force, and assumed the President realized it, too. But he had no way of guessing whether Theodore was bluffing. "There are many ways to cook a stew, Mr. President," he said.

Theodore, always amused by his heavy accent, bared his teeth. "You're something of a chef, Philippe. What do you suggest?"

"I am an expert chef."

"Well, I'm willing to sample your stew."

"First, Mr. President, the Colombians should be given a single, final offer."

"If we could, that's what we'd do. But Secretary Hay can't pin down the legation, and Marroquín is as slippery as an eel on an oily river bed."

"Perhaps I could submit an offer on your behalf—unofficially, of course. Then I wouldn't be interfering in your direct negotiations."

Theodore thought for a moment. "There's nothing to lose, I suppose."

"What do you consider a fair payment, sir?"

"An indemnity of no more than ten million, and an annual payment of two hundred and fifty thousand," Theodore replied promptly.

"I shall send President Marroquín a telegram," Bunau-Varilla replied, "and with your permission I shall cut your figures slightly. A few hundred thousand here, a bit less there will look more authentic."

"As you please, but I've learned that money alone won't produce results. Something else is needed." Theodore looked and sounded grim.

"Your State Department, Mr. President, might suggest to the government of Colombia that you will be forced to terminate your negotiations with them and deal instead with Nicaragua."

"Secretary Hay is prepared to use that threat," Theodore said impatiently. "But I don't know whether it would be effective. The Colombians know you're involved in all this, and that your New Panama Canal Company won't get a penny of the forty millions that we'll be paying you if things work out."

"There is another threat you hold, sir. The people of Panama will benefit from a treaty with the United States. They will grow prosperous if you build your canal there. And they will be unhappy, violently unhappy, if the Colombian government refuses to make a treaty with you. I might even say they would secede from Colombia."

Theodore stared at him, wondering if he realized he was spouting arrant nonsense. "Are you speaking of the Indians in the Isthmus of Panama, Philippe?"

"The Indians, of course. But the thousands of other Panamanians as well."

"They're Colombians."

"They are Colombian subjects, Mr. President, but not Colombians."

Theodore was on the verge of contradicting him. If Bunau-Varilla knew his history, he would realize that Panama had been settled by adventurers from Spain, South America, and, in fact, men from a dozen or more nations who had been stranded there while attempting to cross the Isthmus. But something in the Frenchman's expression made him pause.

"The Panamanians are patriots, Mr. President."

Theodore was silent for a long time. "I see," he said at last.

"Should it be necessary, I may go there myself to—learn more about these patriots."

The tension mounted swiftly. "What makes you think," Theodore asked, phrasing his question with care, "that the Panamanians may revolt?"

"The leaders of several groups in Colón and Panama City have expressed their feelings to my associates."

Although the reply was vague, Theodore did not press for more specific details.

"I know the situation is explosive," Bunau-Varilla said, "and will become much more intense if President Marroquín refuses to make a treaty with the United States."

Again there was a protracted silence, and Theodore looked out of the window at the workmen repairing the White House. "I trust," he said, trying in vain to speak casually, "that you'll keep me informed of any developments that may be significant."

"Of course, Mr. President."

"There may be some details, Philippe, that neither the State Department nor I will want to know." There was an edge of anxiety in Theodore's voice.

Bunau-Varilla smiled reassuringly. "You may trust me to be discreet, sir. After all, the interests of the United States and of my company are identical."

Secretary John Hay worked so assiduously to obtain a favorable treaty that Concha, the Colombian minister to Washington, protested in writing. The United States, he declared, was denying the very sovereignty of his country. But Hay remained adamant, refusing to modify the American claims, and the weary, disgusted Concha resigned his post in November 1902. His place was taken by Dr. Tomas Herrán, a self-styled realist, who proved far more amenable, and rapid progress was made in fashioning an agreement.

President Marroquín, whose unstable government was threatened by opposition to the pending treaty by his political opponents and some members of his own regime, was caught in a dilemma from which there seemed to be no escape. Complaining bitterly to Arthur M. Beaupré, the American minister to Colombia, he declared, "History will say either that I ruined the Isthmus and all Colombia by not permitting the opening of the Panama Canal, or that I permitted it to be done, scandalously and grievously injuring the rights of my country."

Theodore's resolve did not weaken. "Accept no terms," he instructed

Hay, "except those which will insure the interests of the United States for all time."

Marroquín, threatened on the outside by the United States and internally by a possible revolution if he gave in, became panicky. "I find myself in a horrible perplexity," he said. "In order that the North Americans may complete the work by virtue of a convention with Colombia, it is necessary to make concessions of territory, of sovereignty and of jurisdiction which the Executive Branch has not the power of yielding. But, if we do not yield them, we will lose more sovereignty than we should lose by making the concessions they seek."

"Tell the Colombians," Theodore said to Hay, "that our patience isn't inexhaustible. They must either complete the treaty at once or accept the consequences. Tell them we'll start dealing with the Nicaraguans, and that we'll do anything else we believe necessary to protect ourselves."

Early in 1903 the United States obtained the terms it considered appropriate from the Colombian minister, and on January 22 the Hay-Herrán Treaty was signed. It provided for the payment by the United States of $40,000,000 to the New Panama Canal Company, $10,000,000 and an annual subsidy of $250,000 to Colombia. In return the United States was granted control, in perpetuity, of a zone five kilometers wide across the Isthmus of Panama. Nominally, Colombia retained sovereignty over the zone, but one clause in the agreement established United States courts there, and granted them legal jurisdiction.

Another clause not only compromised Colombia, but insulted her government and people. She was specifically forbidden to make any claim on the New Panama Canal Company for a portion of the $40,-000,000 the French stockholders were being paid. Many Colombian officials who had shown a reluctant willingness to accept a treaty because they hoped to obtain some part of the sum being paid to the Company bitterly assailed the clause, arguing that the United States had no right to dictate such terms to a sovereign people.

On January 25, three days after Dr. Herrán had signed the treaty, he received instructions from Bogotá telling him to forward the document unsigned. The embarrassed minister, who believed he had obtained the best possible arrangement in hard bargaining, made no attempt to withdraw, however.

President Marroquín refused to associate himself with the treaty in any way, and forwarded it to the Colombian Senate without comment of any kind.

The fate of the agreement was made clear by Beaupré in a confidential letter to Secretary Hay, written in Bogotá on April 15: *The Colombian press displays bitter hostility toward what it represents as the attempt of a stronger nation to take advantage of Colombia and rob her of one of the most valuable sources of wealth which the world contains. If the proposed convention were to be submitted to the free opinion of the Colombian people it would not pass.*

"Tell Beaupré," Theodore ordered Hay, "that the United States will consider any modification whatever of the terms of the treaty as practically a breach of faith on the part of the government of Colombia."

The issue simmered all through the spring and early summer of 1903. Marroquín used delaying tactics and did nothing; the Colombian Senate, rather than be forced to vote on the treaty, remained in adjournment.

Theodore was losing his patience and temper. "Make it as strong as you can to Beaupré," he told Secretary Hay in mid-July, "that those contemptible little creatures in Bogotá ought to understand how much they are jeopardizing things and imperiling their own future."

Bunau-Varilla privately reported to the White House that the political fever in Panama was rising, and that a revolution there was a distinct possibility if Colombia rejected the treaty. Within a few days stories appeared in many newspapers throughout the United States, indicating that a revolt might be imminent. Correspondents assigned to the White House asked the President to comment on the matter.

"Since I am not a Colombian nor a resident of the Isthmus of Panama," he said, "I cannot judge the feelings of the people in that part of the world. I can only repeat what I have said many times in the past. I hope Colombia signs the treaty in the immediate future. It is good for her as well as for the United States and the rest of the world."

On August 12, unable to procrastinate any longer, the Colombian Senate rejected the treaty, and in a move that was legally unnecessary but nevertheless demonstrated the solidarity of all political factions in the country, the lower chamber of the national legislature concurred.

Theodore's self-control vanished. "We may have to give a lesson to those jack-rabbits," he told the Cabinet. "They're entitled to precisely the amount of sympathy we extend to other inefficient bandits."

The collapse, he was convinced, was due to the desire of Colombian politicians to obtain the sum the United States expected to pay the stockholders of the New Panama Canal Company. In a memorandum to Secretary Hay, sent in late August, he wrote, *They are mad to get hold of the $40,000,000 of the Frenchmen, and they want to make us a party to the gouge.*

His observations were seemingly substantiated by a report from Bogotá, widely circulated by the press, that Colombia had tried, in vain, to deal directly with the New Panama Canal Company. Cromwell and Bunau-Varilla said they knew nothing of any such offer, but deplored the thinking of some American officials who believed the United States should open negotiations with Nicaragua.

They also urged Theodore not to abandon the plan to build a canal across the Isthmus of Panama, and Cromwell wrote to him, *Your virile and masterful policy will prove the solution of this great problem.*

At some time in October Bunau-Varilla disappeared from Washington. No one knew when he had departed or where he had gone, but it was freely rumored that he had sailed to the Isthmus in order to learn at first hand what the people there thought and felt.

Suggestions were made to the President by members of the Congress and others that the United States should actively support a revolution of Panamanians, or, at the very least, the President should issue a firm statement insisting that Panama would be the site of the canal. Theodore refused to consider either approach. On October 10 he learned that the influential magazine, *Review of Reviews,* was planning to publish an editorial stating that a revolution was the only sensible solution.

William Loeb made several telephone calls, and after he learned that the editorial would be strong, Theodore immediately wrote a confidential letter to Albert Shaw, the magazine's editor. *I cast aside the proposition made at this time to foment the secession of Panama,* he said. *Whatever other governments can do, the United States cannot go into securing, by such underhand means, the secession. Privately, I freely say to you that I should be delighted if Panama were an independent State, or if it made itself so at this moment; but for me to say so publicly would amount to an instigation of a revolt, and therefore I cannot say it.*

A few days later two deeply sun-tanned young men, both lean, were admitted to the White House by a private entrance. Loeb was waiting for them there, and took them at once to the private office of the President, who was in conference elsewhere. They were told to wait, and sat down, but before they could exchange more than a word or two, Theodore bustled into the room.

Both of the young men leaped to their feet and stood at attention. "Captain Thomas B. Humphrey, sir!" the taller said.

"Lieutenant Grayson Murphy, Mr. President!" the other declared.

Theodore shook their hands and invited them to sit. "Secretary Root tells me you're officers in the Regular Army who have been on leave of absence for some time."

"Since March, sir," Humphrey said.

"I take it you've been seeing the world." Theodore appeared genial and relaxed.

"One small part of it, sir," Murphy replied. "We traveled extensively in Colombia and Venezuela, we toured through the Caribbean, and lately we've spent most of our time in the Isthmus of Panama."

Theodore, still nodding pleasantly, muttered something unintelligible.

Captain Humphrey, who had been in awe of the President, felt less tense. "You might say we've been taking postgraduate courses in geography and politics, sir."

Theodore stiffened. "I assume your travels were made on your own initiative and at your own expense?"

The young officers glanced at each other uncertainly, but Humphrey was quick to understand. "Certainly, Mr. President!"

"Good. Conditions down there aren't too stable these days, and some people might jump to false conclusions. I assume you wore only civilian clothes."

"Yes, sir," Murphy said. "We were ordered to leave our uniforms at home."

Theodore's eyes became cold. "Orders, Lieutenant? You were enjoying a leave of absence!"

"I—ah—was confused for a minute, Mr. President," the abashed Murphy said.

Humphrey found it somewhat easier to balance on the unexpected tightrope. "We drew some maps, Mr. President. Purely for our own amusement. Because of our professional interest in these matters, we made notes on the location of Colombian military garrisons, and we've indicated on the maps where our Navy might be able to land Army units and Marines. Secretary Root thought you'd like to see them."

"As a historian, I'm curious. And I'm always relieved when there's a diversion these days," Theodore said casually.

Humphrey opened a satchel and took out a sheaf of maps, charts, and sketches.

Theodore studied them intently, and was obviously impressed. "These are excellent. I hadn't expected—that is to say, I'm surprised at the thoroughness of your detail work."

"The crosses enclosed in circles are potential sites for our artillery emplacements, sir," Lieutenant Murphy said.

"I'm capable of reading a military map, young man." Theodore sounded annoyed.

Again the officers exchanged glances, and, not knowing how to proceed, remained silent.

"Bogotá is located so far inland that I'd call it virtually impregnable, except in a long campaign. It certainly wouldn't be easy to march several divisions and their supporting troops across that rugged terrain."

"In our opinion, sir," Humphrey replied, finding it safe to take refuge in a technical military discussion, "an attack on Bogotá wouldn't be necessary if the purpose of a campaign was that of taking and holding the Isthmus of Panama."

"I know of no nation that would want to engage in either type of campaign," Theodore said.

"I was speaking theoretically, Mr. President," Humphrey said.

"To be sure, Captain. You're showing these maps to the War Department planning staff, no doubt. They're always interested in theoretical exercises, too."

Both officers assured him that the maps would be made available to the War Department, and Lieutenant Murphy added, "If some country wanted to seize the Isthmus, no attack on Colombia itself would be necessary, sir."

Theodore looked up from the map and peered at him. "Why is that?"

"The jungles in the southern part of the province of Panama and the northern section of Colombia proper are impenetrable, sir. No troops could march through them."

"So I've been told," Theodore said, "but I don't trust hearsay evidence."

Captain Humphrey laughed wryly. "We spent several weeks in those jungles, Mr. President, and it's a miracle we're still alive. The heat is unbearable, the terrain is impassable, even for light infantry, and it would take engineers months to cut a road. Civilized men always come down with yellow fever there, and I've never seen so many poisonous snakes and insects, not to mention savage Indians who are head-hunters and cannibals. An American infantry regiment couldn't survive for a week in those jungles. I'm just using a theoretical example, sir."

"And the Colombians couldn't persuade one of their regiments to go into the jungles," Lieutenant Murphy added. "Their troops are poorly disciplined, and they'd rebel. That's a flat prediction, sir, and I'm willing to stake my future in the Army on it."

Theodore made another attempt to sound jovial. "Well. You've had some fascinating experiences, gentlemen. I've often wanted to visit Panama."

"You wouldn't want to go there right now, Mr. President," Captain Humphrey said. "There's a nasty insurrection brewing."

"Really?" Theodore raised a bushy eyebrow.

"A revolt will break out at any time, sir. The people of Panama desperately want our canal, and will do anything, take any risks and use any violence that's necessary in order to get it."

Theodore's face became impassive. "You've spoken to some Panamanians?"

"Scores of them, Mr. President, including most of the leaders," Captain Humphrey said. "We lived with them—"

"Did they know your identity?" Theodore interrupted.

"No, sir. We let it out, you might say, that we represented some New York financial interests who want to open new hotels in Colón and Panama City if a canal is built."

"They gave us a very warm reception," Murphy added, and stifled a broad smile.

"The success or failure of a revolution will depend on the response of the Colombian forces in Panama," Theodore said. "How resolute is the Governor?"

"We've met Governor de Obaldia many times, sir," Humphrey said. "In fact, he's been a house guest of one of the more prominent Panamanian patriots, Dr. Manuel Amador."

Theodore knew that Dr. Amador was the physician on the staff of the Panama Railroad & Steamship Company, a subsidiary of the New Panama Canal Company, and both Bunau-Varilla and Cromwell frequently mentioned his name. But the President could not reveal the extent of knowledge to junior Army officers. "Doesn't Governor Obaldia have his own palace?"

"Well, sir," Humphrey said, "the official story the Panama *Star and Herald* printed claimed that the palace was being repaired, but we didn't see a single workman anywhere near the place the whole time we were in Panama City."

"Everybody is being very coy," Murphy said, "but we got the definite feeling that Governor Obaldia sympathizes with the Panamanian patriots and won't lift a finger against them if there's an insurrection."

"That's an unusual attitude. Do you know what caused it?"

"I'd say it's the usual, Mr. President," Murphy replied. "The Governor isn't a wealthy man, and he supports his wife and children on a small salary. An enterprising politician in Bogotá can find a way to dip into any funds that are being passed around, but a provincial governor doesn't get too many opportunities."

"If our assessment of Governor Obaldia's character is correct, sir," Humphrey said, "Amador and the others have promised to pay him off, and he's made a deal with them. Maybe they've already paid him something. Nobody, including Dr. Amador, was willing to discuss the subject with us, and we couldn't pry too hard."

"So much for the civilian authority." Theodore couldn't curb a quick smile, but sobered again. "That puts the issue squarely up to the Colombian garrisons in Panama."

Humphrey took a sheaf of notes from the satchel. "Would you care to read these, Mr. President?"

Theodore shook his head. "It wouldn't be appropriate, but Secretary Root might want to see them."

"He does, sir."

"Good. Can you give me a summary?"

"There are eight hundred troops, most of them infantrymen, stationed in the Panama City forts overlooking the Pacific, sir, and approximately four hundred at Colón on the Atlantic side. By our definition they're not good soldiers. Their discipline is a joke, and we've shuddered when we've seen them on parade."

Theodore shook his head. "Don't underestimate them. They're armed, and they'd be fighting Panamanian civilians who have had no military training at all."

"I'd bet on the people of Panama, Mr. President," Lieutenant

Murphy said. "In fact, if I had any money to invest, they'd get it. They have a reason to fight, but the Colombian troops have none. Most of them are illiterate men who were conscripted, and they've been stationed in Panama a long time. Too long. That heat eventually rots you, and eats away all your energy."

Theodore was not ready to drop the matter. "Will they obey orders?"

"To the best of their ability, Mr. President," Captain Humphrey said thoughtfully, "I believe they will. That means the key man is the Colombian commander in Panama. He's a General named Huertas, and we've seen him evening after evening in the saloons on both sides of the Isthmus, drinking with Gabriel Duque, who owns the *Star and Herald*. We know that Duque is a Panamanian patriot who is very close to Dr. Amador."

"That doesn't necessarily mean General Huertas sympathizes with them."

"Forgive me for correcting you, sir," Humphrey said, "but in that part of the world it does. Two colonels who didn't like the General's friendship with Duque and criticized him openly for it were transferred to little jungle outposts where they can do no harm. Duque was very careful when we talked to him, but he didn't seem in the least worried about the General."

"We've also talked with Colonel Shaler, the American who is superintendent of the Panama Railroad," Murphy declared.

"I've heard of him," Theodore said.

"He was very frank, and believes that Huertas will not only hold his troops in their barracks when the revolt breaks out, but will take command of the Panama irregulars."

Theodore roared with laughter, removed his glasses and wiped tears from his eyes. "Unbelievable! The more I hear, the more it sounds like fiction!"

"Every word is the truth, Mr. President." Humphrey sounded hurt.

"I beg your pardon, Captain. I'm not denying the validity of your observations. But I can't help wondering whether there are any honorable men down there."

"A great many, sir," Humphrey replied, "and that's one of the Panamanians' two great weaknesses. President Marroquín and his people are devoted Colombians, and they're worried. There's been so much rumored and printed about a revolution that the Colombian authorities know they're sitting on the edge of a volcano ready to erupt. Marroquín is a very able man, and one of these days, soon, he's going to reinforce the garrisons in Panama with fresh troops."

"How many of them?" Theodore demanded.

Both of the officers shrugged. "If he's smart, and he is," Murphy said, "he'll send some of his best regiments."

"How will he get them into Panama?"

"By sea, Mr. President." Humphrey leaned forward in his chair and spoke earnestly. "The second—and greater—weakness of the Panama conspirators is their lack of a navy. They don't have a single ship, and wouldn't know how to sail a battleship—or even a gunboat—if someone presented one to them as a gift."

"I can't imagine who'd do anything that stupid," Theodore murmured.

"A division or two of Colombian troops could put down an insurrection with ease, sir," Humphrey continued. "And although the whole Colombian navy couldn't put up much of a fight against a single small American or British squadron, it does have the strength to seal off both ends of the Isthmus. If Marroquín's gunboats blockade Colón and Panama City while his new regiments engage the rebels, the revolution will collapse."

Theodore was silent for a moment, then abruptly rose to his feet. "This has been a pleasant and instructive interlude for me, gentlemen," he said as the officers quickly stood. "I'm grateful to you for the distraction." He shook hands with them and escorted them to the door. "One final word. Under no circumstances will you reveal to anyone except Secretary Root that you've been here, seen me, or discussed affairs in Colombia and Panama."

"Yes, sir," they replied simultaneously, both aware they had received an order from the Commander-in-Chief.

When the door closed behind them Theodore paced the length of his office for a quarter of an hour, then rang for Loeb. "Bill," he said, "notify the Cabinet there will be a meeting at two o'clock this afternoon."

Loeb glanced at his watch. "I'm not sure I can round them all up that soon, Mr. President."

"I want every last member here." Theodore became waspish. "I know they're in the habit of enjoying long lunches, but this is one day they'll have to endure a little inconvenience."

as their President within a few days, and who was already acting as the new nation's Chief Executive, made a long, emotional speech. Significant portions of it were duly reported by newspaper correspondents from the United States, who had hurried to Panama when rumors of an impending revolution had reached their height.

"The world is astounded at our heroism!" Dr. Amador declared, tears rolling down his face. "Yesterday we were but the slaves of Colombia. Today we are free. President Roosevelt has made good! Free sons of Panama, I salute you. Long live the Republic of Panama! Long live President Roosevelt! Long live the American Government!"

In Washington, the White House and State Department refused to comment on the developments. It became known, however, that on the morning of November 5, Secretary Hay, acting on instructions from the President, sent a telegram to the United States consul at Panama City, directing him to recognize Dr. Amador's government. An official of the British Foreign Office in London, refusing to be quoted by name, professed to be shocked by what he termed the "indecent haste of the Americans."

Philippe Bunau-Varilla closed his suite at the Waldorf-Astoria and, accompanied by his wife, traveled to Washington in a private railroad car attached to a regularly scheduled train. To the surprise of no one and the amusement of cynics in the press corps, he announced that President-designate Amador had appointed him as Panama's first minister to the United States. The United States accepted his credentials on November 10. Colombia protested vehemently but in vain.

On November 17 Secretary Hay and Bunau-Varilla signed a treaty granting the United States a zone across the Isthmus of Panama for the purpose of building and operating an interocean canal. The terms of the agreement were precisely the same, in all details, as those contained in the treaty that Colombia had rejected.

Theodore preferred to say nothing, but the pressure on the White House was so great that he finally agreed when Colombia frantically and belatedly offered to sign the treaty by executive decree. "In their silly efforts to damage us they cut their own throats," he said. "They tried to hold us up, and too late they have discovered their criminal error."

Questioned about the recognition of the new Republic of Panama by the United States, he replied, "Nothing could be more wicked than to ask us to surrender the Panama people, who are our friends, to the Colombian people, who have shown themselves our foes."

I don't think that any family has ever enjoyed the White House more than we have, Theodore wrote to Kermit, who had gone off to school with Ted at Groton.

In all probability the President was right. Guests continued to move in and out of the Executive Mansion in a never-ending stream, "Princess" Alice was the most popular young lady in Washington society, and the younger children, their friends and pets could be found almost anywhere at any time. The energy of the children, like that of their father, was boundless.

The year 1904 was a presidential election year, and some of Theodore's friends were worried, believing that some of Alice's escapades, like the highly publicized incident in which she set an automobile speed record between Boston and Newport, Rhode Island, might be harmful to him. Author Owen Wister finally summoned the courage to raise the subject during a private White House chat, and asked, "Mr. President, isn't there anything you can do to control Alice?"

Theodore laughed. "I can do one of two things," he said. "I can be President of the United States or I can control Alice. I cannot possibly do both."

The New York *Herald* marveled at the President's self-control. *It is unlikely that any President has ever worked as hard as does Mr. Roosevelt. It is also unlikely that any other President has ever relaxed as graciously or enjoyed himself more fully.*

Theodore appointed a commission to organize the building of the Panama Canal, and establish the Zone under the jurisdiction of the United States. He also displayed a keen interest in yellow fever, which had forced De Lesseps to abandon his plan to build a canal, and held meetings with medical authorities who held various, often contradictory opinions on the best methods of curbing and eradicating the disease. Simultaneously, not satisfied with his personal program of keeping himself physically fit, he began taking lessons in judo.

To the alarm of the Standard Oil Company, which was afraid it would be prosecuted on anti-trust charges, Theodore established a new Executive Department, that of Commerce and Labor. With the help of Senator Lodge and other friends he persuaded Congress to approve, privately indicating to a few friends that he had no intention of moving against Standard Oil until he won both the Republican nomination and the election. He went on another brief hunting trip, taking advantage of his presence in the West to make several "non-political" speeches, and, while traveling on his private train, designed a new sailboat that he ordered built for the children's use at Oyster Bay the following summer.

The forthcoming election loomed larger in his thinking, and he was afraid he might not win the nomination. The party regulars did not trust him, he told Lodge and William Howard Taft, who became Secretary of War in February 1904 when Root temporarily retired from the government. Therefore, he said, the probable candidate would be Mark Hanna. The fear nagged at him, but Hanna became ill, and no one was more shocked than Theodore when he died in mid-February. Thereafter the President's opponents in the party quietly conceded his nomination.

Members of the diplomatic corps continued to hike through Rock Creek Park with Theodore, no matter what the weather, and French Ambassador Jules Jusserand felt the time had come to register a protest. He enjoyed walking, he told his colleagues, but tramps through ice and snow in raw weather were too much. His opportunity came one blustery winter afternoon.

The presidential party plowed across Rock Creek Park, with Theodore, in knickers and boots, in the lead. A cold wind stung the faces of the diplomats and aides, but Theodore, as usual, seemed impervious to the elements. Jusserand, bringing up the rear, was the most uncomfortable member of the group, having responded to the White House invitation in formal afternoon attire.

At last the party reached the Creek, which was swollen, its current rapid, and the French Ambassador breathed a silent sigh of relief. Now, he thought, the President would turn back, and the day's ordeal would be ended. But, to his horror, he saw Theodore strip off his hunting jacket and start to unbutton his shirt.

The other members of the party exchanged uneasy glances.

"We'd better strip," the President said. "Otherwise we'll wet our clothes in the Creek."

There was no choice, and the rest of the party, miserable and shivering, hurriedly undressed.

Theodore paused at the bank to make sure the others were ready, and was startled when he saw that Jusserand was as naked as the rest except for a pair of lavender kid gloves. "What's this, Jules?" His voice echoed through the deserted woods.

"With your permission, Mr. President," the Ambassador said, "I will keep these on. Otherwise it would be embarrassing if we should meet ladies." Not waiting for a reply, he jumped into the icy water and began to swim toward the far bank.

Theodore thought the incident was riotously amusing, and, if he understood the diplomatic rebuke, chose to ignore it. The President and the unfortunates he asked to accompany him continued to take brisk constitutionals.

The Roosevelt children displayed a genius almost as great as their father's for making news the American public was eager to read. Ethel and a classmate, riding home from public school on a trolley car, pressed their faces against the window and made faces at a gentlemen riding in a carriage. Other passengers noticed that the top-hatted man in the carriage was responding in kind, and a member of the Chicago *Tribune* staff recognized him as the President.

Archie and several friends, among them a son of Secretary Taft, were caught one afternoon while throwing spitballs at a portrait of Andrew Jackson in a White House gallery. Archie was spanked by his father, which normally would have been the end of a domestic incident, but the matter became public knowledge when Theodore wrote notes in his own hand to the parents of the other culprits, urging that similar punishment be inflicted on them.

John L. Sullivan, the heavyweight boxing champion of the world, spent the better part of an afternoon at the White House, but neither he nor the President would disclose whether they had retired to the gymnasium for a friendly bout. Theodore confined himself to a single comment: "John L. is the finest who ever wore mitts."

Cecil Spring-Rice called the work of poet Edward Arlington Robinson to Theodore's attention, and soon thereafter Robinson received an invitation to the White House, where presidential praise was lavished on him. When Theodore learned that Robinson was living in genteel but almost desperate poverty, he quietly obtained a minor Treasury Department post in New York for the poet, enabling him to continue his creative work.

Archie was sent to bed with the measles, and was disconsolate because his friends were not allowed to visit him. Quentin thought the sight of his calico pony might cheer him, and, with the help of a stable boy, managed to wedge the animal into an elevator for a ride to his brother's bedroom. Unfortunately for the boys, the commotion they caused disrupted a formal presidential reception for the Justices of the Supreme Court. Photographs of Archie, Quentin, and the pony appeared in virtually every newspaper in the country.

James R. Garfield, son of the assassinated President, was appointed by Theodore as Commissioner of the Bureau of Corporations in the new Department of Commerce and Labor. Garfield had already acquired a reputation as an ardent reformer, and Wall Street was afraid the Administration would step up the pace of its anti-trust campaign. But Garfield, under orders to offend no one before the presidential election, did nothing. The financial community breathed a collective sigh of relief, and J. P. Morgan, invited to the White House for lunch, offered Theodore a campaign contribution.

Henry C. Payne, the newly appointed Postmaster General, discovered corruption in his Department, and immediately called it to the attention of the President. "I suppose," he said, "you'll want me to tread lightly until the election is out of the way."

"You'll make every effort to expose fraud, Henry," Theodore replied, "and you'll bring charges against every man who is guilty of wrongdoing, no matter who he is or how high his seat in the government. I may have to mark time politically in an election year and let some of my programs wait, but I can't and won't place my own good name as a reformer in jeopardy. I'd rather lose the election."

In the months that followed twenty-nine separate cases of fraud were uncovered, and among the officials indicted was Perry S. Heath, secretary of the Republican National Committee. Theodore stole the ammunition of the Democrats by announcing each indictment himself and solemnly promising that every case would be prosecuted with vigor.

The death of Mark Hanna made it necessary to find a new chairman for the Republican National Committee, and prominent Republican senators, led by Nelson Aldrich, called at the White House to urge the election of a New York banker whose colleagues and friends would, thereafter, be generous in their contributions to the party's election fund. Theodore listened, nodded and occasionally bared his teeth in an amiable grin.

Aldrich, who was beginning to understand him, felt that he was quietly balking, and obtained the support of Speaker Cannon and Senator Lodge. "They're the only men whose advice he takes," Aldrich said. "He listens to Joe Cannon because the House will rebel if he doesn't, and I guess he listens to Cabot because he wants to. Anyway, I think they can whip him into line."

Again Theodore listened, grinned and tugged at his mustache. Then, heeding no counsel except his own, he dictated to the National Committee the election of his own personal candidate, George B. Cortelyou, his Secretary of Commerce and Labor, and an ardent advocate of reform in government, conservation of natural resources and other liberal causes. Wall Street and the Old Guard of the Republican party were equally disappointed, and the New York *Times* suggested in a scathing editorial that Cortelyou would not inspire wealthy Republicans to open their purses.

The Old Guard, Wall Street, and the *Times* were mistaken. Cortelyou threw himself into his new work with ferocious enthusiasm, set up new Republican organizations in Democratic strongholds, and soon won both the respect and confidence of business leaders throughout the nation.

Everyone in Washington, Theodore included, waited anxiously in the early months of 1904 for the Supreme Court to render its verdict in the Northern Securities case, which had started on its long legal journey to the highest tribunal almost two years earlier. And excitement ran high on the morning of March 14 when a clerk on the staff of an Associate Justice leaked the news that the verdict would be announced that day.

Shortly before noon the Court announced that, by a five to four vote, it upheld the action of the government. The huge railroad trust was ordered dissolved.

Justice John Marshall Harlan wrote the majority opinion. Dismissing the claim of counsel for the National Securities Company that the directive to dissolve it was a violation of state sovereignty, Marshall said such a contention would "mean nothing less than that Congress, in regulating interstate commerce, must act in subordination to the will of the states when exerting their power to create corporations. This view cannot be entertained."

Justice Oliver Wendell Holmes delivered the minority opinion. The tremendous size of the railroad trust, he declared, was an inevitable incident in the development of American railroads, and was not a legitimate reason to compel the combine to be dissolved.

Justice Department officials and liberal members of Congress hurried to the White House to offer the President their congratulations. With one giant smashed, the trust-busting campaign could proceed as the government saw fit, and the evils of monopoly in every major industry soon would be halted.

Presidential Secretary William Loeb thanked the callers and promised to deliver their messages. But, he informed them, President
Roosevelt, who was deeply gratified by the verdict, was unable to receive visitors at present.

Had the callers looked out of the windows they might have seen
a thin-lipped Theodore being driven out of the White House grounds
through the rear gate. Thirty minutes later a breathless messenger
searched Capitol Hill for Senator Lodge, and an hour passed before
Lodge was located and was told that the President awaited him at
his house.

Lodge hurried home and found Theodore pacing up and down his
small, book-lined study. "If I'd known you wanted to see me—"

"You," Theodore roared, pointing a finger at him, "are directly responsible for that man's appointment!"

Lodge hastily closed the door.

"Don't deny it, Cabot!"

The Senator from Massachusetts was not cowed. "I can neither
affirm nor deny a charge until you make your accusation in plain
English."

His haughtiness took the edge off Theodore's anger. "You recommended Holmes. I appointed him to the Supreme Court because you
told me he was the best judge in the country. You said he was a
humanitarian—"

"So he is." Lodge remained icily calm.

Theodore's temper soared again. "I could carve a judge with more
backbone than his out of a banana!"

Lodge chuckled, and, unable to stop himself, laughed so hard that
he wept. "Forgive me," he said at last, wiping his eyes with a neatly
folded handkerchief, "but I found the image of the President carving
a banana irresistibly amusing."

"Holmes' vote in the National Securities case was anything but
amusing."

"Ah, so that's it."

"He betrayed me!" Emotion choked Theodore and thickened his
voice.

"Nonsense."

"Of all members of the Court, I expected him to sympathize with
this Administration's efforts to limit the powers of wealthy monopolists. Instead it was Harlan, who voted in '95 in favor of the trusts,
who gave us today's victory."

"As it happens, I was having lunch with Justice Holmes when I was told you had come to see me."

"Oh, you were!" Theodore became bitterly aggressive again.

Lodge stared at him for a moment. "Sit down, Theodore!" he commanded, addressing him by name for the first time since he had assumed the presidency.

Startled, Theodore obeyed.

"We'll forget for the moment that you're the President of the United States. And I hope our friendship is strong enough to survive the observations I feel compelled to make. But say them I must. You're behaving like a spoiled, undisciplined child. You're furious because someone you admire—or at least wanted to admire—has had the temerity to disagree with you."

There was a long silence, and Theodore grew pale. Then, his color returning to normal, he said meekly, "Quite possibly you're right, Cabot."

Lodge took a chair opposite him. "I'm relieved to hear you admit it."

"On the other hand, you may be wrong. And I think you are. Holmes voted as he did out of cowardice. He enjoys the friendship of railroad millionaires like Harriman—"

"That's a disgusting accusation. Don't make it unless you can prove it!"

Theodore gnawed at his mustache.

"I don't know whether Justice Holmes and Mr. Harriman have ever met, or would even know each other by sight. And neither do you." Lodge spoke in the severe, clipped tones of a schoolmaster. "Personally, I'm inclined to doubt that they've ever become even slightly acquainted. They don't belong to the same clubs, and to the best of my knowledge they have no mutual friends."

Theodore's glasses had become fogged, and he removed them. "That was very stupid of me. I had no basis for saying it." He seemed to concentrate on polishing his glasses.

"Well, at least you said it only in front of me. It makes me ill to think of the consequences if you'd spoken like that in the hearing of newspapermen."

"I lost my temper." Theodore sounded plaintive.

"Yes, I know. And when that happens, you become reckless. A President of the United States, particularly one who hopes to be nominated and elected within the next seven and a half months, must learn to control his tongue."

"Don't lecture me, Cabot. I simply find it inconceivable that Holmes voted as he did."

"Grant him integrity, Theodore!"

"I find it difficult. I read some of his decisions on the Massachusetts bench, and I've also read a number of his opinions since I made him a Supreme Court Justice. He's always shown great sympathy for the common man—until now."

"His decision was based strictly and exclusively on his interpretation of the law," Lodge said. "He was telling me about it in detail at lunch, and I'm sure he'd be happy to explain his position to you, too. I suggest that you sit down with him at the White House, and—"

"Not yet," Theodore said. "Eventually I'll meet with him and discuss the case. But I'll have to wait until this damnable temper of mine cools, or I'll disgrace myself. Again."

"There's no harm done." Lodge sat back in his chair. "And you've cleared the air."

"Not really. Nothing will rid me of my disappointment in Holmes. He should have been an ideal man on the bench."

Lodge knew it would be useless to pursue the matter. Theodore was incapable of forgiving anyone who opposed him in what he considered a matter of principle. "Forget Justice Holmes for the present, and celebrate your victory! Shall we drink a glass of champagne?"

Theodore suddenly remembered he had eaten no lunch. "I'd prefer fruit juice," he said.

Lodge smiled and went out of the room to give the order to a servant. When he returned, he stood for a moment, shaking his head. "For a man who has won a great victory over the monopolists, over the combined financial might of the nation's most powerful banking interests, you don't appear very pleased."

"I've won a single battle, not a campaign. The rest of my work lies ahead."

Lodge drew in his breath.

"I know what you're thinking, Cabot. George Cortelyou is going to find it difficult enough to persuade wealthy Republicans to contribute to this year's campaign fund."

"Not if you observe your own motto. Walk very softly, and please don't brandish any clubs, large or small."

"You think I'm something of a bumbler, Cabot, but I have just enough horse-sense—"

"In my opinion," Lodge interrupted, "your political instinct is more highly developed than that of anyone I've ever known in public life."

"I wouldn't want to admit it to anyone else, but I'm inclined to agree." Theodore recovered his aplomb, and with it his good humor.

"However, your singleminded devotion to the causes you favor can sometimes cause you unnecessary problems. If you're as wise as I think you are, you'll do nothing and say nothing that will antagonize anyone in the Republican party between now and the time the convention opens in Chicago. That means keeping your mouth closed on every subject that may be controversial, particularly your trust-busting ideas."

"If I didn't know you so well, I might resent your feeling that you need to spell out the obvious."

"And after the convention," Lodge continued, "we'll examine the situation again."

"We won't know much until the Democrats nominate their candidate, but there are certain principles I intend to follow, no matter who he might be. I'll concentrate my campaign on the Panama Canal, free Cuba and the pacification and development of the Philippines. I'll stress our domestic prosperity. And I'll step up the pace of my demand for conservation. How does that sound?"

Lodge laced his fingers and looked up at the ceiling. "The Democrats are certain to demand lower tariffs."

"That's a subject I don't intend to touch! The Democrats want too much, but we'll undoubtedly have to lower tariffs if we're going to make any substantial gain in our international trade." Theodore held up his hand when his friend started to interrupt. "Just listen to me for a minute longer. I give you my word I'll side-step the tariff question."

"I hope you'll remember that."

"Cabot," Theodore said, hunching forward, "more than anything else on this earth, I want to be elected to a full term in my own right. I'm an accidental President. I've had to tread lightly because I wasn't the choice of the voters, and there isn't much satisfaction in knowing I slipped into the White House through a side door."

"No one the Democrats nominate will stand a chance against you."

"I want to be elected so much that I've lost my objectivity. I don't know whether you're right. I don't like dodging and ducking, but I'll do nothing to jeopardize my chances. All I want—all I'll ever want for the rest of my days—is another four years as President. And I'm going to make that principle very clear to the electorate—"

"Is that wise, Theodore? Obviously you realize that under the Constitution you could serve still another term four years from now."

"Of course I'm well aware of it, but four more years will be enough. I can accomplish all I want to do in that time."

Lodge regarded him for a moment, then smiled. "It's going to be the most hectic four years this country has ever known, I'm sure."

Senator Aldrich, Speaker Cannon and others who would have preferred another candidate for President realized they had no choice. An incumbent President was virtually impossible to dislodge without disavowing all the achievements of his Administration, and, with Mark Hanna gone, no other potential Republican candidate of stature existed. "Regardless of what we may think of TR," Aldrich said at a private caucus of party leaders, "he's dominated the country for almost four years. We're stuck with him."

The conservatives felt it only fitting, however, that a member of the Old Guard become the candidate for Vice-President. And Theodore, himself painfully aware of the Vice-President's impotence, his isolation and inability to exert any real influence in the planning or execution of legislative programs, was amenable. Congressional leaders and party chieftains held endless discussions, and finally selected Senator Charles W. Fairbanks of Indiana as the President's running-mate.

A tall, quiet man who was chairman of the Republican party in Indiana, a state that might swing either way in the election, Fairbanks rarely made speeches, always voted the orthodox Republican line and exerted his persuasive influence principally in the Senate cloakrooms. Again Theodore accepted the decision of the Old Guard, with only one reservation. He wanted to meet informally with Fairbanks several times, since they were only slightly acquainted, so they could work together with greater ease and efficiency.

"I'll be accused of surrendering to the conservatives," Theodore said to his friend, Nicholas Murray Butler of Columbia University, "but I'll take Fairbanks because there simply isn't anyone else. There's a conspicuous lack of talent in the higher ranks of the party these days."

One day in late May, about a month prior to the Republican convention, Senator Fairbanks was invited to join the President at the White House for a private lunch, the first of their meetings. He arrived punctually, an austere figure in a frock coat, his only adornment a small pearl stickpin neatly centered in his black and gray cravat. An usher guided him to the President's suite in the Executive Wing, and there William Loeb greeted him with an apologetic smile.

"I'm sorry, Senator," he said, "but the President has been delayed by an unexpected emergency."

Fairbanks, who had half-anticipated a slight, looked down his nose.

Secretary Loeb cleared his throat. "He asked me to tell you there has been a death. In the family."

The Senator's attitude changed immediately. "Obviously, then, this isn't an opportune day for a meeting."

"He's looking forward to your visit."

Fairbanks was mystified. "Was it someone close to him?"

"I wouldn't say the President's personal relations with the deceased were particularly close." Loeb stifled a smile as the sound of a loud, slightly off-key tenor voice bawling a hymn drifted in through the open windows.

The dignity of the potential candidate for Vice-President was somewhat shaken.

Loeb went to the windows, looked out and beckoned. Fairbanks joined him, and together they saw one of the strangest processions ever to wend its way across the White House grounds.

In the lead was Archie Roosevelt, in overalls, pulling a toy truck. Directly behind him walked the First Lady, who was engaged in earnest conversation with her son, and following them were several other youngsters, Quentin Roosevelt and boys whom Loeb identified as sons of Secretary Taft and Commissioner Garfield. Ethel Roosevelt walked alone, self-conscious and embarrassed at the age of thirteen, wishing herself elsewhere and apparently trying to pretend it was a coincidence that she happened to be walking in the same direction as the others.

Bringing up the rear was the President, who was enjoying himself hugely as he sang.

Archie halted, and the children gathered behind him, Ethel carefully standing apart and staring at some shrubs on the far side of the lawn. There was a brief consultation, and then the President called to a gardener, who approached with a spade. Archie tried to dig into the ground with it, but the tool was too large and heavy for him to handle, and the other boys, each taking a turn, encountered similar difficulties.

The President, still singing, removed his coat and handed it to Mrs. Roosevelt with a flourish. Then, in his vest and shirtsleeves, he energetically dug a hole.

Archie took an object from the toy truck and placed it in the hole. He started to weep, but his father said something to him, so he blinked back his tears and stood erect. Mrs. Roosevelt read something, the President sang again, and filled in the hole.

When the children stooped to place flowers on the earth, Fairbanks could contain his curiosity no longer. "May I ask—"

"One of Archie's pets expired this morning," Loeb said. "His name, I believe, was Peter Rabbit."

The ceremony ended, the President donned his coat as he walked briskly toward his office, and he was in high spirits when he entered his own suite. "I hope I haven't kept you waiting long," he said as he shook the hand of his potential running mate, "but a private matter took precedence over everything else. I'm sure you realize it was urgent, as I wouldn't have allowed any ordinary business to prevent me from being on hand to greet you when you arrived."

A man who held no public office, at least for the present, found it easier to relax in the President's office than did members of the Administration whose work was studied and weighed, week after week, by a man whose coldly calculating eyes seldom matched his ready grin when he was weighing government business. Elihu Root had been the most outspoken member of the Cabinet in his years of service as Secretary of War, but now, as a corporation lawyer who would admit only that he "dabbled a bit" in politics, he felt even freer to speak his mind.

Leaning back in the overstuffed leather chair that others usually left vacant because of the President's preference for it when in a restless mood, he hooked his thumbs in the pockets of his vest and stared up at the ceiling. "Your nomination is assured," he said, "and you know it. Fairbanks will be accepted by acclamation as your running mate. You don't have a worry in the world, so I wish you'd stop fuming and fretting and fussing. Leave the handling of the convention to men who've been doing that sort of thing for years. Everyone knows you're the President, so there's no need for you to be the convention's stage manager and chief janitor as well."

Theodore, roaming the office, was not amused. "We have no idea who'll be nominated by the Democrats, so we can't leave any important details to chance."

"Absolutely nothing will be left to chance." Root sighed. "And the Democrats can nominate Bryan, or anyone else they please. It won't matter. The people are going to give you a term in your own right, and you know it."

"Complacency is a statesman's worst enemy," Theodore said.

"Mr. President, when you start creating third-rate epigrams, you need a rest. Why don't you play some tennis? Or take a ride? There's a fine breeze this afternoon."

"I've already boxed for an hour. And I took a long walk with Ted and Kermit. They came home from school yesterday."

"I saw them on my way in. Go rowing with them. It's something you've been wanting to do all spring."

"The Democratic press is keeping a sharp watch on me, Elihu, and I'd be criticized for neglecting my work."

Root lost patience with him. "Why are you so nervous?"

"In politics, nothing can be taken for granted."

"Except your nomination and election."

"My nomination, yes. But I think everything done at Chicago should point directly toward the election. Have you written your Keynote Address yet?"

"I've made some notes I plan to expand on the train going out there."

"Your speech is the real reason I wanted to see you before you left," Theodore said.

Root knew him too well to be offended. "You can trust me to present everything you've done here in the most favorable light."

"I have more confidence in you than in myself," Theodore replied quickly. "But I thought it would do no harm to discuss a few basic points with you. I hope you intend to stress the acquisition of the Panama Canal Zone."

"Naturally."

"If I were the temporary chairman, making the Keynote Address, I'd tell the full story of Panama. I'd include all the details."

"All of them?" Root raised an eyebrow.

"All that are pertinent." Theodore remained composed. "I'd also emphasize our guarantees of Cuba's independence, and our enlightened administration in the Philippines, where we're setting an example the colonial powers will find it difficult to copy. I'd bear down hard on our insistence that every nation observe the Open Door policy in China, giving everyone a chance to trade there without snatching territory. And I'd balance that with our striking enforcement of the Monroe Doctrine. The Venezuela business is a perfect example." He paused for breath.

"Anything else?"

If Theodore was aware of his friend's sarcasm, he ignored it. "Oh, yes. The establishment of the new Department of Commerce and Labor is a major achievement. So is Interior's program of preserving forests and irrigating wastelands. I hope you're remembering all this, Elihu."

"Every word," Root said, and did not laugh.

"You know, far better than anyone, what this Administration is doing to maintain the Army and Navy at maximum strength. And our victory in the Northern Securities suit deserves special mention."

In spite of his tolerance, Root was becoming annoyed. "What would you suggest I say about the tariff question?" There was a hint of malice in his voice.

Theodore frowned. "That's a delicate problem, and we can't promise the people more than we can reasonably hope to give them. A majority of Republicans in both the Senate and House want no change in the protective tariff, and would fight me to the end if I tried to reduce duties."

"So they would."

"On the other hand, the minority pushing with the Democrats for a tariff reduction is fervent. And it grows larger every year."

"So you're caught in the middle."

"For the present, I suppose. Along with the people." Theodore raised his voice. "As strongly as I believe in the duty of the Executive Branch of the government to lead, we can't do the impossible."

Root deemed it expedient not to show his amusement. Only rarely had he seen Theodore hesitate and temporize, and he was enjoying the novel experience. "Perhaps," he said with a straight face, "I'd better not mention tariffs."

"You can't ignore the subject, Elihu!" Theodore became alarmed. "The Democrats would crucify us! We'd be stupid if we handed them a campaign issue."

"Call in a secretary, Mr. President, and dictate a statement on the tariff. I'll repeat it word for word in my speech."

"I wouldn't insult you by telling you what to say. I'm sure you can find some diplomatic way to straddle the issue without offending either wing of the party." Theodore went to his desk, sat down and bestowed his most ingratiating smile on his friend. "No one can handle this sort of dilemma with greater finesse than you, and I'll be happy to follow your approach when I start campaigning."

"Where do you stand on the tariff, Mr. President?" Root sounded innocent. "I don't believe I've ever heard you express your position."

"I hope," Theodore replied vaguely, "to draw the party together. But it can't be done overnight, and in the meantime, with an election to be won, I'd rather not expose myself to unnecessary enemy sniper fire."

The Republicans convened in Chicago, and dutifully went through the prescribed routines. On June 23 President Roosevelt was nominated for another term by the unanimous vote of the delegates, who congratulated themselves by parading, shouting, and singing for an hour. Then, after naming Senator Charles W. Fairbanks for Vice-President, they went home.

The task of the Democrats, who met at St. Louis in early July, was infinitely more complex. Not only were they faced with the task of finding a candidate able to compete with a President who was popular everywhere in the country, even in the traditional Democratic strongholds of the South, but they had to rid themselves of the radical image created by the peripatetic William Jennings Bryan.

Determined not to nominate Bryan again, they conducted a diligent search for someone whose appeal to the business community might win them badly needed financial support. Finally, on July 9, they nominated Theodore's old friend, Justice Alton B. Parker of New York. Then, still trying to impress potential contributors with their conservatism, they named the richest man in West Virginia, Henry G. Davis, as his running mate. Davis, who was eighty-one years of age, was too old to campaign actively, and promptly disappointed his party by refusing to give a penny of his own money to the campaign fund.

Tradition prevented the President from making extensive tours. He was expected to remain at his desk, guiding the nation while others spoke on his behalf, and Theodore tried to live up to the part expected of him. His family went off to Oyster Bay, and although he longed to join his wife and children for the swimming, sailing, and camping trips he relished, he stayed at the White House, uncomplainingly enduring Washington's summer heat.

Judge Parker, who was a gentleman, conducted a quiet, dignified campaign that made it relatively easy for Theodore to hold himself aloof from the battle, and the summer passed slowly. But the Democratic newspapers were dissatisfied, knowing their candidate was waging a losing struggle, and early in the autumn Joseph Pulitzer wrote a sensational editorial that filled the entire front page of his New York *World*. In it he attacked the integrity of the Roosevelt Administration, and other Democratic newspapers quickly followed his example.

Parker, goaded by the press, made a speech claiming that the Administration was corrupt.

Theodore lost his temper, and, shrugging off the advice of his supporters, who urged him to ignore the charge, issued a blistering reply. Since Parker had no real evidence to support his claim, that should have ended the matter, but Theodore was not satisfied. Casting aside tradition, he went on a whirlwind tour that took him to New York, New England, and Pennsylvania, to Chicago, St. Louis, and Denver. Accusing his opponent of uttering "wicked falsehoods," he fought savagely, disregarding the cries of anguished Republicans who believed he was impairing the dignity of the presidency.

"I was willing to wage this campaign as a tennis match," he said, "but when I'm accused of dishonesty, I climb into the ring—without gloves."

The friends who were closest to him accepted his reaction with resignation, and on his birthday, October 28, Elihu Root sent him a brief note: *I congratulate you on attaining the respectable age of forty-six. You have made a very good start in life, and your friends have great hopes for you when you grow up.*

Theodore laughed until tears came to his eyes, and paid no further attention to the Democrats' charges.

He was rewarded when the voters went to the polls on November 8. His popular vote of 7,628,834 was the largest ever accorded any presidential candidate, and he defeated Judge Parker by a staggering 2,540,067 votes. The electoral vote was 336 to 110, Missouri went Republican for the first time since the Civil War, and the victory was the greatest achieved by the Republicans in more than thirty years.

Theodore was ecstatic, and without consulting anyone, issued a statement to the press. "On the 4th of March next," he said, "I shall have served three and a half years, and this constitutes my first term. The wise custom which limits the President to two terms regards the substance and not the form; and under no circumstances will I be a candidate for or accept another nomination."

Senator Lodge, among others, was distressed when he read the declaration in print the next day. *I hope,* he wrote, *that you won't regret that declaration in years to come. I wish you had considered the matter at greater length and waited until a calmer moment to speak your mind.*

I have taken your lecture to heart, Theodore replied, *but I can imagine no circumstances that might impel me to seek what would be tantamount to a third term. So don't scold me again, and instead, think of all we're going to do in the next four years!*

In his exuberance he spoke bluntly to other friends and relatives, and the press heard a rumor that, at a private lunch given in his honor by Douglas Robinson, his enthusiasm was greater than his discretion. According to persistent but unsubstantiated reports, he told a group of startled financiers, "Now that I shall come into my office in my own right, watch out for me!"

The guests refused to discuss the affair, and one, who insisted that his identity not be disclosed, confined himself to the tart comment that "the President is capable of speaking for himself."

Theodore grinned amiably but made no reply when asked by a group of correspondents whether he had made the alleged remark.

"It doesn't really matter whether he said it or not," Secretary of War Taft confided to several intimates. "I'm sure that's the way he feels, and I won't be surprised if the fireworks start exploding the very day he's inaugurated."

V

1905–1909

Tomorrow I shall come into office in my own right. Then watch out for me.

THE INAUGURAL ADDRESS which Theodore delivered on March 4, 1905, was hailed by the press throughout the civilized world as a dignified, sober appraisal of a nation coming of age. He wrote it in his own hand, with editorial help from Cabot Lodge, and delivered it, under fair skies, before a vast crowd assembled below the east portico of the Capitol.

The American people, he said, were richly endowed with the wealth of natural resources. "We are the heirs of the ages, and yet we have had to pay few of the penalties which in old countries are exacted by the dead hand of a bygone civilization." The nation, he declared, had faced perils with vigor and effort, and had surmounted them. Now she faced new perils: "The conditions which have told for our marvelous material well-being, which have developed to a very high degree our energy, self-reliance, and individual initiative, have also brought the care and anxiety inseparable from the accumulation of great wealth in industrial centers."

Upon the resolution of these new problems, he said, depended the welfare of the American people and, perhaps, of mankind itself. "If we fail, the cause of free self-government throughout the world will rock to its foundations." But the United States need not fail; the qualities she needed were those which she had demonstrated in the past, qualities "of practical intelligence, of courage, of hardihood, and endurance, and above all the power of devotion to a lofty ideal." He did not spell out the pragmatic solutions he had in mind.

In promising a new era in foreign affairs, his words were those of a statesman. "Toward all nations, large and small," he declared, "our attitude must be one of cordial and sincere friendship. We must show not only in our words but in our deeds that we are earnestly desirous securing their good will by acting toward them in a spirit of just and generous recognition of their rights. But justice and generosity in a nation, as in an individual, count most when shown not by the weak but by the strong."

Above all, the President promised action. "Be ye doers!" he urged his fellow citizens, and indicated he intended to set an example for them.

After a private lunch with family and friends, diplomats, high-ranking members of his Administration and Congressional leaders, Theodore took his place in the reviewing stand to watch the inaugural parade that moved down Pennsylvania Avenue. And within moments his dignity had vanished, his reserve had melted away.

Tears of laughter rolled down his face as he watched the marshals of the parade, solemn in top hats and cutaway coats, trying with small success to maintain their balance as they rode spirited mounts at the head of the line. He stood, waving his arms, whenever a band played "A Hot Time in the Old Town," and many bands played it. Bareheaded and red-faced, he cheered when a contingent of his Rough Riders rode past the stand.

When he saw a group of Puerto Rican leaders in the line, he could not resist the opportunity to twit those who believed the United States should hold no colonial outposts. "They look pretty well for an oppressed people, don't they?" he demanded. No one answered, so he pointed a finger at Senator Augustus O. Bacon of Georgia, leader of the anti-imperialist bloc, and repeated the question. Bacon flushed, kept silent and thereafter voted consistently against the Administration.

The appearance of a regiment of Filipino Scouts gave Theodore another chance to ridicule the foes of American expansion. No troops, including the cadets from West Point and Annapolis, were better drilled than the Scouts, who showed their obvious pride in themselves as they swept past the reviewing stand. "The wretched serfs are disguising their feelings admirably!" Theodore shouted, and his shrill laugh sent Senator Bacon and several others home for the rest of the day.

The afternoon was a personal triumph that sometimes resembled a family picnic. The younger Roosevelt children took turns perching on their father's shoulder and dipping into a sack of rock candy he held for them. Although the day was cold, he consumed several cartons of ice cream, and the fresh air whetting his appetite, he also ate a num-

ber of frankfurters on buns, urging Supreme Court Justices, foreign ambassadors, and members of his Cabinet to follow his example. *The
aroma of mustard and grilled sausage meat,* the Philadelphia *Inquirer*
observed, *drowned the more delicate scents of the perfumes worn
by the wives and daughters of the great men. Only a campfire was
needed to convey the illusion that Teddy and his friends were relax-
ing on a hunting trip.*

That night, as the celebrations continued, Edith wondered whether
she might need campfires on the White House lawn to cook refreshments for the guests who arrived in droves. About two thousand had
been invited to drop in for an informal reception, but Theodore was
so carried away by the spirit of the day that he asked countless others,
sometimes cupping his hands and asking whole delegations marching
past the reviewing stand to join him after dinner. When more than
six thousand men and women had crowded into the public rooms of
the White House, the gates were closed. A number of dignitaries were
locked out, much to their annoyance, and William Loeb was kept busy
for days writing letters of apology.

John Morley, the noted English author and statesman, was present
at the day's festivities, and was fascinated by Theodore's inexhaustible energy. Watching the President, long after midnight, still shaking
hands with guests, exchanging jokes with friends, chatting in earnest
with Cabinet members and newly elected Senators and Congressmen,
Morley could not restrain himself.

"Mr. Roosevelt," he told those standing near him, "is an interesting
combination of St. Vitus and St. Paul. Do you know the two most impressive things I have seen on my tour of your country? Niagara Falls
and the President of the United States, both great wonders of nature!"

On the morning of March 5, as an augmented, weary household
staff cleared away the debris, the President arrived early at his office
to wrestle with the problems he had promised to solve. And in spite
of the optimism of his inaugural address, he knew he faced a troubled,
complicated future. Not the least of his difficulties was that of winning
the support of Congress, which regarded him with nervous suspicion.
The Old Guard maintained its firm control of both Houses, and he
knew he would encounter stiff opposition to his long-range plans,
which included the establishment of firm freight and passenger rates
for railroads, the curb of corporate abuses by large companies, and
the expansion of his conservation program. He enthusiastically endorsed Gifford Pinchot's recommendations, including the acquisition

and preservation of more forest lands, the irrigation of deserts, and unqualified opposition to the exploitation of water power by private interests. If necessary, he was ready to fight the Old Guard on these issues, as well as on another close to the hearts of American manufacturers, that of the tariff.

The Republican party long had advocated high tariffs in order to protect American products in domestic markers, but Theodore was convinced that such a shield was no longer necessary, and, in fact, was harmful to American interests. Other nations raised duties on American goods in retaliation, thereby cutting off foreign markets. Plants that made everything from heavy machinery to consumer goods were growing at such a rapid rate they would soon need the right to sell abroad if they hoped to maintain their rapid rate of expansion. And Theodore was becoming increasingly convinced that the United States would sell more to foreign nations than she would buy, if tariff rates were lowered.

He would be accused of adopting the line long advocated by the Democrats, to be sure, but the charge did not worry him. The opposition, as he told Taft, had been premature in advocating tariff cuts, which would have been harmful to young American industries. Now, however, they would benefit. *Prepare a set of figures to support a campaign for a lowered tariff*, he scribbled in a note to Taft, who was acting as Secretary of State because the elderly Hay was ill. *We needn't avoid something good for the country just because the Democrats favored it. But make sure your figures can be substantiated. Aldrich, Cannon & Co. will howl for our blood.*

Shortly after nine o'clock Theodore put domestic considerations out of his mind when a foreign visitor was announced. Cecil Spring-Rice, Councilor of the British Embassy at St. Petersburg, looked very pale, and had deep smudges under his eyes. But Theodore greeted him cheerfully.

"Springy," he said, "you look as though you need a cold bath and a long hike in fresh air."

"I need a cold bottle of champagne to undo last night's damage," Spring-Rice replied, sinking into a chair and groaning. "I also need a more considerate host, who won't call me to the White House at the crack of dawn."

"I've been working for hours."

"I don't have the constitution of a bull moose, Mr. President, and I'm embarrassed by your insistence that I come to Washington. Our

Embassy thinks you want me to engage in some hanky-panky behind the Ambassador's back—"

"Which happens to be true."

"—and I've made a dreadful tactical error. I was wrong to accept Henry Adams' invitation to stay with him. I know of nothing worse than the moralizing effrontery of a Boston Puritan at breakfast after the inauguration of a mutual friend. I'll need a long sea voyage back to Russia to recover my health and my aplomb."

A laughing Theodore ordered some coffee for his guest, then became brisk. "Springy," he said, "I'm grateful for your friendship, and I give you my word that no one except your Prime Minister and Foreign Secretary know you're here for anything other than a social visit."

"You must think the Foreign Office is peopled by fools." Spring-Rice became reflective. "If so, you may be right."

Theodore became silent while the visitor was served coffee, and waited until they were alone again. "I have something in mind so daring that I can trust only a few members of my own Administration with it, and I can speak freely to no British representative except you."

The diplomat sipped his coffee and held his cup close to his face, inhaling the aroma. "It's too bad we can't return to our carefree youth, but I try, I really do, to accustom myself to the thought that you've become one of the most powerful and influential men on earth."

"I'm serious, Springy. I had a reason for writing to you privately in St. Petersburg and begging you to come here unobtrusively."

"The fact that I'm here," Spring-Rice replied tartly, "proves I take you at your word."

"Hear me out. I'm very much worried by the Russian-Japanese War."

"So are the people with whom I deal in St. Petersburg. In fact, Mr. President, be assured on the highest authority that Czar Nicholas hasn't enjoyed a good night's sleep since the war broke out more than a year ago."

Theodore decided to ignore his old friend's flippant attitude. Spring-Rice's eyes had become alert behind his façade. "When the war started, Secretary Hay and I were afraid Russia would win a crushing victory, which would have made her the most powerful nation in both Europe and Asia."

"Our Foreign Office hasn't been insensitive to the possibility."

"Nor have the French."

"Any change in the balance of power is a threat to every established nation, but you and the French have too much prestige to show your concern. Bill the Kaiser is a bit more open about it, since he's trying to expand Germany's spheres of influence—"

"And President Roosevelt's position is similar to that of Kaiser Wilhelm, but public opinion in the United States isn't prepared for foreign ventures, so you must act with greater circumspection."

"I sometimes wish you weren't so bright, Springy."

"I have the honor to call the President of the United States a cheeky liar. If you didn't admire my mind, you wouldn't have sent halfway round the world for me."

Theodore couldn't help laughing. "I suppose you knew I was secretly hoping the Japanese would pull ahead."

"Naturally."

"I wonder," Theodore challenged, "if you can tell me how I feel about the war now."

"Certainly, Mr. President." Spring-Rice was one of a very few who dared to light a cigarette in Theodore's presence without first asking permission. "The Japanese capture of Port Arthur two months ago was so unexpected and so smashing a victory that you're now afraid Russia will be trounced. If Japan becomes the strongest power in the Pacific, the United States will feel menaced."

"Precisely. For the good of this country, I'd like to see the war end before either side becomes too powerful. And I'm sure that Britain, for her own reasons, must feel the same way."

"To be sure. But we're all observers, nothing more, so what can we do?"

"Britain can't do much of anything. But I can. The United States is relatively new to the game of international power politics. I very much want to offer our services as a mediator."

Spring-Rice blinked. "You have the courage of the perennial amateur! How do you propose to bring this miracle to pass?"

"Through you. I've just assigned one of our best diplomats to Russia, George Meyer. But he isn't known in St. Petersburg, and you've won the confidence of Czar Nicholas. I'm hoping that you and Meyer, between you, can persuade him to accept American mediation."

"Isn't it dangerous to go through your own regular diplomatic channels?"

Theodore bared his teeth in a confident smile. "George Meyer and I went to Harvard together."

"Then you may be safe enough. I make you no promises, Theodore, but I'll try. Provided you'll grant me permission to stop off in London and tell Prime Minister Balfour your plan, in confidence. I couldn't act on your behalf without his knowledge."

"He already has an inkling of my intentions, and I've assumed you'd speak with him."

"I'll accept, then, but don't count on anything. Nicholas is like all Russians, suspicious and afraid of trickery. Also, he's hoping to recoup his Port Arthur losses."

"I've been studying the military and naval situation," Theodore said, "and he'll be disappointed. Apparently it hasn't occurred to him that the Japanese fleet is inferior to his."

"That's what our Admiralty says."

"Your Admiralty is so efficient that you and we will stand on the same side for years to come, Springy."

"You're far too blunt to be a diplomat, Mr. President."

"I thank Heaven I'm not."

"But you're trying to play a diplomatic game, and you may be badly burned."

"I feel it's a risk I must take."

"How will you persuade the Japanese to accept mediation when they're already winning the war?"

"I don't yet know, frankly. I wanted to enlist your help first."

"If you fail, and it becomes public knowledge," Spring-Rice said, shaking his head, "you and the United States will look ridiculous." He changed his mind about expanding on the theme when he saw the expression of stubborn incredulity on his friend's face. Theodore's greatest strength as well as his greatest weakness, the Englishman thought, was his inability to admit even the possibility of failure.

Baron Kogoro Takahira, the Japanese Minister to the United States, courteously but firmly rejected President Roosevelt's suggestion that he and Count Cassini, the Russian Ambassador, meet secretly on "the neutral soil of my office." When the appropriate time came, Takahira said, his government and that of Russia would meet in direct negotiations. In the meantime there was a war to be won.

George Meyer's reports from St. Petersburg were not encouraging, either. On two occasions he had conferred with the Czar, but Nicholas had been evasive and had changed the subject when the American envoy had suggested that he accept mediation. Cecil Spring-Rice returned to Russia, but his luck was no better. The Czar preferred to discuss the relative merits of Russian and English literature with him, and would not be pinned down.

The opposition of the two principals to American intervention of any sort infuriated Theodore, and none of his intimates who were familiar with his scheme were surprised when it assumed the proportions of a holy crusade. "It's bad enough that the Russians and Japanese are slaughtering each other," he said in a visit to the bedside of John Hay. "But we can't stand aside when a continuation of the war might involve every other major country!"

The elderly Secretary of State, his health becoming more precarious each day, smiled feebly. "The real danger, Mr. President, is that the United States will be drawn in if you persist in offering our services."

"We have no choice!" Forgetting he was in a sickroom, Theodore raised his voice.

"Have you ever seen a busybody interfere when two men are having a fight in a bar? It's human nature for both of them to turn on him."

"I haven't been near a bar since my Dakota days, but I believe I could handle myself as well now as I could then."

Hay knew it was useless to persist. The President was convincing himself it was his mission to halt the Russo-Japanese War, and no argument, no logic, no threat could change his mind.

But Theodore made no progress in his efforts. Both Taft and Lodge, who were thoroughly familiar with his plan, urged him to exercise patience, but he refused. "The peace of the world depends on my efforts," he said.

Unable to obtain that peace, he went West on an extended hunting trip. "The President," Taft said, "is the finest man I've ever known, but it disturbs me when I see him sulk. I suppose everyone has minor faults, though, so I don't mean to criticize him."

The hunting trip caused a lull in America's one-man crusade. Meanwhile the grand fleets of the Russians and Japanese met in the Battle of Tsushima Strait in the Pacific on May 27, and the following day correspondents traveling with Admiral Heihachiro Togo, the Japanese commander, cabled the news around the world that the greatest naval action in history had been fought. The results were stunning: almost without exception the entire Russian fleet had been sunk or captured.

Theodore hurried back to Washington, arriving late on the night of May 31, and the following morning Secretary Taft arrived at the

White House for breakfast. As usual on such occasions, the kitchen staff had been alerted, and William Howard Taft's customary breakfast of fruit, cereal, pancakes, eggs, and steak were prepared for him. He ate steadily, enjoying his meal in spite of his superior's irritability.

"You have every reason to rejoice, Mr. President," he said, eating steak and fried potatoes with obvious relish. "George Meyer sent a cable in code early this morning. Czar Nicholas received him and Spring-Rice last night, and is willing to accept our mediation now."

"Of course he is!" Theodore glowered at the amiable, heavy-set man who sat opposite him. "There's been no doubt of it in my mind ever since I first learned of the battle. Nicholas is knuckling under, Will, because he has no choice. It's the Japanese who worry me!"

"If I had just destroyed my enemy's fleet," Taft said, helping himself to another slice of toast and buttering it, "I'd refuse to accept a mediator's intervention. I'd demand a surrender!"

"And if you were the Japanese, you'd be dead wrong! Russia has been weakened, but hasn't been beaten to her knees so badly that she'll surrender. You don't force the surrender of a giant that size by cutting off a foot or a hand. The war can drag on for years, and the Japanese will become more arrogant all the time. The entire situation in the Pacific must be stabilized—and soon—or our own position in the Philippines will be threatened. This war must be ended before we're forced to fight the Japanese ourselves."

"I've been devoting a great deal of thought to the subject, Mr. President—"

"So have I!" Theodore snapped, and ground his teeth.

Taft remained unperturbed. "I don't see how a victor can be forced to sit down at a bargaining table—and persuaded to accept decisions made by an outside party."

"Ah, that's the point. We don't force her. We cajole her."

"How?" Taft looked puzzled as he ate the last of his steak. "A delicious breakfast, Mr. President."

"Would you like another steak?"

"No, I don't want to put on too much weight."

Theodore concealed a grin behind his napkin, then sobered. "As I see it, Japan should return all of Manchuria that she's captured to China, which has the primary right to the territory."

"She won't."

"I disagree. I'm willing to support her claim to the Port Arthur area."

"She won't thank you for that. After all, she captured Port Arthur."

"True, but there's something else she wants—Korea. A barren, use-less land, if ever there was one, and the Almighty in His infinite wis-dom only knows why any ambitious, self-respecting country would want that burden."

The President, Taft thought, could display monumental ignorance of matters that did not interest him. A brief study of a map of the Far East would reveal the reason for the Imperial Japanese government's desire to control Korea: the peninsula on which she was situated dom-inated an area which Japan, Russia, and China each needed if she hoped to dominate the Pacific seaways of the Orient. But no one, not even the most trusted of associates, dared to point out such basic facts to Theodore Roosevelt when his mood was other than reflective.

"Japan needs support, Will. The British and French won't give it to her. Bill the Kaiser thinks of Tokyo as his rival in the East, and will do absolutely nothing that might benefit Japan. But if one major na-tion, just one, will support the claim of the Japanese for a protectorate over Korea, no other nation can stop her without risking the start of a world war."

Secretaty Taft was startled. "You'd actually go that far, Mr. President? You'd back the Japanese claim?"

"Certainly," Theodore replied emphatically. "I don't want to be crass about it, and I wouldn't offer them a horse trade in so many words. But they can be very subtle, I've discovered, and I feel reasonably sure they'd be very quick to accept us as a mediator in the war."

"The Koreans don't want to become wards of Japan," the former Governor-General of the Philippines said.

Theodore gestured impatiently. "No inferior, barbarian people ever wants to be civilized by a more advanced nation."

Taft busied himself stirring his coffee. The culture of Korea, as any-one who had lived in the East knew, was older than that of Japan, and her traditions in literature and art were almost in a class with those of ancient China.

"So the advantages are obvious," Theodore continued. "Every na-tion will benefit, including Korea. And, with luck, peace can be re-stored."

"Some people—including our own—might not see it that way," Taft replied cautiously. "In fact, the Administration might be criticized for making a crude deal."

"Oh, we won't be open about it, and we certainly won't put our offer on paper. What I want to do, Will, is invent some logical-sound-ing reason for you to go to Manila on an inspection trip. No one will think it particularly significant that I'm sending you, of all men, to investigate a situation in the Philippines. I'll put a warship at your disposal. You can travel faster than you could on the commercial lines."

"I see. And you'd expect me to stop in Tokyo."

"You get the idea! The Japanese will understand that we don't intend to advertise our support for their Korean claim at present, but they'll accept a promise made by a man of your rank as binding."

The Secretary tried to weigh the possibilities of American involve-ment far beyond her desires in Far Eastern affairs. "I suppose," he said dubiously, "that the whole thing could be arranged and worked out."

"There's no reason it can't! There's no real difference between for-eign and domestic politics, Will. Give a senator or congressman or governor something he wants, and he'll support you when you de-mand repayment. Scratch another country's back, and she'll scratch yours! I tell you, diplomacy is too simple a game to be left in the hands of diplomats!"

"Count Cassini had a fit," Theodore told Secretary Hay on a visit to the old man's bedside, "when he learned that Will Taft visited Tokyo on his way to Manila. But the Russians can't prove a thing."

John Hay mistrusted the unorthodox venture, but was too feeble to argue against it. His health declined so rapidly that his family, afraid to let him linger in Washington during the blistering summer months, moved him to his summer home at Newbury, New Hampshire, where, on the first day of July, he died.

Theodore led a host of dignitaries to his funeral, and on board the train that carried him back to Washington managed to persuade Elihu Root to return to the government as Secretary of State. "We have a chance to win recognition for the United States as a great world power, Elihu. Join me, and you won't regret it!"

Root could not resist, and, accepting the offer, became active in the extraordinary experiment in personal diplomacy. On July 29 he was summoned to the White House by a jubilant Theodore, who had just received a long, coded cablegram from Taft.

The Secretary of War had met for the better part of a day with Prince Taro Katsura, the Japanese Premier, and both men had been frank. As a token of his good will, Katsura had indicated that his na-tion had no interest in acquiring the Philippines. He welcomed

American support for Japan's claim to Korea, and, based on it, planned to send troops to occupy the small country. At the same time he indicated an awareness of American domestic politics, in particular the President's delicate position.

He knew Senate ratification of a formal treaty of alliance would be necessary, and realized that approval of the Japanese-Korean claim might not be forthcoming in such a treaty. There were officials in Japan, too, he said, who were reluctant to acknowledge, in public, the necessities of power politics. Therefore he was willing to accept the President's private assurances.

The jubilant Theodore sent a cablegram to Taft. YOUR CONVERSATION WITH COUNT KATSURA ABSOLUTELY CORRECT IN EVERY RESPECT. WISH YOU WOULD STATE TO KATSURA THAT I CONFIRM EVERY WORD YOU HAVE SAID.

Within a week Baron Takahira called on the President and informed him of the Japanese government's hope that he would "of his own motion and initiative" invite the belligerents to negotiate a peace treaty.

"The battle is half won," Theodore told Root, and, summoning Cassini, informed him with brutal candor that the Czar would be foolish to reject mediation. Russia's military situation had deteriorated so badly, he said, that she could no longer hope to win the war.

Others felt as he did, among them Kaiser Wilhelm, who urged his reluctant and stubborn cousin, Nicholas, to save face and meet the Japanese under American auspices. Nicholas, his mood changing, suddenly agreed.

Theodore found overnight he had attained his objective: he had become a mediator.

The pace quickened. Japan appointed two representatives, Minister Takahira and Baron Jutaro Komura; Russia swiftly countered by naming Count Sergei Witte, "a giant who looks like the proverbial Russian bear," as Theodore called him, and Baron Roman Rosen.

Consulting no one and blithely ignoring diplomatic precedent as well as the problems of a face-to-face confrontation, Theodore invited both delegations to a lunch on board the presidential yacht, the U.S.S. *Mayflower*. The affair would be held on August 5, he said, asking neither side if it approved, and the yacht would be anchored in Oyster Bay.

"Theodore," Root confided to friends, "has no understanding of protocol, no sense of diplomacy and is rushing into this meeting with the sensitivity of a blindfolded bull moose. If he isn't careful, we'll be at war with both Japan and Russia, but he just laughs when I try to warn him."

The fascinated world watched the preparations for the meeting, and heard rumblings of discontent on both sides. Count Witte made it plain, in a press interview, that he would not tolerate a toast being offered to the Czar after the offering of a toast to the Japanese Mikado. Baron Komura swiftly countered by saying that Japan would regard it as a shocking and unacceptable insult if the Mikado were not toasted first.

The forthcoming luncheon soon assumed musical comedy aspects which, although amusing, threatened the success of American mediation efforts. Seemingly insoluble problems were raised, and the press gloomily predicted that the war might drag on interminably. Komura demanded the privilege of being seated on the President's right; Witte countered by saying it was his right, not his privilege, and that the Czar would order him to withdraw unless he received the honor. Minister Takahira expressed the hope that a Japanese dish would be offered as the main course. Baron Rosen insisted that anything other than a Russian main course would be a disgrace.

A scant forty-eight hours before the meeting was scheduled to take place, both delegations revealed that high-ranking military and naval officers in full uniform, wearing all of their decorations, would accompany the civilian leaders. The American press immediately created a domestic crisis. Would the United States allow herself to be shamed? Or would the President draft some of his own top-ranking Army and Navy officers to act as subordinate hosts? The President, coming ashore from a sailing picnic with his sons, merely grinned.

A final explosion took place on the evening of August 4. Witte, insisting that a count in the Russian hierarchy outranked a baron in the Japanese nobility, declared that he, of course, would take precedence in entering the dining room. Baron Komura indignantly declared that the war would be fought for another decade unless he went into the dining room ahead of Witte.

Such substantive questions as that of Russia paying indemnity, the settlement of international boundaries and the guarantees against another outbreak of war seemed to be forgotten.

Robert Bacon, the President's Harvard classmate, on leave from his partnership in J. P. Morgan & Company, had just been appointed Assistant Secretary of State, and some reporters thought his unfamiliarity with public office might be responsible for his rectitude. He arrived at Oyster Bay by train, and was surrounded by newsmen, but refused to say a word before being whisked away in a presidential carriage. Secretary Root, who followed by automobile a short time later, made an attempt to smile as he saw the correspondents gathered near the entrance to the Roosevelt estate, but the press representatives of twenty nations agreed that he looked very grim.

August 5 was a hot, bright day, and members of the *Mayflower's* crew were at work by dawn, scrubbing decks and polishing brass. At sunrise other sailors were seen carrying cartons and bags of provisions from the Roosevelt kitchen to waiting boats, which took them out to the yacht. Press attempts to discover the contents of the cartons before they were loaded on the boats were foiled by a small contingent of United States Marines.

At nine o'clock Mrs. Roosevelt went out to the *Mayflower*, escorted by the President's brother-in-law and Naval Aide, Rear Admiral William S. Cowles, who, the press noted, was dressed in civilian attire. Two hours later the First Lady returned to her house, which led the reporters to believe that she had taken a hand in supervising the preparation of the meal. A committee of newsmen went to the house to ask her for the menu, but she sent her regrets through William Loeb, who said that full details would not be available until later in the day. He offered no explanation.

Secretary Root, Assistant Secretary Bacon and two junior State Department officials were taken out to the *Mayflower* at 11:30 A.M. The Chicago *Tribune* correspondent wrote that "all four looked as though they were going to the dentist for molar extractions."

The President, who had enjoyed a swim and a game of tennis with his elder sons earlier in the morning, emerged from the house shortly before noon, resplendent in what he called his "diplomat's suit." His high, stiff collar seemed to annoy him, and he carried his top hat. He was accompanied by his dapper young Military Aide, Lieutenant Douglas MacArthur, who also wore a cutaway and striped trousers. Several of the American reporters, who knew that MacArthur had brought his Army dress uniform with him, were surprised that he was not wearing it.

One question was already answered. The United States would not try to compete with Russian or Japanese admirals and generals. Instead, the President was choosing to emphasize the peaceful purposes of the occasion, and had not even invited any of his own top commanders.

A score of press boats circled around the *Mayflower* like vultures; they were kept at a reasonable distance by two Coast Guard cutters, but were close enough to hear shouted conversations and see everything that took place in the open. They watched a grinning President bound up the ship's mahogany ladder, go inside and return to the deck, chewing something. Apparently he had tasted something in the galley, and found it good. In any event he was laughing, which was more than could be said for any of his sour-faced subordinates.

The Japanese were the first delegation to arrive, and were carried out to the *Mayflower* in two Coast Guard cutters. The President, leaning out over the railing, cupped his hands and bellowed his informal greetings. His shrill voice echoed across Oyster Bay, and Baron Komura, who had rarely displayed any emotion in public other than anger, was seen to laugh without restraint.

The Japanese were piped aboard, Admiral Cowles and Lieutenant MacArthur whisked away the military and naval officers for a tour of the yacht, and the President, Secretary of State, and other high-ranking Americans sat down in the sunlight on the open deck with Baron Komura and Minister Takahira. The importance of these tactics was not recognized until later, when it was realized that Theodore had been deliberate in seating his guests. The Japanese were conscious of their short stature in the presence of Occidentals, and the President was putting them at their ease.

The Russians arrived a quarter of an hour later, and were taken to the *Mayflower* on board the same Coast Guard cutters. European newsmen, among them correspondents of the *Times* of London, *Le Figaro*, and the *Allgemeine Zeitung*, were astonished by the President's informality. Returning to his place at the rail, he again roared greetings across the water.

No one, the *Times* of London correspondent wrote, *including the Japanese and Russians, knew whether he was presenting one side to the other, and, if so, which to whom. Mr. Roosevelt's performance was a masterpiece of ambiguity and deliberate confusion, cloaked in the guise of hearty American informality.*

The German correspondent was even more lavish in his praise. *Roosevelt,* he wrote, *is a genius. In Germany we have many geniuses, and those who know them realize they are simple men in all but medicine, physics, astronomy or whatever the special field of the individual may be. The President of the Americans makes the study of man his special field, and in it he pretends to be simple, which makes it possible for him to manipulate these others.*

A flurry of handshakes followed as the Russians were piped onto the yacht, and the delegates were so busy shaking hands that they were able to observe the amenities with each other without suffering much embarrassment. Then everyone sat again, at the President's insistence, and by now it was apparent to the newsmen that he was sparing the sensitivities of the Japanese.

For the next twenty minutes Theodore Roosevelt delivered one of the rapid-fire monologues to which his relatives and friends long had been accustomed. On this occasion he chose to speak in French, and tortured the language with such abandon that the correspondent of *Le Figaro* winced whenever an occasional phrase drifted across the water. Theodore told several stories of his hunting exploits, illustrating them with broad gestures, then pointed out the sights of Oyster Bay, loaning the guests field glasses so they could see his children jumping from the deck of a sailboat into the Bay.

Theodore appeared completely relaxed, and was behaving as though his guests were like hundreds of others he had entertained, that the affair itself was just another friendly lunch party. His monologue was light and witty, no one else was given an opportunity to speak, and nothing of consequence was said. Eventually the correspondent of the Denver *Rocky Mountain News* understood why the President insisted on speaking in his fractured French.

If he made a mistake that mattered, and he certainly made many in grammar and syntax that did not, he could not be blamed. Neither delegation could accuse him of favoring the other or slighting a crowned head. If the truth be known, the delegates could not pause to think of such things. They were obliged to listen to their host, the President of the United States, and needed to exert all of their efforts in an attempt to understand what he was saying.

A gong chimed, signaling the first moment of crisis. Everyone stood, preparatory to going into the dining room, and the tension on the deck of the *Mayflower* was evident from the press boats. But Theodore did not falter. He linked one arm through that of Witte, the other through that of Komura, and proceeded with them at what the New York *Tribune* referred to as "his San Juan Hill trot." Half-leading and half-dragging them, he charged into the dining room.

Admiral Cowles and Lieutenant MacArthur, bringing up the rear with the Japanese and Russian admirals and generals, followed their instructions to the letter. They herded everyone inside with brusque, jovial informality, and the civilians who preceded the military men were jostled and pushed. Eager to get out of the way, they hurried, and entered in no particular order.

Subsequent details were provided the press by William Loeb. The guests saw a large, round table in the center of the dining room, with a variety of dishes piled on it in buffet style. The President put one hand between Komura's shoulders and the other in the small of Witte's back, then shoved them toward the table, genially requesting them to help themselves. Chairs lined the bulkheads, and everyone was free to sit where he pleased. No one was placed at the President's right or left; in fact, he was too busy playing the host to sit, and ate his own meal while standing. Thanks to his maneuvering, however, Komura and Witte found themselves next to each other.

The dishes were without exception simple, and all were American. There was a cold chicken salad, sliced Virginia ham, codfish cakes in a cream sauce, hard-boiled eggs, Maine lobster, and chopped steak wrapped in bacon. Reporters from the Midwest were delighted to learn that a potato salad, served with sliced cucumbers and onions, was popular. A salad of peaches and apples made fruit growers in Georgia and Michigan happy. No region of the United States was neglected, and only American recipes were used.

After everyone had helped himself and found a place, waiters in white jackets served champagne, and the President raised a hand. Several crises had been averted, but another now loomed.

For the first time Theodore spoke in English. "Gentlemen," he said, "I propose a toast to which there will be no answer, and which I ask you to drink in silence, standing."

A hush fell over the assemblage.

"Let us drink," he said, "to the welfare and prosperity of the sovereigns and peoples of the two great nations whose representatives have met one another on this ship. It is my most earnest hope and prayer, in the interest of all mankind, that a just and lasting peace may speedily be concluded among them."

The guests drank the toast, and when they sat down to eat, Elihu Root relaxed for the first time. Theodore, who had planned every move, every word, had been far more successful than the Secretary of State had allowed himself to hope.

Throughout the meal the waiters continued to pour champagne

from chilled bottles, and the atmosphere began to thaw. At the end of the meal Theodore escorted Komura and Witte to his living room, while Root took Takahira and Rosen to the open deck, leaving them sitting in the sun. Substantive conversations now began in earnest between the two sets of diplomats, while Theodore, Root and Bacon, sometimes together but more often singly, drifted back and forth, smiling amiably, occasionally entering the conversations for brief periods but taking care not to make their intervention obtrusive.

The reporters on the press boats could see the Japanese Minister and the second-ranking Russian representative speaking and gesturing. Both remained calm, unruffled and in command of themselves. They shook hands with obvious warmth when their superiors emerged from the living room, also smiling, and it was evident that the meeting had been an auspicious start.

Theodore was hailed throughout the civilized world for his triumph, but he refused to take the credit. "Thank the wives of the members of the United States Senate," he said. "They gave me their favorite home-state recipes for the dishes we served."

Four days later formal peace negotiations were opened at Portsmouth, New Hampshire, where the United States Navy Yard offered the delegates the privacy they needed, in a small community. Theodore was present to act as host, intervene at the request of one side or the other, and, as he told Root, "lock the gates to prevent either from walking out."

Russia was forced to give the Port Arthur area, already occupied by her enemy, to Japan. But she stubbornly refused to pay indemnity, and would not give up Sakhalin Island, which the Japanese coveted.

France and Germany quietly went to work in an attempt to soften the Russian stand, while Theodore held a private meeting with the Japanese delegates. "You're getting just about everything you've wanted," he said. "I heard Witte tell you that Russia is willing, privately, to recognize your sphere of influence in Korea. And she'll include a clause in the treaty, agreeing to evacuate the portions of Manchuria she still holds. If she'll give you half of Sakhalin Island, take it and don't be greedy. The alternative is the death of hundreds of thousands more men on both sides."

The Japanese agreed to accept the southern half of Sakhalin, and the Russians, their prestige intact, said they would be willing to give up that much. A tentative agreement was signed on August 23, and both sides awaited final word from home. Czar Nicholas finally ratified the terms on August 29, and the Japanese delegates received Tokyo's approval the following day. The Russo-Japanese War was ended.

"This is the happiest news of my life," Pope Pius X said in a statement issued by the Vatican. "Thank God for President Roosevelt's courage."

The Pope's reaction was echoed by the leaders and people of virtually every civilized nation on earth. The United States gained so much standing that she won instant recognition as a great power, her stature rising simultaneously with that of Japan. And Theodore Roosevelt overnight became one of the world's foremost citizens.

He received the official congratulations and thanks of every major government, letters from grateful individuals all over the globe clogged the White House mail room, and the world press was unanimous in recommending that the Nobel Prize committee recognize his services to mankind. Encouraged by the applause, Theodore redoubled the efforts he had already initiated to settle a dispute between Germany and France in North Africa. Simultaneously playing on the French love of logic and Kaiser Wilhelm's insatiable vanity, he was able to guide the two European powers to a peaceful solution of their argument.

Again the world hailed him, but there were many in the United States who did not cheer. Senator Bacon, who had not forgotten his humiliation on Inauguration Day, made an impassioned speech in the Senate. "Why must we meddle in the affairs of other nations?" he demanded. "We don't need Europe or Asia. Let's mind our own business, and we'll become more prosperous, more powerful, more secure!"

Isolationists in all parts of the country rallied to Bacon's banner, and scores of newspapers printed firm editorials agreeing with him. Theodore found himself in a strange and ironic position: he was being honored abroad, but his fellow Americans were criticizing him.

He complained to Taft when the Secretary returned home from the Orient, but, for once, his loyal subordinate gave him little sympathy. "You aren't as popular in some parts of the world as you may think, Mr. President. Japanese troops are pouring into Korea, and that's one country where you couldn't win an election!"

The return of Secretary Taft catapulted Alice Roosevelt into the headlines from which she was never far absent. She had accompanied his party to Japan and the Philippines, and an official member of the group, Republican Congressman Nicholas Longworth of Ohio, had been exceptionally attentive to her. A few hours after the party debarked in California, Washington newsmen asked the President whether his daughter was engaged.

Theodore had sworn that Alice could do nothing that would surprise him, but this situation was unlike any he had anticipated. "You'll have to ask her," he said cautiously.

The press did ask her, and Alice replied with an enigmatic smile that closely resembled her father's famous grin.

Other stories about "Princess" Alice appeared in print throughout the country. On board ship, it was said, she had jumped into the swimming pool fully clad. She had, it was rumored, pushed Nick Longworth into the pool. She had demonstrated stamina worthy of a Roosevelt by dancing every night until the early hours of the morning, and then had reappeared on deck soon afterward for long pre-breakfast walks.

Was she injuring her health? the reporters asked the President. Did she get enough sleep?

Theodore issued a formal statement on the subject, written in his own hand. *I am proud,* he wrote, *that my daughter, Alice, does not stay in the house and fold her hands and do nothing. She can walk as far as I can, and often she walks several miles at the pace I set for her. She can ride, drive, ski, shoot—although she does not care much for the shooting. I don't mind that. It is not necessary for her health. She gets plenty of outdoor exercise. That is necessary.*

The subject was closed.

That of Alice's romance was not, however; romance was in the air. Earlier in the year, in March, Theodore had given away his favorite niece, Eleanor, in marriage to a distant cousin, Franklin D. Roosevelt, and accounts of that wedding reception still appeared in the newspapers from time to time. Society and women's page writers delighted in recounting that most of the wedding guests had followed Theodore into the library of the house at 6 East 76th Street in New York City, and had been enthralled by one of his monologues. A few had commented that young Franklin Roosevelt, whose personality closely resembled that of the President, had responded to the challenge by telling some stories of his own. It had been implied, but never stated that the shy Eleanor had been virtually forgotten at her own wedding.

No one believed for an instant that Alice would permit anyone to slight her, and the press kept a close watch on her and the Congressman from Ohio. When Longworth carried his violin to the White House, headlines announced that he was serenading Alice. When they went for a stroll in Rock Creek Park, more than one hundred reporters trailed after them, ruining their privacy.

No one knew what Alice said to Theodore and Edith on the subject, however, nor did the press learn of the Congressman's request for a private meeting with the young lady's father. The meeting was held, however, and Theodore gave his consent. Late in the autumn of 1905 the President and Mrs. Roosevelt announced Alice's engagement to be married.

The whole world was curious about the balding, thirty-six-year-old legislator. Even King Edward VII, one of the many with whom Theodore maintained a steady correspondence, wrote from London to inquire about him. Theodore obliged His Majesty with a cheerful, candid reply: *Longworth is a good fellow, one of the younger men who have really done well in Congress. He was from my own college, Harvard, and there belonged to my club, the Porcellian, which is antique as antiquity goes in America, for it was founded in colonial days; he was on the varsity crew, and was, and is, the best violinist who ever came from Harvard.*

The wedding, on February 17, 1906, was the international social event of the year. Alice was the first daughter of a President to be married since Nellie Grant had made headlines thirty-two years earlier, and the wedding was the first in the White House since the marriage of President Grover Cleveland to Frances Folsom on June 2, 1886.

The wedding gifts were dazzling, and even the avid reporters soon lost count of them. They came by mail and messenger from Republicans and ordinary citizens, Democrats and office-holders. They came from thousands whom the bride and bridegroom had never met, from chambers of commerce and clubs, from companies and individuals, from incorporated cities and towns and from state legislatures. They came from the King of England, the Czar of Russia, the Kaiser of Germany, the King of the Belgians, the Emperor of Japan, and the Dowager Empress of China.

The American people, living vicariously through "Princess" Alice, were dazed. One priceless gift was a Gobelin tapestry. The press used astronomical figures in describing the cost of the jewelry. A dispatch from Havana said the Republic of Cuba was contemplating giving Alice a deed that would have made San Juan Hill her property and that of her heirs in perpetuity. No one knew whether the story was accurate, but the gift of Cuba turned out to be jewelry that cost the taxpayers of the little island nation far more than some jungle real estate.

After the excitement of the event died away, Congressman Longworth returned from his honeymoon to help push his father-in-law's ambitious reform program through a reluctant 59th Congress. The task was staggering, but Theodore pounded ceaselessly at his favorite themes, aided by Lincoln Steffens, William Allen White, and the other editors and newspaper writers whom he called the muckrakers.

He fought valiantly for a bill that would provide fair railroad shipping rates beneficial to the American consumer, but the railroads and major shippers fought back. They were careful, however, afraid that an irate public might retaliate. The Chicago *Tribune,* in a frank editorial, declared, *Many Senators and Congressmen are perfectly willing to serve the railroads and big shippers, but they have no desire to arouse a popular sentiment that might deprive them of their seats.*

A new reform Senator, Robert M. La Follette, who had gained national prominence as Governor of Wisconsin, came to the White House in the hope that he could join forces with the President. Theodore received him eagerly, but both men were soon disillusioned.

"Roosevelt," La Follette said, "is willing to compromise. I'm willing to fight to the end because I'm sure we'd win. He ought to use all the power of his office. He ought to send a special message to Congress, and if he fails, he ought to appeal to the next Congress. If he fails again, he ought to go over the heads of Congress to the people."

"La Follette is a fighter," Theodore said, "but he isn't a realist. A President may be able to break the spirit of Congress and push one piece of legislation through, but he'll do it at the expense of the rest of his program. A fair railroad rate is important, but so are a great many other things. I'm willing to settle, temporarily, for at least a partial achievement that will improve the situation. I'm willing to defer my ultimate goal so I can get some kind of improvement."

The Old Guard opposition was led by Senator Nelson Aldrich, who demonstrated what the President termed "almost diabolical cleverness" in attempting to thwart Theodore's purpose. But the White House made temporary alliances with any who were willing, including a number of Democrats not highly regarded in their own party. The Hepburn Bill of 1906, which gave the Interstate Commerce Commission limited but specific powers to set railroad rates, gave the President a victory which many of his progressive followers failed to recognize.

He, however, encountered no such difficulties. "Maybe I got an arm instead of an arm and leg," he told Henry Cabot Lodge, "but when the idealists stop sulking they'll realize we've moved a major step forward in curbing the big business monopolists."

Meanwhile a far more vicious struggle in which virtually all Americans were involved on one side or the other was building toward a climax. For many years the chief chemist of the Department of Agriculture, Dr. Harvey W. Wiley, had been requesting passage of a law accurately labeling preserved foods and beverages, and making the adulteration of foods harmful to health a Federal offense punishable by imprisonment.

Dr. Wiley's efforts had achieved little prior to the late summer of 1905, when some of the President's friends, including his personal physicians, had become interested in his crusade. In the late autumn of 1905 Theodore had invited Dr. Wiley to the White House for a talk, and, based on what he learned, recommended, in his annual message to Congress submitted in December, the Federal regulation of interstate commerce in "misbranded and adulterated food, drinks and drugs."

Senator Weldon B. Heyburn of Idaho prepared a bill, which was conspicuously supported by Senators Albert J. Beveridge of Indiana and Porter J. McCumber of North Dakota. Senator Aldrich kept the Pure Food Bill bottled up in committee, however, and hopes for its passage were dim.

But in January 1906 *Collier's Weekly* published the climactic article in a series by Samuel Hopkins Adams exposing quack patent medicines, and public opinion began to stir. In February an idealistic young novelist with strong Socialist beliefs, Upton Sinclair, startled the nation. Thoroughly documented by painstaking, accurate research, which was described in graphic, often brutal detail, *The Jungle* described the operations of the meat-packing industry. As an indictment of the methods used by the major meat-packers to intimidate their employees, it aroused indignation, and the people were shocked by Sinclair's basic charge, that meat was tainted, in part because the packers were so indifferent to public health that they slaughtered diseased animals, in part because of their unsanitary operations.

Theodore read the book in his usual single sitting one evening soon after Alice's wedding, and was horrified. The next morning he summoned Senators Lodge, Beveridge, Heyburn, and McCumber to his office. "How true are Sinclair's charges?" he demanded.

None knew, although McCumber suspected they might be completely accurate. "I know there are cattlemen in the Dakotas who have sold diseased cattle to the packers, Mr. President."

"I had the same hunch when I was a rancher, but I couldn't prove it," Theodore replied. "Sinclair's book has an authentic ring, but I don't know how much we can depend on his findings. I hate to condemn any man because of his politics, but Sinclair is an out-and-out Socialist, which may mean he's an idiot!"

Only Cabot Lodge dared to laugh.

"I've written him a letter this morning challenging his Socialism— and asking for facts. If he's right, I want to use an expanded and revised version of your Pure Food Bill to end these monstrous abuses, Senator Heyburn."

"We'll need more facts than somebody who is just an author can give us, Mr. President."

Theodore tugged at his mustache, and his eyes became glacial behind his glasses. "I don't necessarily agree. My own profession is that of an author."

There was an uneasy silence, which Lodge finally broke. "It seems to me," he said, "that there should be an independent investigation of the situation."

"There must be several," Theodore told him. "I've already asked Commissioner of Labor Charlie Neill to conduct one, and I've put in a call to Jim Reynolds—a social worker who is an old friend of mine—to make another. Do any of you gentlemen have time to make one of your own?"

"I'll take the time," Beveridge said.

"You won't be popular with the Old Guard, Senator. Nelson Aldrich will make life difficult for you."

"Aldrich and I already have an understanding," Beveridge replied with a slight smile. "We speak only on official business, and only when absolutely necessary."

"I want action," the President said after the general laughter subsided. "If Upton Sinclair is anywhere near right, the health of the American people has been endangered."

The senators later agreed that, in spite of his usual tendency to dramatize and exaggerate, he might be right.

Senator Beveridge's brief but intensive investigation verified the major claims made by Sinclair in *The Jungle*. Neill and Reynolds, pooling their findings, submitted a long, documented report in writing to the President. Meantime, while they were preparing it, the major Chicago meat-packers learned what was in the wind, and took energetic measures to protect themselves. *A flood of paid butchers' lobbyists,* wrote author Mark Sullivan, who had joined in the crusade for pure foods, *has descended in a tidal wave on Washington, with tainted blood on its hands and in its hearts.*

The President called a strategy meeting at the White House, and it was decided to advance meat inspection legislation on parallel lines with the Pure Food Bill rather than take the time to incorporate such provisions in a new, rewritten measure. Beveridge had already told his fellow Senate members about his own investigation, and many of them, Old Guard included, were horrified. There was only token opposition when he presented a meat inspection measure as an amendment to the Agriculture Appropriations Bill, and not even Aldrich, who was opposed to all Federal controls of industry, put up a real battle.

The situation in the House was far different. Speaker Cannon refused to believe that some of his wealthy meat-packer friends might be negligent of public health. And Chairman James W. Wadsworth of the Agriculture Committee was even closer to the packers. In fact, he regularly sold them cattle from his farm at Geneseo, New York. The lobbyists were everywhere in the corridors and offices of the House, and Wadsworth, refusing to act, would not release the Beveridge amendment from his Committee to the floor of the House.

"I'll have to take off my boxing gloves and fight bare-fisted," Theodore said, and on May 26, 1906, he sent Wadsworth a letter that was brutal, blunt and openly threatening. The facts reported to him by Neill and Reynolds, he declared, were *hideous and disgusting. I was at first so indignant that I resolved to send in the full report to Congress.*

But he had realized that the release of the report might strike a crippling blow to the meat-packing industry, one of the nation's largest. As President he wanted to do all he could to aid in the continuing growth and development of all American industries. At the same time he could not lose sight of the unalterable fact that the protection of the American people was a fundamental responsibility of his office.

So he had decided, after due reflection, to withhold the Neill-Reynolds report if Wadsworth would lend his immediate, full support to the Beveridge amendment. *I should not make the report public with the idea of damaging the packers,* Theodore concluded, not bothering to tread very quietly as he brandished a nail-studded club. *I should do it only if it were necessary in order to secure the remedy.*

Wadsworth and the other congressmen friendly to the packers were afraid of a direct confrontation with the President, but used evasive tactics to obtain their ends. They allowed Beveridge's measure to be sent to the House, but there emasculated it with a number of deftly worded amendments.

"They must think I'm bluffing," Theodore said. "An artillery salvo may convince them that something they've heard about me is wrong. I don't talk just for the pleasure of hearing the sound of my own voice."

A special presidential message was sent to Congress, urging the speedy passage, intact, of the Beveridge amendment. Attached to it was a portion of the Neill-Reynolds report, carefully labeled *"Preliminary."* In order to give his message full exposure, Theodore called a press conference. Copies of the message and the partial Neill-Reynolds report were handed to the reporters, and the President repeatedly emphasized that the full report, which he called "nauseating," might be released "in the public interest."

His message, combined with Sinclair's novel and the continuing efforts of Sullivan and others, created havoc. The packers' products, including smoked and canned meats, gathered dust on the shelves of butchers and grocers. Housewives throughout the United States and Canada refused to buy them, even when prices were dropped. In Western Europe and other foreign markets orders fell off alarmingly. In all, according to conservative estimates made by the packers themselves, their business declined sixty percent.

Facing certain ruin, they reversed their stand. A meat inspection bill, they realized, would restore public confidence in their products at home and abroad. Congressman Wadsworth sat down to write a new, mild version of the Beveridge amendment.

But Theodore refused to follow the precedent he had set in dealing with the railroad rate bill, and would not compromise. "I insist," he said, "upon a thorough and rigid, not a sham, inspection."

Writing a firm letter to Wadsworth, which he promptly made public, he called the substitute amendment "very, very bad."

Congressman Wadsworth, ill-advised, replied in writing to the effect that the President was "wrong, very, very wrong."

Theodore's patience was exhausted. Wadsworth was called to the White House and subjected to the full force of a presidential temper tantrum. He emerged white-faced and obviously shaken after a two-hour conference, and went straight to the House, where he submitted a new version of the Beveridge amendment that, in many respects, was even stronger than the original.

Federal meat inspectors, the measure provided, would be appointed under the civil service laws. The Federal government would bear the cost of inspection in order to make certain there would be no cheating. Most important, all meats and meat products that met the Federal sanitary inspection standard would bear a government stamp of approval; those that failed would be denied it. And the right of packers to procrastinate by appealing the rulings of inspectors in the law courts was curtailed.

Theodore's victory was so sweeping that House opposition to the Pure Food Bill also vanished, and that measure, too, was passed into law without further debate. Wadsworth was so badly crushed that, later in the year, he lost the House seat he had held since 1881, and was forced to retire to his farm.

Progressive Republicans, muckrakers, and the Democrats who had been advocating reforms for years under the banner of William Jennings Bryan began to press for other radical measures, among them a strict child labor law and a new system of Federal taxation based upon the income of the individual taxpayer. The President's program, which he called the Square Deal, was a resounding success.

He continued to win other laurels, chief among them the Nobel Peace Prize for 1906. This honor burnished his already vast international reputation, but his friends were puzzled when he expressed only quiet pleasure instead of his usual, exuberant joy.

Only Secretary of State Elihu Root learned the real reason for his reaction. "I'm very happy, naturally," Theodore told him. "But when something like this happens, I can't help wishing I'd been awarded what I wanted most and what was unfairly denied me, the Medal of Honor."

"I will tolerate no diminution or perversion of the principles that are making this nation great," Theodore said in the autumn of 1906, and did his best to prove it. "Coolie labor" from Japan, China, and Korea was being imported into California, which struggled to overcome the problems, including a lowering of the standard of living, caused by these poverty-stricken, ignorant peasants. San Francisco, which had suffered a disastrous earthquake and fire in April, was encountering more difficulties than other parts of the state, having brought in thousands of poor Orientals to help rebuild the city.

Theodore sympathized with the Californians, but lost his temper when San Francisco adopted rigid segregation laws for its schools. He intervened, exceeding his Constitutional authority, but the Californians were so unyielding that, in the following year, he was forced to send Secretary Taft back to the Orient to work out an agreement with the Japanese and Chinese to prevent immigration by individuals certain to create problems in a different civilization.

In other matters, however, he remained adamant. Aware of the rising tide of anti-Semitism caused by a heavy influx of poor Jewish immigrants from Russia and other nations in Eastern Europe, he deliberately made his own feelings clear. He appointed Oscar S. Straus of New York as Secretary of Commerce and Labor, the first Jew in American history to win a Cabinet seat.

He also proved that he did not carry a grudge against those who had opposed him. In the Congressional election campaign he generously supported Speaker Cannon and other Old Guard members who had fought his railroad, meat inspection, and pure food legislation. They were patriots as well as good Republicans, he declared, and therefore deserved the full support of their constituents.

The Roosevelt family continued to thrive, although friends sometimes wondered how Edith could stand the grueling pace of the social life her husband took for granted as normal. Whether at the White House in Washington or Sagamore Hill at Oyster Bay, however, she remained unflustered, a gracious hostess able to cope with the guests who arrived in a never-ending stream.

Contrary to predictions, marriage did not tame Alice. Still sharing her father's relish for everything in life, she was outspoken on every subject that came to her mind, actively helped advance her husband's career and feared no one. Ted, who had recovered from a delicate eye operation, was doing well at Harvard, where Kermit soon would join him after graduating from Groton. Ethel, who was maturing rapidly, was still sufficiently athletic to win tennis matches and swimming races from the boys who were interested in her. Archie and Quentin were still the terrors of the White House, where they and their many pets blithely interrupted state functions, private dinners, and their father's office routines.

Theodore had never been busier, but insisted on maintaining his physical fitness program. He hiked, rode, and boxed daily, and on his relatively brief, infrequent summer semi-holidays at Sagamore Hill he swam, went boating and took his children on camping trips. "They think I'm the best cook in the world," he told Edith. "It's lucky they never grow tired of bacon and eggs for breakfast or steak and potatoes for supper. It's all I know how to cook."

One evening in the autumn of 1906, while preparations were being made for a presidential visit to the Panama Canal Zone, Theodore brought an unusually large stack of papers to the family living room. After his customary bedtime romp with the younger children, he settled down in his easy chair, with the documents piled on a table beside him. He worked in silence, occasionally scribbling notes to staff members, and seemed to be concentrating hard on everything he read.

Edith, who had been leafing through magazines, glanced at him. "I know I shouldn't ask, but is something out of the ordinary happening?" she asked.

"Just the expected crises. Nothing earth-shattering."

She detected a strain in his voice, and quietly studied him while pretending to accept his statement at face value. "I haven't seen you bring so much work upstairs in months, that's all."

"I've fallen a little behind the past couple of days, and the backlog can become sky-high in no time, you know. There ought to be a special office, that of Assistant President. The man who holds the job would do nothing but sign official papers."

He appeared to be squinting, and Edith continued to observe him.

"I must spend at least an hour and a half a day just signing my name. Think of all I could do with that extra hour and a half!"

All at once she knew what was wrong. He was holding the papers close to his face as he read them, and seemed to find it difficult to focus.

Theodore became aware of her scrutiny, and attempted to smile blandly, but succeeded only in looking guilty.

"What's the matter, dear?" Edith managed to speak calmly.

"Why, nothing at all—"

"Theodore!"

"I'm having some new glasses made. A somewhat stronger prescription." He waved in an offhand manner and pretended to return to his work.

"You hadn't told me."

"It slipped my mind. The doctors came to my office this morning."

"Well."

"That's not unusual. They often do that when I'm busy. It's easier for them to come to me than—"

"How many doctors?"

"Two. The eye specialist we called in yesterday, and—"

"You haven't seen an eye specialist for several years."

Theodore put down his papers, closed his fountain pen and put it in his inner coat pocket with exaggerated patience. "I suppose you'll have to know."

"I should hope so!" Her façade of tranquillity had deserted her, and she was openly concerned, obviously angry.

He laughed without conviction. "There was a minor incident yesterday in the gym, when I was boxing."

She waited when he paused, her tension growing.

"My sparring partner really fooled me. After feinting with his left, he shot a right jab—"

"Who was your sparring partner?"

"A young captain. Army. Fine boy, and a first-rate boxer. He'd have done well in the professional ring—"

"Who is he?" she insisted.

"I conceal very little from you, but I prefer to mention no names. I don't want his career hurt by something that wasn't in any way his fault."

"I think," Edith said, "you'd better tell me the whole story."

"I'm trying. In my own way. But there isn't much to tell." Theodore displayed unusual nervousness, and, removing his glasses, polished them vigorously. "You and the doctors and I must remain the only people who know this. I can't allow anyone else to hear of it. That must be understood."

"I can't remember," Edith said, her teeth clenched, "when I last screamed."

"My left eye was damaged." Theodore sounded matter-of-fact, almost indifferent.

She jumped to her feet, went to him, and, holding his head between her hands, looked closely at the injured eye.

"You can't see a thing," he told her. "No one can, I'm relieved to say. It will make no difference of any kind in my appearance."

"How bad is the damage?" Edith tilted his head slightly toward the light.

"I'll have very little sight in the eye. It will be useless for reading or writing."

"Will you be able to see at a distance with it?"

He hesitated. "Not really."

"In other words, you've lost your vision in your left eye."

"Well, more or less." Theodore managed a grin. "But the doctors say my right eye will become somewhat stronger to compensate."

Edith knew he was telling her he had become virtually blind in one eye, and she exerted a great effort in an attempt to match his quiet acceptance of the situation. "How much will it affect your activity? I'd like to talk to the doctors myself."

"By all means, my dear. Please do. I've already informed them I don't plan to make any changes in my routines, and they aren't arguing with me. I'll admit they insist I give up boxing—"

"I should hope so!"

"—and I suppose I'll have to go along with that much. I don't want to be unreasonable. But I'll make no other changes. My right eye will soon adjust, and I'll be able to read and write as much as ever."

"I'm sure the doctors will want you to be careful—"

"Edith," Theodore said sternly, "I have many years of a full life still ahead, and I absolutely refuse to coddle myself. In fact, I'm going on a hunting trip after we come back from Panama, and if necessary, I'll do some target shooting until I become proficient with the one eye."

She realized his mind was made up, and that nothing would persuade him to exercise caution.

"I refuse to let anyone feel sorry for me. It would be even worse if people claimed I was failing to live up to my obligations. So no one —and I include the children, family, old friends like Cabot—must ever know about this little handicap. I'm sure I can promise you that not one person on this earth will ever guess I'm using only one eye."

She wasn't certain whether he was being courageous or foolhardy.

He hooked his spectacles over his ears and reached for another official document, ending the discussion.

Edith returned to her chair, wanting to talk about the affliction, but not knowing what to say.

"I must admit to you," he said in a small, wistful voice, "that I'm going to miss boxing. It's been an important part of my life for so long." For some moments there was no sound in the room but the scratching of his pen, and then he chuckled. "But this will give me the chance to improve my judo. You know, that's a bully sport!"

The confidential War Department memorandum that reached the desk of the Commander-in-Chief in the autumn of 1906 related the purported facts of an unfortunate incident that had taken place in the dusty town of Brownsville, Texas, in mid-August. But Theodore did not view the matter as complicated, and he had no way of knowing that his reaction to it, combined with subsequent complications, would haunt him for the rest of his life.

On the surface, the facts were simple. Three companies of the United States 25th Infantry Regiment arrived at Fort Brown, on the banks of the Rio Grande, a few miles from Brownsville, on August 1. The troops were Negroes, commanded by white officers. Many were veterans with fifteen years of service in the Regular Army, and had accumulated distinguished records. Six were winners of the Congressional Medal of Honor, the nation's highest military award, which the President himself still privately coveted.

The white citizens of Brownsville were less than overjoyed by the presence of their new neighbors, and the black troops reciprocated in kind. Feelings ran high, some of Brownsville citizens officially protested the presence of the troops, and on the night of August 13 the regimental commander, Major Charles W. Penrose, took the precaution of restricting his men to quarters.

A few minutes after midnight shots were heard, apparently in Brownsville. The men were ordered to fall in, with their rifles; a roll call was made, and only two soldiers, who had been given passes earlier in the evening, were not present. By this time between one hundred and two hundred shots had been fired, according to later estimates.

A company commander was sent to Brownsville to find and bring back the two men who were absent with permission. He returned with several town officials, including the mayor, one Dr. Comb, who informed the horrified Major Penrose that a civilian had been killed and a police officer wounded by rioting Negro troops. These reports subsequently were found to be totally lacking in foundation.

The troops were restricted to their barracks. At daybreak all rifles were inspected and found to be clean. Soon thereafter Dr. Comb returned with a number of empty cartridge cases and several unfired shells, which had been found in the town. Several Brownsville citizens then appeared to inform the major that they had seen ten or fifteen Negro soldiers advancing through the town the previous night, firing their Springfields.

Major Penrose could not imagine how his men could have been responsible. His only explanation, which he included in his report to the War Department on August 15, was that some of the troops had stolen out of the garrison but had managed to return in time for roll call.

The Inspector General's Office conducted an investigation. Its report, prepared by Major A. P. Blocksom, concluded that the troops were guilty and that many who had not taken part in the raid must have known it had been planned.

The President received the War Department report early in October. He was furiously angry, but deliberately waited until November 7, after the Congressional election of 1906 had been held, before acting. His caution was well advised. According to figures later published in the Washington *Post*, a switch of one-half the Negro votes in Cincinnati would have defeated Congressman Nicholas Longworth. The New York *Herald* estimated that a substantial change in the national Negro vote would have reduced the Republican majority in the House of Representatives from 59 to 14. The Chicago *Tribune* said it would have dropped even farther.

Theodore summarily ordered the one hundred and sixty men of the three companies "discharged without honor and forever barred from re-enlistment." In his order he referred to the "atrocious conduct of the troops" and their "lawless and murderous spirit." His temper rising, he concluded that the "act was one of horrible atrocity, unparalleled for infamy in the annals of the United States Army."

In his final paragraph the President declared, forcefully, that the action he had taken was in no way based upon the fact that the soldiers whom he deemed guilty were Negroes.

Secretary of War Taft was afraid the President had gone too far. An attorney of note who, after his own term as President, would serve with distinction as Chief Justice of the United States Supreme Court, he saw some gaping holes in the President's stand, and pointed them out to him. Not one of the raiders had been positively identified by the Army or the citizens of Brownsville. Not one soldier had admitted his guilt. No witnesses could prove the shots had been fired by the troops, and Taft thought it possible that townsmen had used ammu-

nition from the Fort Brown arsenal, firing the shots themselves in order
to cause trouble for the men of the 25th Infantry.

Equally important, Taft felt, it was possible that the President's order
was unconstitutional. Due process of law had not been observed. No
court-martial had been held; not one soldier had been formally accused and tried. Nor had any action been taken in the civilian courts.

Theodore, however, remained adamant.

Then, two days after directing the severe punishment, he wrote,
*When the discipline and honor of the American Army are at stake,
I shall never under any circumstances consider the political bearing of
upholding that discipline.*

*To show you how little the question of color enters into the mat-
ter, I need only point out that when a white officer was alleged to
be guilty, in speaking of the incident, of commenting unfavorably on
the black troops generally, I directed an immediate investigation into
his words, and suitable proceedings against him should he prove to
have been correctly quoted.*

On November 8, having dispensed justice according to his best
lights, Theodore put the matter from his mind and sailed for the Panama Canal Zone with Edith on board a battleship, the U.S.S. *Louisiana*,
which was escorted by two powerful armored cruisers, the *Tennessee*
and the *Washington*.

As he wrote to his children, he had a bully time in the Canal Zone.
In fact, he enjoyed himself so much that one afternoon, in the blistering tropical heat, he spent more than three hours on the driver's seat of
a huge steam shovel, scooping out earth for the "big ditch" of his
dreams. Edith and several other members of the party, unable to tolerate the sun and dust, returned to the ship, but the Navy officers
who comprised his escort remained with him as an appreciative audience.

The presidential party returned home by way of Puerto Rico, where
Theodore's genuine interest in the island's development and his un-
reserved friendliness toward the native leaders he met proved, to his
own subsequent satisfaction, that he was himself in no way anti-Negro.

When he returned to Washington he discovered that a national
storm had broken during his absence. The champion of the Negro
cause, who called the matter "an American Dreyfus Case," was Republican Senator Joseph B. Foraker. The devotion Foraker displayed
in behalf of the dismissed soldiers over the next two years demonstrated the sincerity of his convictions to most Americans, but not to

the President. Foraker was a friend of Standard Oil, a company the Administration had attacked on anti-trust grounds, and so, as Theodore said on many occasions, "He's my enemy. He's trying, on strictly personal grounds, to embarrass me."

The press throughout the North supported Foraker, who in speech after speech hammered home the theme that the dismissed soldiers were innocent. And even the newspapers that consistently admired the President and his works condemned his harsh actions in the case.

Pained and hurt, insisting he was misunderstood, Theodore took immediate steps to put his sentiments on the record. His first chance came in his annual message to Congress, which he prepared soon after his return home. Scornful and angry, he denounced the lynching of Negroes in the South as "a perversion of all that is American."

He also asked Congress to provide "ample funds" for Negro education. "It is out of the question," he declared, "for our people as a whole permanently to rise by treading down any of their own number. The free public school, the chance for each boy or girl to get a good elementary education, lies at the foundation of our whole political situation. This is as true for the Negro as for the white man."

If he hoped to end the controversy, he hoped in vain. At the annual dinner meeting of the Gridiron Club, the Washington newspaper correspondents' association, members of the press ridiculed the President in several satirical sketches. Theodore laughed without humor in the appropriate places, and then rose to his feet. In a long, rambling speech devoid of his usual wit he defended himself; then he rashly attacked Senator Foraker, who sat only a few feet away.

Foraker requested and was granted the opportunity to reply. For a quarter of an hour the Ohio lawyer picked the President's handling of the Brownsville case to bits. His manner that of a cool and detached prosecuting attorney, he made the President look foolish, and he concluded with the ringing assertion, "His actions, gentlemen, were illegal. They were unconstitutional. Above all, they were unjustifiable."

The applause in the dining room was deafening.

Belatedly the correspondents noted that the President was on his feet again, his face apoplectic, his arms waving madly. Lodge and Taft sat nearby, and although they knew he had lost complete control of himself, they did not dare interfere in the presence of the press corps.

"Neither the Senate nor the Senator from Ohio has the right to interfere in this case!" Theodore roared. "Only the President, acting in his Constitutional capacity as Commander-in-Chief, had the authority to act. And the President acted!

"The only reason I didn't have the guilty hanged was because I couldn't find out which ones actually did the shooting! I studied this case, and I tell you, some of those men were bloody butchers!"

Glaring at Foraker, he turned and stamped out of the room in a silence as pregnant as the applause for Senator Foraker had been deafening.

Cabot Lodge caught up with him before he could reach the new presidential limousine. "You idiot!" he exclaimed, not caring that he was addressing the President of the United States. "You've ruined yourself!"

Theodore had recovered his good humor, and grinned. "I'm an idiot, all right, but the boys will forgive me. They know where I stand."

"Don't be too sure of that."

They walked in silence toward the new automobile, and Theodore tugged at his mustache. "They shouldn't have called on Foraker to speak. But they did. And he spoke." Again he was reflective. "I can't abide the man, but if I'd been in his boots, I'd have said much the same things. I don't have the heart to blame him for that speech."

The evidence in the Brownsville case, the President told his Cabinet, was insufficient. Therefore he had decided to reopen the whole matter. The Secretary of War was ordered to review the findings. And Attorney General Charles J. Bonaparte was directed to send his assistant to Brownsville for the purpose of making a completely new, independent investigation.

On January 14, 1907, the President sent a special message to the Senate on the subject of the Brownsville incident. Repeating that reliable witnesses had seen the Negro troops making a raid, he nevertheless backed down somewhat from his original, adamant stand. *If any soldier of the 25th Infantry who was dismissed from the Army can prove his innocence,* he wrote, *he will be reinstated. But upon any such man is the burden of thus clearing himself.*

Foraker, in a swift rebuttal echoed by senator after senator, charged that the President was perverting the very essence of the English common law upon which all American jurisprudence was based. "Under our system, as every schoolboy knows," he said, "a man is innocent until he is proved guilty!"

Theodore stubbornly refused to admit he might have been wrong, but he tried, repeatedly, to prove he was not prejudiced against the black man. In a directive that was highly publicized, he ordered Secretary of War Taft to form a Negro battalion of heavy artillery, the Army's first. And in 1908 he sent a very firm letter to the Nashville, Chattanooga & St. Louis Railway Company, threatening it with the strongest legal action at his command unless it provided Negro passengers with dining and sanitary facilities. The company complied, but the Negro press greeted the President's efforts with restrained applause.

In March 1908 a special Senate committee conducting its own investigation of the Brownsville affair voted by a slim majority that the President had been right. A minority—and the press—indicated that Republican committee members might be worrying about the coming presidential election, which was less than eight months distant.

Senator Foraker, himself scheduled for retirement, made the most brilliant speech of his career, and proved to the satisfaction of many millions of Americans that the dismissed troops were innocent.

Theodore's resolve at last was shaken, and he ordered the Justice Department to investigate the matter anew. In December 1908 he sent still another message to the Senate, reopening the case. Only a few soldiers were guilty, he said, and the others had been intimidated by them. Therefore he was directing the War Department to conduct hearings in the individual case of every dismissed soldier who requested it. If found innocent, he would be given full and unqualified reinstatement.

This action, he believed, was in keeping with American traditions of justice. He had done everything in his power to be fair.

Until now the most distinguished of American Negroes, Booker T. Washington, Theodore's friend, had maintained an embarrassed silence. Finally, however, he spoke out, writing, *The bulk of the Negro people are more and more inclined to reach the decision that even though the President did go against their wishes in dismissing the soldiers at Brownsville, he has favored them in nine cases out of ten, and the intelligent portion of the race does not believe that it is fair or wise to condemn such good friends as President Roosevelt and Secretary Taft because they might have done what they considered right.*

It is not the part of common sense to cherish ill will against one who has helped us in so many ways as the President has.

The reinstatement of about one-third of the dismissed Brownsville troops following War Department hearings during the years after Theodore left the White House convinced him that he had been vindicated. And he insisted to the end of his days that he had been right in everything he had done. Admittedly the Brownsville matter was one of the most controversial and persisting problems of his second term as President. In the *Autobiography* he later wrote, however, he did not mention the subject.

"I sometimes feel only despair," Cabot Lodge said in July 1906, "when I contemplate Theodore's affinity for impossible causes. I ask myself where is he leading us, and when I find out, I wish I hadn't been so curious."

The Senator's feelings were shared by most Americans that summer. The Roosevelt family had gone off to Oyster Bay, and Theodore, alone at the White House, spent even more time than usual in the company of intellectuals he admired. Among them was Professor Brander Matthews of Columbia University, with whom he discussed literature, and through Matthews he became interested in an unusual project. Steel magnate and philanthropist Andrew Carnegie had made a large donation to an organization known as the Spelling Reform Association, of which Matthews was a prominent member.

"English is the most difficult of languages," Matthews told his friend, "principally because of our archaic spelling. We still spell words as we did five hundred years ago, not the way they're pronounced today."

Theodore was fascinated, and Matthews gave him a small pamphlet the Spelling Reform Association had published. In it were a number of suggested spelling simplifications, among them "thru" for "through" and "bot" for "boat."

I thoroly aprov, the delighted Theodore wrote to the Columbia educator. *The new speling maks sens!*

The President sought converts, but Cabinet members shied away and his friends made excuses. *There's no ful lik an old ful,* Henry Adams said in a note to Cecil Spring-Rice.

But Theodore persisted, and when Presidential Secretary William Loeb, who had no real choice, finally succumbed, he decided to strike a bold blow for simplified spelling. Members of the Association were elated when they learned that Loeb had been instructed to use the new spelling in presidential correspondence. Not satisfied with this radical departure from tradition, Theodore instructed the Public Printer to use the Association's pamphlet as an official spelling guide in all the documents it published.

The press was overjoyed, and the Louisville *Courier-Journal* launched the first salvo. *The President's name,* it declared in an editorial, *should be speld Rucevelt, the first silabel riming with goose.*

Wat r we kuming 2? asked the Cleveland *Plain Dealer* in mock wonder. *R Presdent thinks of wundrus things!*

The New York *Times* adopted a pontifical tone. *We rely upon the American press to save the nation's sanity, particularly that of school spelling teachers. The newspapers will take the kindly view that the President's heterographical freaks are misprints, and will correct them into English.*

President Charles W. Eliot of Harvard, asked to comment, laughed until he wept, but refused to say a word for publication. President Nicholas Murray Butler of Columbia merely shook his head. President Woodrow Wilson of Princeton, one of Theodore's greatest admirers, contented himself with a murmur. "Every man is entitled to his own opinions, but I must reserve mine. They are not fit for print."

Senators and Congressmen, including Theodore's strongest supporters, were unable to resist the opportunity to exercise their wits at his expense. Their views were given a full airing, and the newspapers duly reported new outbursts of ridicule through the late summer and autumn of 1906. No opportunity was lost, and even the Washington correspondents joined in the fun. In September, when the President was watching a Naval review from the *Mayflower,* a vessel bearing a huge sign reading, *PRES BOT* sailed around it.

He made his pleasure obvious. Cupping his hands, he shouted across the water, "Thank you, gentlemen! A most delicate compliment."

The nation responsible for the language in the first place was not amused. *The President's American,* the *Times* of London declared, *is usurping the King's English. The United States has gone too far.*

When the Supreme Court convened in the autumn for its new term, it saw fit to render a judgment insofar as its own business was concerned. *Any citation of a previous decision, made by this Court,* the reserved Justices informed the Solicitor General of the United States in a firm memorandum, *which invokes the new spelling, is not a literal quotation.*

Theodore was somewhat bewildered by the growing opposition. "I've never known so many people opposed to progress," he told Cabot Lodge.

"It all depends," the Senator from Massachusetts replied, "on your definition of progress."

In December the House of Representatives entered the controversy. Badgered by the President on such diverse matters as meat inspection, the railroad rate bill, the fight against monopolistic trusts and the immigration of "coolie labor" into California, the Congressmen were no longer in a playful mood. A resolution was passed directing that all government publications, including those issued by the Executive Department, observe standard spelling practices. If the U. S. Government Printing Office and others who published government documents failed to comply, the resolution said, the House would refuse to vote the necessary payroll appropriations for the offenders.

The machinery of the government threatened to creak to a halt, and Theodore capitulated. *I could not by fighting have kept the new spelling in,* he wrote Professor Matthews, *"and it was infinitely worse to go into an undignified contest when I was beaten. But,* he added in a final burst of defiance, *I am mighty glad I did the thing anyhow. In my own correspondence I shall continue to use the new spelling.*

He kept his word, and for the rest of his life used the Association's pamphlet as his guide.

"I am worried about Japan," Theodore said in April, 1907, to Senator Eugene Hale of Maine, whom he had summoned to a very private White House conference. "Sometimes I wonder if I let her win too much in the peace treaty with Russia. She's too big for her breeches."

The bewhiskered, enigmatic Hale, who was chairman of the Senate Naval Affairs Committee, was not impressed. Rumors had reached Capitol Hill that the President was seeking a large appropriation from Congress for the purpose of building major additions to the fleet, and Hale suspected an ulterior motive might be responsible for the unexpected conference. He nodded, but said nothing.

Theodore pretended to be unaware of his silence. "We maintain diplomatic proprieties with Tokyo, to be sure," he continued. "Our relations with the chief civilians in their government are good enough, and we're fairly friendly with those who haven't forgotten that we helped her win a great many peaceful concessions from the Russians. They're gentlemen."

"Are there some who aren't, Mr. President?"

Theodore searched through a pile of documents beside him.

The one he picked up, Hale noted, was at the top of the heap.

"I think you'll be interested in the secret instructions I recently sent Leonard Wood in Manila. They're detailed orders outlining his defense responsibilities in the event that the Japanese invade the Philippine Islands."

The Senator glanced through the long telegram. "I'm no expert in these matters, but it seems very thorough, very complete."

Theodore reached for the paper. "It should be. These orders represent the combined efforts of the best planners in both the Navy and War Departments. I thought this would indicate how seriously I regard a threat of war with Japan."

"I'd be even more interested, Mr. President, in seeing some reports from General Wood that might indicate any threatening moves the Japanese may be making against the Philippines."

Theodore's ruddy face turned a shade deeper. Although Leonard Wood was his close friend, the general had disappointed him by telling a group of Congressmen who had visited Manila that he believed the United States would remain at peace in the Orient. "Leonard has been kept so busy administering the affairs of the Filipinos and putting their house in order that he's had little time to see what might be happening in Tokyo and other places."

Hale nodded and waited.

"I wonder if you remember that I transferred four battleships to the Pacific last month."

The Senator couldn't suppress a smile. As the President well knew, he had made a fiery speech demanding the reason for the transfer, but the Navy had not given him a satisfactory reply.

"A letter from a colleague and dear friend of mine explains itself." The President reached into the pile again, then waved a communication from Rear Admiral Alfred Thayer Mahan, former Superintendent of the Naval Academy, who was universally recognized as the world's most renowned naval historian and strategist.

The letter was long and complicated, but Hale dutifully tried to wade through it.

Theodore impatiently snatched it from him. "Let me summarize. He criticizes me severely for the transfer."

"Aha!" Hale rubbed his hands together. "Mahan and I don't often agree, but I don't see how any sensible man could fail to wonder why the Navy Department was so extravagant."

"The Navy obeyed a directive from the President, and isn't responsible. The President assumes full responsibility." Theodore's mustache appeared to bristle.

Hale was embarrassed. Never a willing debater, he had no desire to become embroiled in a face-to-face argument with a belligerent and defensive Chief Executive.

"Listen to this." Theodore wanted to avoid unpleasantness, too. "Here's the crux of Mahan's stand. *What is accomplished by the dispatch of these warships? Our main fleet, stationed in the Atlantic, would be deprived of the firepower of these ships in the event of sudden hostilities in Europe or Latin America. Also, as is obvious, a scant four ships, no matter how superior the seamanship and gunnery of commanders, officers and men, could do little damage to the powerful Japanese fleet that swept from the seas the entire Imperial Russian Navy.* Do you follow his logic, Senator?"

Hale felt he was being maneuvered. "Of course, Mr. President."

"*Should the Japanese threat be sufficiently serious to warrant the taking of defense measures, I recommend the transfer of the entire fleet to the Pacific.* That's Mahan's advice, Senator!" Theodore bore down hard. "The entire fleet!"

"But he didn't say he regards the threat as serious, Mr. President. He put it on a conditional basis."

"I need scarcely remind you that Constitutional responsibility for the determination of a threat to our security is vested in the Commander-in-Chief." Theodore glowered for an instant, then softened. "I'm trying," he said, his tone becoming almost conspiratorial, "to bring you up to date. Of course, you may have your own sources of information—"

"All I know is what I read in the public prints, Mr. President. The responsible press, that is. Hearst and Pulitzer would have the country believing that what they call the yellow peril is real, but I've seen no evidence indicating any intention on the part of the Mikado's government to invade us."

"No, we haven't reached that point." Theodore lowered his voice dramatically. "Yet."

"Correspondents in Tokyo have been writing that there's some anti-American feeling there, and I can't blame the Japanese. The sixty thousand of their nationals who have come to California have been having a bad time there."

"Seventy-five thousand, Senator, and I can't blame them, either. Our citizens on the Coast haven't been very hospitable, and the Japanese

are a proud people who feel they've won a major war and are entitled
to the respect of the world. And so they are! We'd feel as they do if
we were in their position."

"If you're able to understand that position, Mr. President, surely you
can work out an accommodation with them that will reduce tensions."

"I'm sending Secretary Taft to Tokyo for the purpose. For the present, that's confidential. I haven't announced it yet."

"Then I don't see your cause for concern, Mr. President. You claim
we're being threatened. Where? How?"

"I have every reason to believe that Will Taft's mission is going
to be successful—temporarily. He'll buy time for us. Japan isn't strong
enough yet for a war with us, and she knows it. It's one thing to beat
an Army and Navy of Russian serfs who hate their Czar. It's something quite different to defeat eighty million free Americans!"

"Then I don't see—"

"Joe Pulitzer and William Randolph Hearst may exaggerate, Senator, but they're right, basically. Japan is an expansionist state. She
has Korea and she wants Manchuria. She can't feel very comfortable,
seeing us sitting on her flank in the Philippines. It was another matter when Spain was still there. She was too weak to be a threat. But
we're a major Pacific power ourselves, the only power there other than
Japan, so it's only natural that our interests clash."

"You're speaking in terms of textbook theories, Mr. President?" Hale
spoke politely, but his expression was skeptical.

"My record indicates my appreciation of the intellectual processes,
Senator, but more than reason is involved here. I'm also a great believer
in mental intuition. My own, that is. Perhaps you'd like to read a
copy of a letter I wrote recently to my friend, Sir George Trevelyan,
the British historian."

Hale shook his head.

"I told him that unless there's a distinct change in climate, a war
between Japan and the United States is inevitable. We won't attack
them, I said, but they'll attack us, perhaps in five years, perhaps thirty."

"I find it hard to believe that, Mr. President," the Senator from Maine
said.

"So the real question is one of judgment, yours against mine. Naturally, I prefer mine. I'll grant you that we've caught no Japanese
spies mining Manila Bay or trying to foment revolution in San Francisco. Nevertheless, I must rely on my instinct."

Hale was not the first to discover that it was painstakingly difficult to counter the President's intuition with logic. "You say we're the only major power in the Pacific other than Japan. Surely Great Britain—"

"Oh, she has many interests there. Hong Kong, her spheres of influence in China, her island protectorates. Australia and New Zealand, too, although they're growing and soon will be able to look after themselves. Britain's lifeline to India lies through Suez, not the Pacific." Theodore's manner was that of a patient classroom lecturer.

The Senator wondered whether he was being patronized, but decided to give the President the benefit of the doubt. "I wish I could see the situation your way," he said, and shrugged.

Theodore became very grave. "I'd like to speak freely, and in confidence. Senator, my political enemies and a very vocal part of the press call me a jingoist. They say I wave the American flag to cover my shortcomings, and that I won't be satisfied until I've established colonies all over the world. You've been hearing that kind of talk about me for years."

Surprised by his candor, Hale could only nod.

"I'm an American, all right. First, last, and always. But I'm no jingoist. Let me read you a paragraph from the instructions I'm drafting for Secretary Taft when he goes to Tokyo. No one except Secretary Root has read this."

Hale didn't want to hear anything that might limit his own freedom of action, and held up a hand.

But Theodore gave him no chance to interrupt. "*The Philippine Islands form our heel of Achilles. They are all that makes the present situation with Japan dangerous. I think that in some way and with some phraseology that you think wise you should state to them that if they handle themselves wisely in their legislative assembly we shall at the earliest possible moment give them a nearly complete independence. I think that to have some pretty clear avowal of our intention not to permanently keep them and to give them independence would remove a temptation from Japan's way and would render our task easier.* There you have it, Senator, and I'm sure you realize that many of my strongest supporters in Congress would be very unhappy at the prospect of giving up the Philippines."

Hale stroked his beard. "I must admit you astonish me, Mr. President. No nation gives up territory it acquires."

"The United States is unique." Theodore looked pleased with himself. "We could have made Cuba a colony, and didn't. Within a very few years Puerto Rico will become self-governing, and if I have any influence at that time, I'll recommend she be given the choice of remaining associated with us or striking out on her own."

"Is that what you have in mind for the Philippines?"

"Not precisely. We can't administer her affairs forever. She's too far from our mainland. So we'll have to set her free some day, with a guarantee that we'll protect her independence. I'd like to see some sort of mutually acceptable arrangement made as soon as the Filipinos can govern themselves. Tensions with Japan will be reduced, and we'll be buying time."

"For what purpose, Mr. President?" Hale found it difficult to follow the leaps of a mind so much more agile than his own.

"We must increase our armed strength in the Pacific," Theodore said patiently.

The Senator was confused. "But the Philippines are our first line of defense."

"At present, yes, but they shouldn't be. Japan could take the islands from us any time she chooses, so we've got to recognize strategic reality. We ought to keep some bases there, of course—military and naval outposts, you might call them. But our real defense lines must be established in Hawaii and Alaska."

"According to your logic, sir, Hawaii is expendable, too."

Theodore became upset. "Never!" he shouted, and pounded his desk. "Hawaii is American, and so is Alaska, and no President will ever consider giving them up. They belong to our frontier tradition—"

"But they're so far from the rest of the country," the Senator protested.

"The telephone is shortening distances, ships are becoming faster all the time, and I have every confidence that new methods of transportation will develop in this century. Change is in the air, and you can feel it!"

It was true, Hale thought, that Roosevelt was an incurable romantic.

"I subscribe to the theory," Theodore said, his manner that of a man who had just mounted a rostrum and was launching into a major address, "that the frontier has formed and molded the character of the American people. We've always had new territories with inexpensive land for immigrants, who are coming in at the rate of more than one million per year. Think of it, Senator! More people are coming here every year now than came from the establishment of the Jamestown colony to the publication of the Declaration of Independence. We're

growing faster in a single year than we did in one hundred and sixty-
nine years! Our changes are exhilarating, and could be frightening if
we had no more frontier lands!"

Hale tried to interrupt, but, when the President was excited, no
man could stem the flow of words that poured from him.

"The Oklahoma Territory is putting her house in order, and I have
every reasonable expectation that she'll be granted statehood this year.
That leaves only two Territories on the North American continent,
New Mexico and Arizona, and we're growing so fast they'll soon become states, too. Then where will the newcomers go? City life doesn't
suit everyone—"

"Immigration may have to be curbed, Mr. President." Hale managed to cut in by speaking loudly and forcibly.

Theodore blinked at him in surprise, his train of thought momen-
tarily broken. "That day may come, much as I dread it. But we'd fail
in our obligation to the people of Europe who want liberty and opportunity if we closed the gates now! I'll fight that with every weapon
I have!" His jaw jutted forward, and he unconsciously took a boxer's
stance behind his desk.

His idealistic patriotism was so naïve that it sometimes became impossible to discuss national problems with him. "As you say, sir, we
aren't being forced to close the gates quite yet." Hale tried to bring
him back to earth.

"Alaska will become a frontier, and so will the Hawaiian Islands.
I don't believe it's too far-fetched to accept the possibility that both
may become states themselves. But no matter what their status,
Japan won't try to take either from us. She knows we wouldn't tolerate any such attempt, not for one minute!"

In some strange way the Senator couldn't quite understand, the
President had returned to the basic theme of their conversation.

"She'll laugh at us, though, if we just sit back on our mainland and
shake a fist at her across the Pacific. Study her history, Senator, and
you'll discover she has a strong warrior tradition. When you've grown
up with a sword in your hand, you don't scare easily, and you may
even snicker if an unarmed man tells you to stay away from his property and behave yourself."

Hale began to see the ultimate point that Roosevelt was trying to
make, and thought it typical of him to put the question on a basis
that might open anyone who opposed him to charges of being unpa-
triotic.

"Tokyo isn't afraid of us. We've had several strong messages warning us not to mistreat her nationals on the West Coast. She's right, but now it's our turn. We must—and I stress that this is essential to us as a sovereign nation—we must make certain she knows we aren't afraid of her."

"How do you propose we do that, sir?" The Senator from Maine became very cautious.

"Why, we increase our Navy, of course." Theodore sounded sweetly reasonable.

"Battleships and cruisers are expensive, Mr. President!"

"It will be a damnsight more expensive," Theodore snapped, "to be dragged into a major war without adequate preparation. If we're strong enough, we may not have to fight."

Hale didn't want to be a target of the President's wrath, and therefore avoided a direct confrontation. "Some of my colleagues might regard your logic as specious, sir."

"Any senator who failed to grasp the significance of increasing our fleet in times like these would be derelict in his duty." Theodore quietly issued his challenge to combat, making it plain that he would not hesitate to launch a personal attack on any legislator who opposed him. "The British fleet is the most powerful on earth, and you don't see anyone, not even Bill the Kaiser, thumbing his nose at the Royal Navy. I'd go straight to the voters to point out these truths, and I'd willingly travel to any state for the purpose!"

Not even the most solidly entrenched members of either House of Congress wanted the President coming to his home and appealing to the electorate over his head. The tactics Roosevelt was threatening to use were unorthodox, so primitive they might be regarded as vicious, but they proved he was not bluffing and meant to do everything in his considerable power to obtain appropriations for a larger Navy. Hale again stroked his beard, deliberately shielding his face with his hand in order to mask his expression. "A loyal senator who was treated in that cavalier a fashion would resent it, Mr. President!"

"Not nearly as much as the voters in his state would resent him. Remember I have a built-in advantage." He grinned cheerfully to lessen the deadly impact. "He'll want to be re-elected, but I'll be leaving public office at the end of my term, so the people of the country know I have no ax to grind but their security, prosperity, and welfare. So, I'm sure, you'll want to explain my position to the members of your Naval Affairs Committee. And I feel certain we'll be able to work together in solving this problem. No one wants to be accused of niggardliness when the entire future of the United States is at stake, at least in the sober opinion of the Commander-in-Chief!"

Theodore used the full power and prestige of his office in his as yet unpublicized campaign to enlarge the Navy. "I want to line up enough support in both the Senate and the House to make very sure that I'll win this campaign," he told Cabot Lodge. "I'm reminded of my term as Assistant Secretary of the Navy, but this round I hold more trumps!"

Word was "leaked" to senators and congressmen that any legislator who opposed the President's program might find it far more difficult to obtain White House approval of his patronage requests. In order to drive the point home, Theodore deliberately procrastinated whenever he faced such a request from a senator or congressman who disapproved of the expansion program.

The Navy itself became its own lobbyist, too. Legislators were invited to Navy facilities in their districts, where roaring cannon saluted them. Parades were held in their honor, they were entertained by admirals and captains, and, more often than not, were invited to make addresses to Navy personnel.

Theodore wrote a "private memorandum" to Secretary of State Root, and copies of the document mysteriously found their way into the cloakrooms of Congress. The memo read: *Tokyo's armed forces are formidable, in a far better state of preparedness for war than our own. It goes without saying that I want to remain on the best possible terms with Japan. I have no desire to harm her interests, treat her unfairly or do her any wrong. Nevertheless, I want still more to see our Navy strengthened and maintained at the highest point of efficiency. No matter what my own feelings, or that of any successor to the Presidency, the United States Navy is and must continue to be the real keeper of the peace in the Pacific.*

The California Assembly added to the tensions between the United States and Japan by passing a bill that limited the ownership of property by Japanese nationals in the state. In San Francisco, roaming bands of self-appointed vigilantes burned a Japanese restaurant to the ground and, in senseless attacks, beat several of the Mikado's subjects. Japan lodged a stiff official protest in Washington, and one of her high-ranking Navy officers, Admiral Gambei Yamamoto, who was passing through the United States en route home from Europe, called on President Roosevelt at Oyster Bay, where Theodore had just joined his family for part of the summer.

The President and the admiral managed to observe the amenities, but the atmosphere was cool. The admiral complained, and the President sincerely expressed his regrets. The admiral made the mistake of continuing to complain until he aroused his host's ire, and then Theodore indicated he was thinking of sending the main fleet of the United States Navy to the Orient on a "good will" cruise. The possible voyage received major press attention, but no one in Washington seemed to know anything about the matter, and Theodore was distressingly vague when correspondents approached him one day while he and Ethel were drubbing Ted and Kermit at tennis.

Secretary Taft left for Tokyo on his new mission, and departed with so little fanfare that newsmen had no opportunity to interview him. He was on the high seas before it was learned that he had gone.

The warships of the main American fleet changed colors, their usual, drab gray being replaced by several coats of dazzling white paint. These vessels put out to sea from several Atlantic ports, under sealed orders, and quietly vanished. There was virtually no speculation in print about the unorthodox maneuver, the President having directed the observation of wartime secrecy precautions.

In September, Theodore and Edith returned to Washington with their younger children, and the journey was enlivened by the repeated escape of a pet snake that Quentin had captured just before leaving Oyster Bay. Theodore immediately plunged into a series of meetings, and his reception rooms were soon overflowing with Executive Department officials and Congressmen. He worked at high speed, and in less than two hours saw the Secretaries of State, Treasury, Navy, and Agriculture.

Then, while busy conferring with the Attorney General and several other Department of Justice officers, the door opened and a breathless ten-year-old boy hurried into the inner sanctum.

"Papa," Quentin said, "look!"

The Attorney General tried to make himself invisible in his chair when he saw the child clutching a four-foot-long snake in one hand and several smaller snakes in the other.

The President chuckled, however, when the boy unceremoniously dumped the wriggling creatures into his lap. "Well," he boomed, "what have we here? A king snake, obviously. And I'm not sure what these others may be."

"Mr. Schmidt told me, Papa, but I forget. He loaned them to me."

"That was kind of him." Theodore turned to the dazed Justice Department officials, who watched in horror as the long king snake coiled itself around his arm. "Mr. Schmidt owns a pet shop nearby, and my sons have been known to spend most of their waking hours there. What prompted Mr. Schmidt to make this noble gesture, Quentie?"

"The trip from Oyster Bay upset my own snake, Papa. He wasn't feeling good—"

"He wasn't feeling well."

"That's what I meant. I took him to Mr. Schmidt for some medicine, and he'll stay there until tomorrow. So Mr. Schmidt loaned me these fellows, and that way I won't be lonely."

"I must thank Mr. Schmidt for his consideration." The President deftly snatched one of the small snakes from the reach of the king snake, which was trying to devour it.

"The little one," Quentin said, "can kill you if it bites you."

The Attorney General of the United States gasped and became pale.

But Theodore remained calm. "I'll have to be careful, won't I, son?" he asked, continuing to hold the snake.

"Aw, it won't matter today. Mr. Schmidt took out his poison sac."

"If I were you," Theodore said, "I wouldn't discuss the problem with your mother. In fact, I wouldn't even tell her you have these—ah—overnight guests."

Quentin laughed. "You don't have to tell me, Papa. Archie and I are going to hide all of them in our room tonight. Mama doesn't like snakes, and Ethel would start screaming again."

"Yes, I dare say," Theodore murmured, and disentangled himself sufficiently to look at his watch. "Quentie, much as I admire these fine pets, you're slowing the wheels of justice." He thrust the snakes at his son. "We'll look up their names and characteristics in one of your nature books tonight, but right now I must deal with some slightly less important problems."

Quentin took the snakes and started toward the door.

"Whatever you do," Theodore called after him, "don't take them near your mother and Ethel!"

"You can count on me, Papa," the boy replied, using a foot to close the door behind him.

The Attorney General and his staff members breathed a collective sigh of relief, and the conference resumed.

In a few moments, however, they were interrupted by hoarse shouts and the crashing of a chair as it toppled over.

"I think, gentlemen," Theodore said, hurrying to the door, "that all of us can guess the nature of this new government crisis." He opened the door a few inches and peered into the adjoining chamber.

Several members of the Senate and House Naval Affairs committees were milling around a tousle-haired boy.

"Don't try to pull the serpent up his sleeve," one of them said, his tone urgent. "You'll be going against the grain of its scales, and it'll become annoyed."

Theodore laughed aloud when he saw the king snake's head protruding from one of Quentin's sleeves. As nearly as he could judge from the bulges, the better part of the snake was draped across the child's shoulders and neck, beneath his jacket.

"What'll we do, then?" someone else demanded.

"Use your head, Senator! We've got to take off the boy's coat so we can set the snake free. Easy, now. Snakes are treacherous!"

Theodore quietly closed the door. "Quentin doesn't realize it," he told the Department of Justice officials, "but he's performing a valuable service on behalf of his country. He's keeping those gentlemen so busy they won't have too much time to wonder why I sent for them the very day I came back to Washington!"

Eventually the shaken senators and congressmen were admitted to the President's office, and Theodore managed to hide his amusement. It was his unpleasant duty, he said, to tell them of a grave development just reported to him by the State Department. Secretary Root had been informed by the British and French embassies that Tokyo was so disturbed by the anti-Japanese activities in California that she was thinking of recalling the staff of its Washington legation and breaking diplomatic relations with the United States.

"Does that mean war, Mr. President?" one of the congressmen wanted to know.

"Not necessarily, although the recall of a nation's diplomats very often is a prelude to war, as you know."

"How do you assess the situation, Mr. President?"

"I hope, with all my heart, that we won't be forced to fight the Japanese. I'm positive they won't start something if they know we'll stay in a war until we win it, and I intend to convey our resolution to them. I'm also preparing certain steps to convince them I mean business, and won't be bullied."

"What steps, Mr. President?"

"I'm not prepared to discuss them yet, not even with trusted members of Congress. I prefer to wait until I hear from Secretary Taft. He should arrive in Tokyo in about three weeks from now—around the middle of October, after his stop at Manila—and his firsthand report should tell us a great deal more about the situation there." In the meantime, he asked that nothing be said in either House to make matters worse.

He realized, however, that he was requesting too much of legislators in a time of increasing international tension. Administration supporters stood in both the Senate and House to express their complete confidence in the President's ability to handle the crisis, while his foes, equally vocal, insisted the United States would be plunged into war unless a belligerent Chief Executive was leashed.

Theodore surprised his friends and critics alike by washing his hands of the controversy. He refused to comment on the debate, either publicly or in private, but indicated that he was in control of the situation.

Then, shortly before noon on October 17, Senator Lodge received a sealed White House envelope, with his name written on it in the President's own hand. He and his wife were invited for "a quiet family dinner" that evening, and Theodore assured him no one else would be present. Lodge knew at once that he was being summoned for a purpose far from casual.

That night Theodore appeared relaxed, but the ladies had no sooner started to chat than he told his guest they should take a stroll around the grounds.

"It's a chilly night," Lodge protested.

"Nonsense, Cabot. You spent the whole afternoon in the Senate, and all that talk drained the air of oxygen. You need fresh air in your lungs." Linking his arm through the Senator's, Theodore led him downstairs and onto the White House lawn, where an early autumn had bared the trees.

They walked in brisk silence on the President's favorite gravel path, which staff members called the Nature Trail, and Lodge, knowing his friend's habits, waited to hear what he had to say.

"Elihu brought me a confidential cable from Will Taft this morning. He's having a bully time in Tokyo."

"Will makes it his business to get along with everyone. I know no one jollier." Lodge deliberately remained noncommittal, and spoke with equal calm.

"Yes, they've been wining and dining him all over the place. If anyone can put on weight eating raw fish and boiled seaweed, Will is the man."

Lodge could hold back no longer. "Has he made any progress in his negotiations with them?"

Theodore stopped teasing him. "Will has never failed me," he said fondly. "He's made what he calls a gentleman's agreement with the Japanese—"

"Any agreement will have to be ratified by the Senate, and heels are being kicked up so hard these days that it might not be easy—"

"Hear me out," Theodore said. "This is one agreement that won't have to be ratified. Will may look sleepy, but no one in this Administration has a finer mind. We and the Japanese have privately agreed to curb emigration to each other's soil. It's that simple."

Lodge was thoughtful for a moment. "But no Americans have been migrating to Japan."

Theodore slapped him on the back. "That's the whole point, Cabot! We don't have to pass any laws or even issue any Executive Orders. Last year only three Americans moved to Japan. What the Japanese do to stop migration here is their business, but I'm assuming they can handle the problem with a minimum of publicity. If the news should leak out, though, they'll have saved face, because the agreement is mutually obligating."

"Very clever," Lodge agreed, then frowned. "But California won't keep all this secret."

"True enough. The way I see it, there's no need for real secrecy, provided we don't make an official announcement of the agreement. I thought you might want to tip off the California Congressional delegation. They'll spread the word fast enough, and that'll take the heat out of the crisis out there."

"I can't imagine," Lodge said testily, "why I'd want to tip them off —unless *you* wanted me to do it."

Theodore chuckled. "You're turning into a crotchety old man. If I asked you to pass along the word, it would become an official request of the President. But if you've learned of all this in a private conversation with me, and out of the goodness of your own heart you can't refrain from saying something, that's quite another matter. Some of the Californians are sure to come to me for corroboration, and I'll be surprised. I'll say I've never before known you to lack discretion. That'll be telling them without openly admitting anything. And no matter how much my enemies in the Senate may scream, they won't be able to pin me down to the admission that we've made a treaty they'll want to reject."

Lodge smiled and shook his head. "I sometimes wonder whether you've brought new subtleties to the White House, or whether the presidency makes a man devious."

"The office," Theodore replied firmly, "sometimes forces even the most direct and blunt of men to use devious tactics. To my knowledge there are two of us who've had to act in ways alien to our own natures on occasion, and Lincoln was the other."

"Lincoln," the former history professor said with some asperity, "was a born politician, a master politician."

"I guess he was, but I'm not. I'm really a very simple and straight-forward person."

Lodge started to reply, then changed his mind when it occurred to him, not for the first time, that Theodore took comfort in thinking of himself in uncomplicated terms. "What does Taft say about the basic issue of war and peace?"

"I'll quote you a significant sentence from his report, but you must regard it as confidential. Agreed?"

"Agreed."

"He said, *The Japanese government is most anxious to avoid war.*"

Lodge halted abruptly on the gravel path. "That's wonderful news!"

Theodore seemed unaware of his joy. "Taft also reports that Japan's finances are badly strained. She hasn't yet paid off the debts she ran up during her war with Russia, and her occupation of Korea is costing another fortune that she can't even begin to amortize for years. Taft says her present financial position makes it almost impossible for her to go to war with us."

"There will be a real celebration in Congress," his friend declared. "Even your worst enemies in the Senate will hail you as a genius!"

"As much as I enjoy praise and watching people who hate me eat humble crow pie, there will be no celebration anywhere, Cabot." Theodore resumed the walk at a faster clip.

Lodge, looking puzzled, hurried to catch up with him. "Surely you're going to release Taft's report! It will make screaming headlines in every newspaper—"

"Not one word will appear in print. Anywhere!" Theodore was emphatic.

"But you can't withhold this news!"

"For the sake of the country, I must!"

No man could argue effectively against a President's claim that he was acting for the good of the nation.

"As you know, Cabot, the fleet has been directed to gather off the coast of Cuba for a voyage to Japan. I'm changing that order. I'm now going to send the ships around the world, and will do all I can to publicize the voyage."

"But there's no longer a need, if the Japanese want peace!" Lodge was becoming indignant.

"The need is greater than ever." Theodore sounded a trifle patronizing as well as patient. "We've had a narrow escape, and Japan's desire for peace this year doesn't mean she'll want it twelve months from now, or even six. When she sees our fleet and realizes how badly she's outgunned, she'll think carefully before she rattles any sabers. By sending our warships to Japan, I'm insuring the security of our first line of defenses in Hawaii."

Lodge studied him closely, was forced to admit he appeared sincere, but couldn't help wondering what other motives might be responsible for his extraordinary reluctance to reveal Secretary Taft's electrifying good news. "You have no other reason?" he asked suspiciously.

Theodore was silent for a moment. "Now that you mention it, there is one. A secondary reason, to be sure."

Lodge's smile was grim.

"I'm sending Congress a special message this week, asking for four new battleships and as many smaller ships as may be needed to support them."

"Four? You won't get them! A battleship costs upward of twenty-five million!"

Theodore tugged at his mustache. "This isn't my first encounter with your Congressional skinflints. Between us, I want two, and I'll get them if I push hard for four."

The Senator from Massachusetts was shocked. "I've seen a good many of your cynical power plays, but there's never been one this blatant. You're holding back the news that there will be peace in the Far East so you'll get the appropriation for new warships!"

"Only because the situation in the Far East—and elsewhere—can change so rapidly. I'm not releasing Taft's report because I need a valid domestic reason satisfying to Congress for the purpose of sending the fleet around the world. It will be a long battle to get the appropriation for the new ships, and I'm counting on the publicity and world re-action to the cruise to put pressure on Congress."

"You're being too clever this time. You're outsmarting yourself, and there will be a rifle shot recoil that will knock you off your feet."

Theodore's gaze was pitying. "I wish you could broaden your horizons and stop looking at these problems through the parochial glasses of a senator."

"And I wish you'd stop allowing the power of your office to warp your sense of right and wrong. What you intend to do is dishonest!"

Theodore was unyielding. "I know I'm right, even if no one agrees with me."

"Ah, then I'm not the only one—"

"Elihu Root is being squeamish, too, but I can't let myself be influenced by either of you. My perspectives aren't warped by a narrow concept of ethics that can't be justified by the pragmatic standards of the twentieth century, and in this instance, regardless of what anyone else may think, I'm convinced that the end justifies the means!"

Congress responded stonily when the President announced the pending cruise of the United States main fleet. The economy-minded said he was extravagant, isolationists insisted the ships had no business leaving home waters, and members of both Houses, knowing nothing about Secretary Taft's report, declared that the dispatch of the fleet was a provocative act and might goad the Japanese into declaring war. A majority of American newspapers picked up the cry, and Theodore was surprised to discover he had misjudged the country's temper.

The opposition made him all the more determined to pursue the course he had set, however. "I'll grant you," he told Elihu Root, "that sometimes circumstances quite properly force the President to bow to public opinion. But one reason the Constitution provides him with a term of four years is to relieve him of pressure when it's essential to the state of the nation. This voyage will be recognized for the next one hundred years as the most important contribution to the preservation of peace made by this Administration!"

The cruise, the White House announced, would begin at Hampton Roads, Virginia, on December 16.

Senator Hale, in an uncharacteristically defiant speech, announced that his Naval Affairs Committee would not authorize the appropriation of funds for the cruise.

Reporters hurried to the White House for a counterblast, but found Theodore calm.

"Funds are already in hand," he said, "to send the fleet as far as Honolulu. It will have to stay there indefinitely, I suppose, until additional funds are voted. If that's what Congress wants, it will have to assume responsibility."

The Senate capitulated, and the necessary money for the voyage was authorized.

On December 16 the President, accompanied by members of his Cabinet, the Justices of the Supreme Court and senior members of the Naval corps watched a grand review of the fleet from the deck of the *Mayflower*. Theodore was in high spirits as he accepted the twenty-one gun salutes of ship after ship, and cheered himself hoarse. Then, as the gleaming white vessels steamed out of Hampton Roads, he accepted the congratulations of the diplomats with the modesty becoming a winner of the Nobel Peace Prize.

The cruise lasted for more than a year, and, amid great fanfares of publicity, the American fleet was greeted everywhere with genuine warmth. The President was particularly pleased by the reports he read, both public and private, of the welcome extended by Tokyo.

Just as he had predicted, Congress was unable to withstand the pressure exerted by a public that, gradually, changed its tune and supported the President. Funds were voted for the immediate construction of two large battleships and seven smaller, supporting vessels.

A number of observers did not accept Theodore's opinion, however, that the cruise was an unqualified success. By showing her muscle, they felt, the United States had contributed to long-range world tensions rather than their relaxation.

Among those who came to hold this view was Secretary of State Elihu Root, who wrote in a memorandum to the President: *Our embassy in Berlin is convinced that the program of naval expansion upon which Germany has embarked was, to a great extent, sparked by the fleet's cruise. There can be no doubt that our maneuvers impressed the Kaiser, who has commented in enthusiastic detail on the subject to many visitors.*

The anti-American elements in Japan have been brought together by the fleet's visit to Tokyo. Our friends there claim that the pressures currently being exerted for the strengthening of Japan's naval forces are, in large measure, due to the power displayed by our warships.

But Theodore refused to accept responsibility for an arms race. "The cruise," he told virtually every White House visitor, "may be the most significant accomplishment of my seven and one-half years as President, and I'm proud of it. I'll be remembered for it when everything else I've ever done has been forgotten."

"Theodore Roosevelt may be remembered," J. P. Morgan is alleged to have said in October 1907 when the controversy over the fleet's forthcoming cruise reached its peak, "as the President who cared so little about his country's financial affairs that he went hunting while Wall Street collapsed."

It was true that the stock market was shaky in the autumn of 1907, and shares of the railroad companies, under presidential attack, were particularly weak. The great business trusts were under assault, and the whole nation had picked up the President's ringing phrase describing some of the nation's most prominent citizens as "malefactors of great wealth."

But Theodore, hunting for bear on a brief vacation jaunt into the wilds of Louisiana, merely laughed when Morgan's purported remark was repeated to him. "I do not," he said, "equate the New York Stock Exchange with the American economy as a whole. Wall Street manipulators are gamblers, no more and no less. But American industry, making products that our growing nation and the growing world need and demand, is as sound as the thousands upon thousands of useful things it manufactures."

The business community did not share the President's optimism, and with good reason. Officials of the Mercantile National Bank of New York were known to control certain stock issues which had been in an unrelieved decline for ten days, and on October 16, 1907, these securities dropped to new lows. Public confidence in the bank itself vanished, depositors staged a run of mammoth proportions, and the institution was forced to close its doors three hours before the usual closing time in order to "prevent an unwarranted panic."

The president and other officers hastily resigned, and it was said that J. P. Morgan had stepped in to pledge the next day's reopening. As it happened, Morgan himself was enjoying a vacation in Richmond, Virginia, but several of his partners were seen entering and leaving the main offices of the Mercantile, and Wall Street, drawing its own conclusions, breathed a sigh of relief.

A news dispatch from Louisiana said the President had bagged a three-hundred-pound bear.

The stock market continued to decline, and on October 21 a rumor swept through New York that the affairs of the Knickerbocker Trust Company, one of the nation's leading banks, were in disorder. Lines formed at the Wall Street headquarters of the bank and its branches, and more than eight million dollars in cash was paid out before the end of the day. Hundreds of depositors who had not yet been served said they would be back the next day.

Morgan hurried home from Virginia, and Secretary of the Treasury George B. Cortelyou canceled a number of appointments so that he, too, could go to New York. They, and a number of Morgan associates including George W. Perkins, spent the day of October 22 conferring in a suite at the Manhattan Hotel. Meanwhile the panic spread to the Trust Company of America and other banks. Telegrams from Chicago, Cleveland, St. Louis, Denver, and New Orleans indicated that the infection was not isolated. San Francisco's canny bankers banded together to declare an informal "holiday," and the maneuver was so effective that their colleagues in other West Coast cities quickly followed their example.

The President, returning to Washington from Louisiana, could not be reached for comment.

That same evening of October 22 Secretary Cortelyou, acting on his own authority, promised to support the banks with twenty-five million dollars in government funds. This move had not been authorized by Congress, but no member of either House questioned Cortelyou's right to pledge the sum.

An additional twenty-five million was forthcoming in private funds. No one in Wall Street was told the source, but it was assumed that Morgan and his associates were responsible. The weary Secretary of the Treasury returned to Washington late that night, leaving the judicious administration of the money, including the Federal funds, in the hands of private banker Morgan.

The stock market steadied on the morning of October 23, and the lines of depositors at banks throughout the nation grew thinner. Morgan and his associates, who habitually avoided interviews, could not be reached by the press, but several employees, refusing to give their names, admitted that "Mr. Morgan and Mr. Perkins and Mr. George Baker are very busy today."

The President's train reached Washington at 11:45 A.M., and he was met by one of the largest delegations of reporters ever to greet him anywhere. "I had a bully time," he said, "and I'm very pleased that I got a bear."

A score of newsmen clamored for a statement on the financial situation. "I've heard no recent details," he replied, "but I can assure you that a dollar will still buy a dollar's worth of merchandise. And the dollars of the American people are safe in the country's banks." Forgetting that his own fortune was invested in securities, he added, "That's where you'll find my money and my family's—in banks."

The market remained firm for the rest of the day, and depositors decided to go home. The panic, it seemed, had ended.

On Friday morning October 25 Secretary Cortelyou issued a statement on Theodore's behalf. In it the President thanked the Secretary of the Treasury for his prompt and patriotic services to the nation, and also expressed his gratitude "to those influential and splendid businessmen who have acted with such wisdom and public spirit."

Reporters sent a message to J. P. Morgan, asking for a comment on the President's generous statement, but the financier continued to maintain his silence.

On October 29, the financial world suddenly and inexplicably fell apart. The clamor of the public for its deposits was so great that the Knickerbocker and four other New York banks failed before the day ended. Scores of others throughout the country, among them many savings banks, also closed their doors. And several major Wall Street brokerage firms were compelled to declare themselves bankrupt.

The plague quickly spread to other segments of American business. Chicago meat-packers regretfully announced the suspension of plans to enlarge the stockyards. The Santa Fe Railroad, with equal regret, indefinitely postponed a seven-million-dollar improvement and expansion program. A new steel company that had started to construct a huge plant on the outskirts of Cleveland, abandoned the project, and, going out of business, sold its attractive site on the shores of Lake Erie.

Reporters clustered outside the Madison Avenue townhouse of J. P. Morgan, where lights burned in the library until a very late hour. But no announcements were made, and the captains of industry and finance who came and went in an unending stream silently pushed through the ranks of the clamoring newsmen. In Washington, meanwhile, members of the press corps laid siege to the White House, where William Loeb politely informed them the President had gone to bed. His attention was called to the lights burning in the President's office, but his only reply was a vague smile that gave them no satisfaction.

Late that night two of Morgan's close associates, Judge Elbert H. Gary of the United States Steel Company, and Henry Clay Frick, the coal and railroad magnate who was a U. S. Steel director, left the Madison Avenue mansion by a side door. They were driven in a new automobile to the Pennsylvania Station, where a one-car special train awaited them, and pulled out the moment they boarded it.

The following morning at eight the pair presented themselves at the White House. "I'm sorry, gentlemen," Loeb told them, "but your appointment with the President is at ten."

"Tell him," the burly Judge Gary replied, "that this is urgent. We've got to see him right now."

"He's at breakfast."

Frick waved impatiently. "Tell the President that millions of Americans will eat no breakfast tomorrow or for a good many tomorrows to come if the business that brings us here isn't settled before the New York Stock Exchange opens at ten!"

A few minutes later the executives were escorted to the President's office, and there Theodore joined them, still absently holding his breakfast napkin. Oddly, he was accompanied by Secretary of State Root.

"I'd hoped Attorney General Bonaparte could join us this morning, but he's out of town," Theodore said after the amenities had been observed.

His remark explained Root's presence. Unwilling to meet representatives of the business community who had become his enemies unless a trusted member of his Administration was present as a witness, the President had made the best of all possible choices. Elihu Root, who had so long acted as legal counsel for J. P. Morgan's interests, still maintained close personal friendships with many of his former associates.

What Gary and Frick did not know was that the President and his Secretary of State planned to use a private communications system should it prove necessary. In the event Theodore lost his temper or became indiscreet, Root would tap on his desk with the upturned bowl of an unlighted pipe.

Before anyone could speak, however, Loeb came in and whispered earnestly in the President's ear.

Theodore nodded, then grinned as he turned to the others. "I must admire your efficiency, gentlemen," he said. "Bill tells me that George Perkins is on the line from the Morgan offices in New York. He asks that the wire be kept open so he can be informed of the results of this meeting the moment we're finished. I've agreed, although I don't know the purpose of this visit. I assume you think it's very critical."

"This can be the most catastrophic day in the history of the United States," Judge Gary said in his deep voice.

"You exaggerate, surely." Theodore, leaning back in his chair, continued to grin.

"He's understating the case," Frick said irritably in a dry, schoolmaster's tone. "The country could be in a state of ruin by nightfall."

Theodore's smile faded. "I don't believe it, and I hope you realize I can't be frightened by bogeymen. From your insistence on meeting before the stock market opens, I'd guess you think it'll drop again today, but a fall in the market doesn't mean the ruin of the country."

Judge Gary made it plain he had no intention of fencing. "In this instance, it does. More corporations than I can possibly mention could be forced into bankruptcy by tonight. Thousands of banks may have to close their doors. Industrial plants will close, land will become worthless and the dollar—including the silver dollar—will be nothing but a scrap of metal."

"Let me illustrate, Mr. President," Frick added. "A loaf of bread costs four cents in the Washington grocery stores this morning, and a housewife can buy porterhouse steak for eight cents a pound. By this time tomorrow bread could cost one hundred dollars a loaf, and steak could go up to five hundred a pound."

Theodore looked at his visitors in cold disbelief, but saw they seemed sincere. Then he flicked a glance at Root.

The Secretary of State read his mind. "Mr. President," he said, "Henry and the Judge aren't alarmists. In fact, I'm wondering what to do about my own investments."

"What's causing this extraordinary situation?" Theodore demanded.

"The problem hasn't changed all month," Frick said. "When there's a lack of confidence and it continues to grow, people lose their heads."

"But our factories have more orders than they can fill," Theodore protested. "Domestic business has never been as good, and our foreign markets are growing, even though tariffs are still far too high. I just can't understand why banks should fail, and—"

"You were a soldier, Mr. President. Did you ever see soldiers panic?"

"Unfortunately, yes."

"Under circumstances that didn't justify panic?" Frick persisted. "Un-

der circumstances that needn't have caused even a ripple if they'd
held firm?"

"I'm afraid so."

"All the same, Mr. President, some of them died. Needlessly. Well,
the same situation holds true in civilian life. In a time of financial
panic, including the unjustified, banks and businesses fail, men lose
their jobs and thousands starve to death. Needlessly." Frick raised his
hands in a gesture of helplessness, then let them fall again.

"And you think all of this will start today?" Theodore asked.

"It started weeks ago, and today will be the climax," Gary boomed.

"It must not be allowed to happen!" The President raised his voice,
too. "I won't tolerate it!"

Root's pipe tapped a quiet warning on the desk.

"How can you prevent it?" Frick made the question seem innocent.

Theodore looked at his Secretary for help, but Root was staring out
of the window at a pile of yellow and brown leaves blowing across
the lawn. "I'll issue a statement expressing my full confidence in the
future of the American economy!"

"You did just that less than a week ago," Gary said.

"I'll make this a stronger statement!" Theodore was becoming frustrated.

"It's too late," Frick said.

Elihu Root intervened before the presidential temper exploded. "If
the situation is as grave as the Judge and Henry say it is—and I'm willing to accept their appraisal—it really is too late, Mr. President."

Theodore recovered his aplomb, and actually managed to sound
cheerful. "It's never been a secret that I'm no expert in the financial
jungle. I've never claimed to be one. But I'm sure you gentlemen could
hire yourselves out as guides in the wilderness. I'm also sure you
haven't come here for the exclusive purpose of scaring me. You've established the problem, and I'm eager to learn your solution."

"The first step," Gary said, "is to restore the faith of the business
community in itself. When that takes place, as we agreed at a meeting
last night in New York—"

"At Pierpont Morgan's house?" Theodore interjected.

"As it happens, yes. When business starts believing in itself, public
confidence usually is restored. I can't guarantee it, but there's nothing
else that can be done." Judge Gary, indifferent to the President's dislike of tobacco smoke, took a cigar from a leather case he carried in
a vest pocket.

Frick cleared his throat.

"If it'll help you think more clearly, I don't mind in the least," Theodore said, and waited.

"There's a major business in New York that's in serious trouble," Gary said. "If it doesn't get help today, first thing this morning, it will fail. And the dropping of that card will trigger the collapse of the whole deck."

"If you'd like to know the name of the company, Mr. President," Frick added, "we'll gladly give it to you in confidence."

Root shook his head almost imperceptibly.

"It might be wiser not to tell me," Theodore said. "I prefer to know only what's essential."

"The basic details are simple, Mr. President," Gary said. "This company can be saved—by an injection of cash into its arteries. Well, among its assets is a majority of stock in a coal corporation known as the Tennessee Coal & Iron Company."

Frick picked up the story. "T.C. and I.," he said, "is a healthy operation. It owns property in five states—or is it six? I'm not sure. Most of it is soft coal of a fairly good grade. Some of my own people have made an investigation, and they assure me that T.C. and I. is a sound investment."

Gary blew a cloud of blue smoke toward the ceiling. "The company that's in trouble has offered its T.C. and I. controlling interest stock to U. S. Steel. We don't know whether to accept or not. In a sense, that's why we're here, Mr. President."

"I can't advise you one way or the other," Theodore said. "Even if I weren't President, I'm not qualified."

"We haven't made ourselves plain," Gary said, still patient. "You must understand, Mr. President, that U. S. Steel doesn't want T.C. and I. We'll have to pay more for the stock than it's actually worth. Mind you, I'm not saying that in the long run we'll lose money."

"It's possible that we may even make a profit," Frick added. "We plain don't know, and U. S. Steel isn't in the habit of gambling. But the general business situation requires something of a sacrifice from everyone able to make one."

"What do you want of me?" Theodore asked, ignoring Root's look telling him that, as usual in business matters, he was being dull-witted.

"We want your assurances, Mr. President, that if we make the purchase, U. S. Steel wouldn't be prosecuted by the government under

the Sherman Anti-Trust Act. We prefer to forget the whole deal,
tighten our hatches and ride out the storm in the months ahead."

"Would you be liable? *Should* the Attorney General prosecute?"

Frick smiled acidly. "We'd regard it as persecution, not prosecution."

"Government action against us would be unjustified," Gary elabo-
rated. "If we acquire T.C. and I., we'll be adding to our holdings of
fuel and possible raw materials sources, but keep in mind that we
have no problem getting either from outside companies. What I believe is important, and I speak now as an attorney, is that we wouldn't
be increasing our steel holdings, so I can see no reason why we should
be liable under the Sherman Act."

Theodore turned to the best corporation lawyer in his Administration for an opinion.

"I know nothing about Tennessee Coal and Iron other than what
we've just heard," Elihu Root said, "but I'm sure the facts of the situation are accurate. Of course, you'll be taking the usual political risks,
Mr. President. Someone is certain to accuse you of accommodating
big business."

"I'm always being accused of something." Theodore ground his teeth
as he tried to pick his way through the maze. At best he understood
the intricacies of financial dealings dimly, so his instincts, on which he
leaned when his intellect failed him, couldn't be trusted. "Obviously,"
he said, "the purchase of this stock would save one bank, or brokerage
firm, or whatever. I don't see, though, how hundreds of banks could
be saved and the panic overcome."

"Carry Elihu's explanation one more step, Mr. President. The reformers and progressives might be unhappy, but the relief in the business community would be enormous." Gary paused, then spoke even
more bluntly. "The directors of every corporation in the country are
convinced you want to scalp them. We'd let it be known that you've
agreed to cooperate with us—"

Theodore frowned.

"I'll put it another way." The steel magnate backtracked smoothly.
"We'd let out the word that you aren't going to beat us with that big
club you're always brandishing. That would be enough."

"Business would be encouraged," Frick said, "and I'm not speaking
only of Wall Street. The reaction all over the country would be immediate. And strong. If bank depositors continued to panic, they'd calm
down fast enough when they found that every bank suffering a run
would pay off to the penny."

Again Theodore glanced at Root.

But the Secretary of State refused to make the final decision, and turned his back.

Theodore resisted the impulse to pace up and down. His pride, as well as the dignity of his office, made it necessary for him to match the somber calm his visitors were displaying. "Under the circumstances," he said carefully, "I don't feel it my public duty to object to the actions you propose to take."

He had gone as far as a President could, and Frick immediately went to the outer office to pass along the good news to George Perkins, who was still waiting in New York on the open telephone line. A short time later the New York Stock Exchange opened, and it soon became evident that Gary and Frick had been accurate prophets. The market held firm, and ample funds were made available, through private sources, to banks that suddenly found themselves in trouble.

In spite of a few panicky flurries in the next few days, every bank in the United States remained open. The stock and commodity markets continued to rally, and within ten days it became plain that the crisis had been resolved. Thereafter the recovery of the business community was swift, corporations revived their expansion plans, and the financial stability of the country was assured.

Hundreds of telegrams and letters congratulating the President, most of them from business and professional men, taxed the facilities of the White House mail room, and Theodore was pleased with the part he had played in averting a serious financial crash. "I'd have been a timid and unworthy public officer if I hadn't acted as I did," he told Elihu Root.

Nevertheless, just as the Secretary of State had predicted, the President was criticized. Democrats wanted to know why he had chosen to save the Wall Street banking and brokerage firm of Moore & Schley, which, it was revealed, was the company from which U. S. Steel had purchased the stock.

A far more serious charge was made within a few months. The steel corporation had paid a total of $45,000,000 for Tennessee Coal & Iron, and even the loyal Gifford Pinchot told Theodore that her assets were worth many times that sum. According to a number of independent estimates, her coal and iron reserves in Tennessee, Alabama, and Georgia, where her major holdings were located, were worth at least $500,-000,000. Some financial and metallurgical experts said they were worth at least a billion.

Attorney General Charles J. Bonaparte became uneasy, and wondered whether he should initiate anti-trust proceedings against U. S. Steel, but Theodore refused. "I gave my word," he said, "and that's the end of the matter."

It was not. The criticism persisted, and the combined, persuasive efforts of Root and Taft were required to prevent a public presidential counterattack. "If you make a statement," the Secretary of State told him, "you'll just keep the fight alive. Say nothing, and it will die away."

"But I was right!" Theodore insisted. "I refuse to believe that Gary and Frick were lying when they told me they thought U. S. Steel might lose money on the deal. Why penalize them for enjoying a stroke of good luck?"

In a more reflective mood, he subsequently spoke more calmly to Taft. "What I did helped the whole country," he said, "and it's a shame that human nature is so treacherous. Now that the fear of a financial disaster has been removed, it's becoming fashionable to point fingers of scorn at the rich. I can't hate any man just because he's wealthy. If his heart is in the right place, I'm for him, and I don't doubt the complete wisdom of my agreement with Judge Gary and Mr. Frick, not for a moment."

In his annual message to Congress, dispatched in December 1907, the President asked for legislation to prevent similar panics in the future. Senator Aldrich unexpectedly cooperated by introducing a bill in the Senate that authorized national banks to issue a half-billion dollars in notes, based on state and municipal bonds, in times of financial emergency. With the support of Speaker Cannon and the Old Guard the measure was passed early in 1908, and Theodore claimed he had been influential in obtaining a major banking reform.

When fresh attacks were launched on the grounds that he had handed the nation's financial future into the safekeeping of a few influential bankers, he merely shrugged. "It takes a banker to understand finances," he declared. "I don't, and the people don't, but I've been learning that the President can't satisfy everyone."

One continuing presidential program, that of conserving America's natural resources, was universally acclaimed, and only the nation's mining, timber, and grazing interests opposed him. They did not dare fight in the open against a solid phalanx of public opinion, however, and Theodore, aided by Chief Forester Pinchot, achieved an impressive series of victories.

By the time the end of his second term was in sight, thirty major irrigation projects, among them the new Roosevelt Dam in Arizona, were under way. Millions of acres of forest land had been set aside, preserved for the people, five new National Parks had been created, as had sixteen National Monuments, among them Mount Olympus in the State of Washington. Fifty-one wildlife refuges had been established, the Inland Waterways Commission had been created, and at a conference of governors held in the late spring of 1908, Theodore began to turn the task of preserving the nation's natural resources over to the states.

"In the past," he told the governors, "we have admitted the right of the individual to injure the future of the Republic for his own present profit. The time has come for a change. As a people we have the right and the duty, second to none other but the right and duty of obeying the moral law, of requiring and doing justice, to protect ourselves and our children against the wasteful development of our natural resources."

A majority of the thirty-eight governors who attended the White House conference disagreed, on both political and personal grounds, with the President's proclaimed principle: the rights of the public are paramount, and those of private interests must take second place. But they knew they would commit political suicide if they opposed a position that had won the unanimous support of the press and public. So, regardless of their own concepts, all of them signed the ringing statement which Theodore called the Declaration of Governors.

It read: *We agree that the sources of national wealth exist for the benefit of the People, and that monopoly thereof should not be tolerated.*

We declare the conviction that in the use of the natural resources our independent States are interdependent and bound together by ties of mutual benefits, responsibilities, and duties.

We agree that further action is advisable to ascertain the present condition of our natural resources and to promote the conservation of the same; and to that end we recommend the appointment by each State of a Commission on the Conservation of Natural Resources, to co-operate with each other and with any similar commission of the Federal Government.

The style and language, Washington press correspondents noted, were similar to the President's. Gifford Pinchot promptly replied that the governors had drawn up the Declaration themselves, with no help from anyone. But the reporters persisted, and Theodore was forced to put an end to the speculation.

"The American people," he said, "don't care who wrote those or any other words. What they do want is the conservation of their natural heritage for their children and grandchildren. I shall support, now and always, every public official who guarantees that future, just as I shall oppose all who do not."

"God help the next President," Cabot Lodge said when he heard Theodore's comment, "if he proves to be less than a dedicated conservationist."

By the middle of 1908, less than a year before the end of his second term, Theodore and the Republican Old Guard had parted company in all but name. In spite of his threats, bluffs, and attempts to rally public support by making strong statements, the President was unable to persuade a recalcitrant Congress to lower tariff barriers. Congress snickered at his efforts to win the vote and equal employment opportunities for women, and he had to content himself with token gestures, hiring female stenographers and clerical help for the White House staff.

The conservatives in both the Senate and House formed a solid phalanx to thwart his urgent demand for a national law that would outlaw child labor. Infuriated, he sent several special messages to Congress on the subject, but they were ignored. Finally, convinced he could not win, he had to be satisfied with a gesture. At his request Senator Lodge sponsored a measure prohibiting child labor in the District of Columbia, and Congress, content to give him an empty victory in order to silence him, passed the bill. Since virtually no children were employed in the District, the new law was indeed meaningless, but Theodore tried to breathe life into it by issuing a public statement to the effect that it served as a warning to the states. The people would hold them responsible for passing their own child labor laws, he said; if they did not, the Federal government would be compelled to act. But the states, like Congress, paid no attention to the threat.

New labor laws were needed, the President declared in another special message to Congress, in order to protect the right of the working man to strike "for just cause." The judiciary should be curbed, too, he declared, because far too often the courts shackled labor by issuing injunctions against unions during disputes with management. And, he said, the nation's criminal codes needed clarification. He thought it unhappily significant that the poor frequently received the maximum punishment the law allowed, but a businessman who defrauded the public rarely went to prison.

In the cloakrooms of the Senate and House, members of the 60th Congress privately referred to the President as "that busybody." His messages were referred to committees, which buried them, and the legislators tried to forget the man at the opposite end of Pennsylvania Avenue.

"Teddy," Senator Aldrich said, "has had his day of glory, and is just trying to make certain that future generations remember him. His record of the past seven years must stand on its own, and it's too late for him to add to it. Let him concern himself with his retirement, a very quiet and inconspicuous retirement, we hope. And let him leave the public business to the elected officials charged with that responsibility."

Angered by Aldrich's remark and deeply frustrated by his failure to obtain legislation he deemed essential, Theodore sat down in late January 1909, only six weeks before he left office, to write a final, blistering message to Congress. Members of his Cabinet and other friends who saw it were aghast, and urged him to tear it up.

"It'll do no good," Robert Bacon told him. "People who've supported you will think you're a poor sport and will become indifferent to you. The indifferent will dislike you, and those who dislike you will hate you."

"Congress," Theodore replied, "seems to be made up almost exclusively of people who already hate me, so I have nothing to lose. And if I can arouse the people this one, last time, there's a great deal to gain."

Turning a deaf ear to his advisers, he sent the shockingly vitriolic message to Congress on January 31, 1909. His attempts to win the Square Deal he had promised the United States, he declared: *are being circumvented, ignored and warped by the representatives of predatory wealth—of the wealth accumulated on a giant scale by all forms of iniquity, ranging from the oppression of wage workers to unfair and unwholesome methods of crushing out competition, and to defrauding the public by stock jobbing and the manipulation of securities.*

Lashing out in an unprecedented manner against Wall Street, he demanded strict regulation of securities controls and the passage of legislation to curb what he called "successful dishonesty." The United States was a God-fearing, moral nation, he declared, and he was certain the people felt as he did about Wall Street, adding, *There is no moral difference between gambling at cards and gambling in the stock market.*

Striking with seeming indiscrimination against everyone who supported the great corporations, he charged that the nation was *filled to overflowing with puppets, petty and venal politicians, editors and lawyers who are purchased by the malefactors of great wealth, puppets who move as the strings are pulled.*

In a final, savage outburst, he even condemned the decent, patriotic citizens *who allow those rich men whose lives are evil and corrupt to control this nation and her destiny.*

Speaker Joseph G. Cannon was so disturbed he walked out of the House while the message was being read. "I never thought I'd hear a message from a President of the United States," he said, "that sounded as though it had been written by an anarchist. In his day Teddy wasn't a bad fellow, but all that applause, which he didn't deserve, went to his head."

"I'll soon be fifty years old," Theodore told Cabot Lodge when they returned to the White House from a canter through the park one spring day in 1908. "Think of it—only fifty when I leave office. I don't feel like someone who is going to retire, and I don't mind telling you I'm miserable."

His friend sprawled in a chair in the second floor family living room and gratefully accepted a glass of iced tea. Anyone who knew the meticulous senator only from his public appearances would have been startled by his informality. "Your mistake," he said, "was that idiotic statement repudiating another term that you issued four years ago. I advise you to forget it."

"Never!" Theodore took an oversized bandanna handkerchief from his hip pocket, carefully wiped dust from his boots and then threw the handkerchief to Lodge, unmindful of the dust that showered onto the rug.

The Senator from Massachusetts chose to ignore the explosive interruption. "You're certain to win the party nomination next month, no matter what the Old Guard thinks of you. A hint will be enough, and you'll be drafted. Unanimously. It can be made to appear that you didn't want the nomination, but that it sought you."

"That would be political sophistry. No man has ever been nominated for an office he really didn't want."

"Are you trying to tell me," Lodge demanded scornfully, "that you wouldn't welcome another term as President?"

"I'm tired," Theodore replied evasively. "I'm tired of politics and politicians—"

"Playing their game—or, rather, forcing them to play yours—is as natural to you as breathing!"

"I'm tired of fighting Congress. And side-stepping the press."

"You've never done that!"

"Ted is of age this year. I've neglected him, just as I've neglected all the children. I'd like to spend some time with him."

"You're the best, most considerate father in the country. What's more, Ted is so busy *he* won't have all that much time for *you!*"

Theodore grinned. "Are you trying to be persuasive on your own account, Cabot, or are you representing a group of some kind?"

"You might say I'm acting as a spokesman for the American people, self-appointed." Lodge dabbed absently at his boots with the bandanna, then rose and handed it to the President. "Here, you'd better hide this away somewhere before Edith sees it and gives you the devil."

Theodore looked around the room, shrugged and stuffed the handkerchief back into his hip pocket. "The people would give my opponent—probably Bryan, from the way the Democrats seem to be moving—the biggest majority on record!"

"Want to bet? They feel you're absolutely necessary to the presidency!"

"If that's really true," Theodore said, "it's the most compelling reason I've yet heard against my candidacy. It's a very unhealthy thing—ruinous to democracy—that any man should be considered 'necessary' to the people, except in some specific emergency."

"You're tailoring your theories to make them fit your situation, and that's philosophical sophistry!"

Theodore gulped the last of his iced tea, then crossed the room to refill it from a huge pitcher. "That's where you're wrong. It sometimes surprises me that after all these years you've never lost that academician's habit of putting other people's thoughts into neat little intellectual cubbyholes."

"Instead of wasting your breath insulting me, which you can do any time, tell me my error." Lodge remained calm.

"I may be wrong, of course." Theodore became gravely deliberate. "But I'm thinking of the bulk of Americans, the plain people, as Lincoln called them. The farmers and mechanics. The little shopkeepers.

The hard-working professional men. They've been my supporters. They're the people who elected me, just as they're the people who elected Lincoln. Well, I don't rate myself with Lincoln, so don't misunderstand me, Cabot. But I feel that in some peculiar sense I'm their President, that I represent the democracy in somewhat the same fashion that Lincoln did. Do you follow me?"

"No, frankly." Lodge toyed nervously with his riding crop.

"I don't mean it in any demagogic way. I make a sincere effort to stand for a government by the people and for the people."

"No one would deny that, not even the Old Guard or the Democrats."

"Then you see why I can't go back on my word and run again."

"I'm afraid I don't," Lodge said waspishly.

"I've become a symbol, not only of our kind of government, but of a clean, honest democracy. Granted?"

"Of course."

"Then the chief service I can render the plain people who believe in me is not to destroy their ideal of me."

"You make it sound good." Lodge sipped his tea. "But I still think you're rationalizing."

"Only time will tell," Theodore said smugly.

"You'll regret it."

"We'll see."

"If you'll give me some more of that splendid iced tea," the Senator said, "I might be willing to listen to your pipe dreams. I'd be delighted to hear how someone who—by his own admission just now—feels he's still young at fifty after serving seven and a half years as President of the United States is going to spend the rest of his useful life."

Theodore refilled his guest's glass, not noticing the small puddle he made on the table.

"Wipe that up!" Lodge commanded.

The bandanna became useful again. "Not an hour ago," Theodore said, "you were telling me you've heard on good authority that Eliot is going to retire in a few months."

"You couldn't be serious!"

"Why not? The pay isn't bad, the atmosphere is fairly congenial, and I'd have a bully forum any time I wanted to speak my mind on issues of the day."

"The Overseers wouldn't like it, nor would the faculty, the alumni and everyone else except the undergraduates, who'd cheer you with the mindless enthusiasm they cheer the fullback!"

"There's nothing wrong with football!"

"You and Harvard wouldn't be able to digest each other," Lodge said firmly. "You've been a member of the Board of Overseers for twelve years now—"

"Thirteen."

"—and every time you've gone to a meeting you've told me you've felt like a bulldog in—what was it?—a symposium of clean, white Persian cats."

Theodore grinned sheepishly.

"You belong right here." Lodge gestured emphatically. "So don't try to fool yourself. I know you, I know Harvard, and I shudder for both of you at the very idea of seeing you become her president. It would be a catastrophe."

"It was just a thought. I wasn't too serious about it. Besides," Theodore added crisply, "they'd never elect me."

The former Harvard instructor breathed more easily. "For a long time," he said, "I've been intrigued by Nicholas Murray Butler's idea that you run for the Senate this fall. Fancy the drama and commotion! Twenty-four hours after you watch the inauguration of your successor, you take the oath of office as a senator!"

"I've been tempted, as you can imagine. Of course, I'd be accused of moving the White House to my Senate office, but I'll probably have to face that sort of thing no matter what I do. And can you just see Nelson Aldrich trying to freeze me in an icebox corner by giving minor committee assignments to a freshman senator?" Theodore's laugh trailed away as a tenor giggle.

"I realize the party in New York wouldn't be too pleased," Lodge said, concentrating on the practical aspects of the situation. "Tom Platt would do everything he could to block you."

"Which wouldn't get him very far." Theodore's mood changed abruptly, and he, too, became pragmatic. "If the President announced his intention of running for the Senate, and appealed direct to the people of New York, there's nothing the Platt machine could do to keep the nomination from him or prevent his election."

"Other than work half-heartedly."

"It wouldn't matter." Theodore was very confident, very firm. "I'm sure the New York electorate, like the rest of the country, would give me any office I want, whenever I might want it."

"Perhaps." Lodge studied him. "You don't sound to me like a man who wants to retire from politics."

"I must!" Theodore scowled and pounded a fist into the open palm of his other hand. "This isn't easy for me, Cabot, but I have no ethical choice, so I'm burning my bridges and making other arrangements."

The Senator had been waiting to learn about those arrangements, but said nothing, hoping his friend would reveal more, provided he didn't feel pressed.

"My first consideration, of course, must be that of earning a living. I'm not wealthy, remember."

Lodge had gathered from some remarks dropped by Douglas Robinson that Theodore's inheritance, which had been prudently invested, was now worth the better part of a million dollars. Someone else in that position certainly would think of himself as comfortably situated, but Lodge long had known that Theodore suffered from a strange fear of poverty.

"What I'd enjoy most would be teaching history at some good university—"

"Any school would be honored to give you a professorship."

"—but those jobs don't pay enough."

Apparently, Lodge thought, he had no idea he was rationalizing, that he had no intention of retreating into quiet anonymity on a secluded campus.

"I'm going to do some books, of course, as much for my own satisfaction as for the royalties they'll earn. Travel, hunting, American morality, eventually an autobiography. But an author needs a steady income, so I've made an arrangement to write twelve articles a year for Lyman Abbott."

"At *Outlook* magazine?"

"Yes, and it'll be a good deal for everyone. Lyman will pay me a flat fee of twelve thousand a year, I'll elect my own subjects, and no one will have the right to change even a comma. I'm looking forward to those articles. First, though, I want to get the stale air of Washington out of my lungs. If I can persuade the Smithsonian Institution or some other organization to pay my expenses in return for natural history specimens, I'd like to go off to Africa for a long hunting trip. What great sport that would be!" Theodore became animated. "The jungles, the veldt, mud flats, water holes—you ought to join me, Cabot."

"I'd rather enjoy the trip vicariously by reading the book you'll undoubtedly write about it," Lodge said dryly.

"I'll never understand how any red-blooded American man could fail to have the time of his life on a hunting trip!" Theodore's expression indicated amused tolerance for the peculiarities of human nature. "I wanted Ted to come with me, but he's so eager to begin his own life and prove himself as a businessman that he doesn't want to take the time. And I suppose I can't blame him. So I'll have a chat with Kermit when he comes home from school."

"It isn't accidental," Lodge said quietly, "that you've chosen Africa. You aren't fooling me."

Theodore's pretended innocence was transparent.

"If you stay at home, you and your successor will be criticized without mercy, and even some of your strongest supporters will claim that you're trying to act as President by proxy."

"That's very shrewd of you, Cabot. I can protect my program in only two ways. I've got to remove myself from the scene for a time, while making absolutely certain that the man who takes my place is dedicated to my principles and their execution."

His flashes of ingenuousness never failed to astonish Lodge. "Any man who lives and works in this place inevitably develops a sense of independence."

"Naturally." Theodore showed sudden irritation. "The President can take orders from no one, including a predecessor. But the right man, someone who believes as I do, will carry on my work and extend it."

"Is there such a man?" Lodge raised an eyebrow.

"There are several. You, for one!"

Lodge raised a hand. "Never. We disagree on many issues—"

"Name them!" Theodore demanded shrilly.

He was so busy expounding his own views on most occasions, Lodge thought, that he didn't listen to the opinions of others. "It doesn't matter. I know my limitations, and I don't care to be President."

"I knew it, so I haven't asked you. But I've had several long talks with Elihu."

"Surely," Lodge said, "you don't believe that Elihu Root is dedicated to your principles!"

"Our thinking," Theodore said, "is identical."

Lodge didn't want to insult him by laughing. "The day he leaves the State Department, he'll return to his practice as one of the country's most eminent corporation lawyers!"

"I was thinking in terms of foreign policy," Theodore said stiffly.

"You have a point there."

"A very important point. We've become a first-rate world power in the past seven years, and our relations with the rest of the world are vital to our survival and growth!"

"Granted," the senator replied. "But I can't picture Elihu Root fighting for your Square Deal or initiating anti-trust proceedings against some of his closest friends!"

Theodore's mustache drooped. "The question is moot. I've used all my powers of persuasion, but he won't be budged. He insists he isn't interested in the presidency. Can you imagine it?"

"Easily."

"Well, I've had to look elsewhere. It's imperative that I find someone I can trust. I've got to hand-pick the right man."

Lodge laughed quietly.

"Perhaps you'll share the joke with me, Cabot." Theodore's manner became frosty.

"How often through the years have I heard you tear Andrew Jackson apart. He came within a hair of ruining the democratic process of government, you've said—"

"So he did!"

"—because he insisted on hand-picking Martin Van Buren as his successor. You've used the phrase many times, the very same you used just now!"

"This is quite different, so there's no comparison. It's vital to the future of the United States that the new President's outlook be progressive, and—"

"I daresay that President Jackson was concerned about the continuity of his policies, too."

"Jackson was a backwoods Indian fighter whose horizons were limited and who had no political integrity. He was the father of the spoils system! And—I shouldn't have to spell all this out, Cabot, not for you— he was a Democrat!"

Lodge wanted no more iced tea, but raised his glass to his mouth in order to conceal his smile. Theodore was far too committed to all of his endeavors to see himself in perspective, so it would be useless to pursue the subject. "With the convention so near at hand, you must have someone else in mind."

"Very much so. Taft."

Lodge neither spoke nor moved.

"Well, Cabot?"

"William Howard Taft is a fine fellow, a man with a good, analytical mind and a good enough grasp on major problems. But I can't for the life of me picture him as President of the United States."

"You've lived in Boston so long that you can't imagine anyone but an Easterner as President."

"I must admit that Governor Hughes of New York would be my own preference. And a logical candidate."

"If I have any voice in the matter," Theodore said indignantly, "Charles Evans Hughes will never become the Republican candidate!"

"He's a progressive—"

"He was rude to me without cause! Do you remember the fuss he made when I didn't consult him before I removed that fellow in Rochester—I can't recall his name—from a Federal post last year? And when I tried to help Hughes by endorsing some of his pet bills—"

"*He* thought *you* were interfering."

"—he started the whole mugwump press cackling with glee when he said he didn't want or need my help. He's selfish and cold-blooded, and I refuse to have anything to do with him!" Theodore drained his glass of iced tea, then searched his pockets for a handkerchief to mop his mustache.

Lodge knew he would consider Governor Hughes an enemy for life, and regretfully abandoned any hope of obtaining his support for Hughes' candidacy.

"What's wrong with Will Taft?" the aroused Theodore demanded. "I defy you to name one officer of my Administration who has served my cause with greater dedication."

"Taft has been devoted to you, not what you call your cause."

"You're quibbling, Cabot, and that's unworthy of you. If you have any legitimate complaint against him, speak plainly."

In spite of the difficulties of raising the argument to an impersonal level, Lodge felt compelled to make the effort. "I hold nothing against him, and I've found him cooperative as well as pleasant. But he simply isn't a man of presidential caliber."

"That's sheer prejudice. Every holder of this office has his own character and style."

"You'll be telling me next," Lodge said with heavy irony, "about the splendid presidential character of James Buchanan."

"Aside from his obvious faults, Buchanan, too, was a Democrat."

Theodore felt he had gained the upper hand, and grinned. "I'm waiting, Cabot."

"You've heard it said that this or that person looks like a President. Taft doesn't."

"Very feeble," Theodore crowed.

"I can't force you to admit what you can't see. But you'll concede—"

"I concede nothing."

"If we're going to let this conversation degenerate into a shouting contest, I prefer to go home. Taft is personally lazy—"

"You're mad. Look at his record as an administrator in the Philippines!"

"He followed instructions, and he was helped by a superb staff. On a half-dozen occasions when I've telephoned him at the War Department, he's been taking a nap."

"I rule out the evidence as irrelevant."

"Would you take a nap during the working day, Mr. President?"

"Certainly not, but it isn't in my character."

Lodge decided to try another tack, even though opposition almost invariably made Theodore all the more determined to get his way. "Watch Taft the next time you see him. Every move he makes is slow and deliberate. He won't stand when he can sit. Ask him for a paper, and even if he's holding it in his hand, you'll have to reach for it."

"A man of his size and weight must find physical exertion of almost any kind both taxing and unpleasant. I'll grant you that he'd be in far better health if he'd ride with me or play tennis, but he doesn't care for sports. And you can't exclude a man from the presidency simply because he won't work up an honest sweat."

"He plays golf."

Theodore gestured contemptuously. "Golf isn't real sport. It's an old grandmother's game."

Lodge laughed. "Now you're trapped. You're proposing that an old grandmother take your place."

"That's sophistry, and well you know it. Twisting my meanings doesn't make Taft less eligible."

"No, but he needs more than the loyalty he's shown you to commend him. Turn him loose without your guidance and supervision, and I'm afraid he'll prove far too conservative for your taste, I'm not saying that he'll necessarily revert to the Old Guard thinking—"

"He won't! It's impossible!"

"—but I honestly do believe you may be making the biggest mistake
of your life!"

The lunch had been bountiful, and Secretary of War William Howard
Taft yawned as he lowered himself into the overstuffed leather chair
opposite the President's desk. "That was a grand meal, but now I feel
sleepy."

It was small wonder, Theodore thought. Rarely had he seen anyone
consume so much food, but it was not his place to criticize another's
personal habits. "Women always like to make changes," he said, "but
don't let your wife or anyone else persuade you to get rid of the chef
when you move in here. He's a first-rate cook."

Taft sat bolt upright, and was wide awake.

Theodore chuckled. "Yes, Will, I've decided you're the best qualified
man in the country to be my successor."

"I scarcely know what to say, Mr. President." Taft was believed
to be imperturbable, but at this moment he was completely flustered.

"Relax and let it sink in. Then say the word, and I'll send notes to
the state chairmen. You'll win the nomination on the first ballot in
Chicago by a landslide. I doubt if anyone will stand against you."

"I've heard all the talk that you'll refuse another term, Mr. President," Taft said heavily, "but Helen has had the idea—I mean—I've
assumed you'd be open to a draft."

"If the convention should make the mistake of nominating me, I'd
go to Chicago and withdraw, in person. But I'm doing several
things to prevent that embarrassment. The most important of them is
to support you openly, now, before the convention."

"I'm flabbergasted." Taft heaved himself out of the chair and went
to the open windows, where, suspiciously close to tears, he stared out
at the White House lawn.

"You shouldn't be. There's been speculation about your possible candidacy for a long time."

"Longer than you might imagine." Taft's voice was muffled. "My
brother, Charley, has been telling me for years that I ought to be President, but I've never been able to agree with him. My one ambition
has been the Chief Justiceship."

"You'll have to set your sights higher now." Never had Theodore felt
more benign or generous.

Taft turned away from the window with a sigh. "I'd still prefer the Supreme Court," he said softly, hesitated and then brightened. "But Helen will be very pleased."

Theodore remembered a long discussion with Mrs. Taft at a reception for the Cabinet. "I'm sure she's always been ambitious for you."

Nodding, the heavy-set man returned to his chair, in control of his emotions again. "Yes, she's wanted the presidency for years, but I always told her it was beyond me."

"She's been right," Theodore said heartily, "and so have I. What do you say, Will?"

"I'm not sure I can handle the job."

"I know you can! What worries you?"

"Well, I'm not very adept at political in-fighting. Of course, Helen is the politician in the family, and she'd join me in the trenches."

Theodore knew the Tafts were very close to each other, and was not unduly disturbed.

"I'm afraid of no one when I must do my duty," Taft continued, "but personal conflicts always make me nervous. For instance, I don't look forward to appointing a Cabinet."

"That problem is easily solved." Theodore bared his teeth in a particularly broad grin. "Elihu has told you, I dare say, that he's decided to run for the Senate. So you'll need a new Secretary of State, but I can help you there. I have a number of exceptionally good men I'll recommend to you."

"That's—very kind of you, Mr. President."

"And I'm sure that—between us—we can persuade the rest of my cabinet to stay on. I think you'll find that Jim Garfield will be delighted to keep Interior so he and Pinchot can go on with their conservation work. And most of the others will feel the same way. Luckily, you know them all well after working together these past four years."

"Yes, of course." Taft cleared his throat. "We—that is—I may develop some new thoughts."

"I'd be disappointed if you didn't." Theodore spoke a shade too heartily. "You're going to be your own man, Will, and you'll want your own people around you. Of course," he added, "we'll have to get you elected first."

"I've never been one to blow my own horn, so I'm afraid I can't look forward with much enthusiasm to a campaign, Mr. President."

"When the Democrats start making absurd charges, you'll work yourself into such a righteous state of wrath you'll want to spend all your time on the stump. Besides, we'll have everyone of importance in the party making speeches for you. Leave that to me. I intend to do everything in my power to help you."

"Under the circumstances, I don't see how I can refuse, Mr. President."

"This is bully, a great day for all of us!" Theodore wrung his hand. "There's just one thing I won't do for you, Will. I believe it would be wrong for me to go out on the campaign trail. This must be your campaign, and I don't want to steal even a little of the limelight from you."

Teddy, the New York *World* observed caustically as the Republican convention opened in Chicago on June 19, 1908, *is the puppet-master supreme. We understand he wrote the platform himself. The candidate is his creature, and so completely does the President dominate the convention that we wouldn't be surprised if he prepares the menus for the delegates' meals. We'd be even less surprised if there were a stampede in his favor, and he won the nomination, in spite of his professed desire to retire.*

The possibility of a last-minute mass movement in his favor on the floor of the convention was very much on Theodore's mind, too, and he had taken steps to prevent it. Henry Cabot Lodge was the keynote speaker, and before he left for Washington he was given special, emergency instructions.

Lodge's address was crisp, and the delegates applauded politely whenever he paused for the purpose. Then, near the end of his talk, he mentioned the name of Theodore Roosevelt for the first time, and Convention Hall erupted. For forty-nine minutes the delegates paraded up and down the aisles, and Mrs. Taft, sitting in the visitors' gallery, could not hide her concern.

Lodge resumed when order was restored, making an effort that, he later confessed to Theodore, was the most difficult ever required in his public career. "President Roosevelt," he said, "has authorized me to make a statement on his behalf."

A tense hush settled over the hall.

"The President," Lodge declared, "retires by his own determination. His refusal of renomination is final and irrevocable. Any man who attempts to use his name as a candidate for the presidency impugns both his sincerity and his good faith. That man is no friend to Theodore Roosevelt."

Many of the delegates wept as they cast their unanimous vote for William Howard Taft on the first ballot.

The following month the Democrats, appropriately meeting in Denver, the silver capital, for the third time named William Jennings Bryan as their candidate. Bryan, who knew the real identity of his opponent, launched an immediate attack on Theodore, and the campaign was under way.

Taft dutifully went on the trail, spurred by long, daily letters of exhortation and advice from the White House. Theodore, still refusing to make any addresses of his own, left no avenue or approach unexplored in his efforts to insure the victory of his candidate. He urged Taft to play less golf during the campaign, and under no circumstances to let himself be photographed in golfing attire, "which the Democrats would call frivolous."

He was equally blunt in more important matters. *Accept Speaker Cannon's support with good grace. You need him, although that need is difficult to remember when his arrogance becomes insufferable.*

No one was surprised when, on November 3, Taft won by a comfortable margin in excess of 1,250,000, and an electoral vote of 321 to 162. "We beat them to a frazzle," an elated Theodore told Taft in a long-distance telephone call to Cincinnati, where the President-elect had gone to await the results. Only rank pessimists were alarmed by the drop in the popularity of the Republican party. The election four years earlier had been unique, everyone else said, and no other man could be expected to match Teddy Roosevelt's record as a vote-getter; he alone was capable of exceeding Taft's margin by three to one.

Theodore continued to pour advice at his successor, which Taft gratefully accepted, and many observers, including the press corps, were surprised that the friendship of the two men remained so close. Some strains on their ties were inevitable, of course. Taft preferred his own Cabinet, and kept only Secretary of the Navy George Meyer and Secretary of Agriculture James Wilson.

The outgoing President was disappointed when Philander C. Knox of Pennsylvania was made Secretary of State. "I'll grant you," Theodore told Senator-elect Elihu Root, "that Knox was my Attorney General for a time. But Will needs someone of your caliber at the State Department. The job requires a powerful battleship, and Knox is just an armored cruiser."

Taft's insistence on giving the Interior Department to Richard A. Ballinger of the state of Washington was a more direct and infinitely more severe blow. Not only was Garfield, one of Theodore's close friends, dropped from a post he had wanted to keep, but Ballinger, although not specifically tied to the Old Guard, was a conservative. And, Pinchot reported, he was close to some of the Northwest's lumber interests that had fought with determination against the conservation program.

Nevertheless, Theodore remained loyal to his chosen successor. "It is the right of every President to appoint his own people," he said, "and I'd be churlish if I felt miffed. I have every confidence in Will. He and I view all questions exactly alike."

Scores of White House lunch and dinner guests heard one refrain in the final weeks of the old Administration. "We're glad to be going home," Theodore told them. "With even the youngest children away at school now, this place is too big for us. We just rattle around in it."

On March 1 Theodore entertained thirty-one special guests at a White House lunch. They were members of what he playfully called his "Tennis Cabinet," and among them were Elihu Root, the displaced Garfield and Bill Sewall, the Maine guide who had gone to Dakota with Theodore. French Ambassador Jules Jusserand sat on the President's right, and on his left was Captain Seth Bullock, a former Rough Rider who was United States Marshal of Oklahoma. Several of the guests wept openly when Theodore thanked them for their loyalty and friendship. Then it was his turn, and tears came to his eyes when his friends presented him with a bronze statue of a Rocky Mountain wildcat.

Edith's eyes did not remain dry, either. A group of Washington ladies presented her with a diamond necklace, and when Theodore saw it he was so moved that he became speechless. "I can't remember another occasion," he later said, "when I couldn't talk."

Eleven members of the Tennis Cabinet gave their friend a silver bowl at a private party held at the home of Garfield, and Jusserand broke down while trying to make the presentation. "You're improving, Theodore," the cynical Henry Adams said. "When you first came to Washington, you inspired only rage. Now people take one look at you, and their eyes fill with tears."

On the evening of March 3 President-elect and Mrs. Taft were the only White House dinner guests. Helen Herron Taft tactlessly revealed that she had already discharged a number of White House servants and had hired others. Edith Roosevelt was shocked by the disclosure, and felt that the loyal staff members should have been retained. The atmosphere became dismal. The incoming President was embarrassed, Helen was still bristling and defiant, and Edith found it difficult to conceal her hurt. Theodore saved the dinner, exerting such wit and charm as he delivered one of his non-stop monologues that the breach, if not healed, at least could be ignored. Edith recovered, and graciously invited the Tafts to spend the pre-inauguration night at the White House.

A cold, driving rain on March 4 made it necessary to hold the ceremonies inside the Capitol. Theodore tried to remain inconspicuous, but his efforts had the opposite effect when he loudly and at length reprimanded the press photographers for concentrating on him rather than on his successor.

After President Taft took the oath of office he delivered his inaugural address in even, measured tones, and some in the audience became restless. But Theodore listened intently, and jumping to his feet the instant the talk was ended, he embraced the new President. "God bless you, old man," he roared, and the crowd gave him its most sustained cheer of the day.

Still afraid he might steal the limelight, he made a deliberate break with tradition by refusing to ride down Pennsylvania Avenue from the Capitol to the White House with his successor. He and Edith made an attempt to slip out quietly by a side door, but most of the press brigade followed them, and one reporter called, "Mr. President!"

"Only one man uses that title," Theodore replied acidly, "and you'll find him in the front of the building. After today I'll answer if you'll call me Colonel, but today I'm not going to say another word. This is President Taft's day. He's news and I'm not, so go to him."

Members of the New York Congressional delegation and a number of friends escorted the Roosevelts to their train at the Union Station, where a waiting band serenaded them and a crowd of several thousand applauded. Refusing the Pennsylvania Railroad's offer of a private train or, at the very least, a private car, Theodore insisted that he and Edith travel "in an ordinary drawing room, like any other private citizens." But so many bouquets of flowers had been sent as parting gifts that the stationmaster had been forced to provide a private car after all.

The last to shake hands was Henry Adams. "Theodore," he said, "we'll miss you," and to his own horror he wept.

Museum that the Smithsonian's collection became the most complete in the world. Edmund Heller, with whom Theodore subsequently wrote a two-volume scientific work of distinction, called him the foremost naturalist on earth, but he himself preferred the title "Bwana Makuba," or Great Hunter, bestowed on him by his native bearers.

I am in my element, he wrote Taft, and he was. Shrugging off several attacks of malaria he had picked up in Cuba, he was impervious to heat, fatigue, and the inconveniences of the jungle. Sometimes he spent as long as twelve hours daily in the saddle, and on other occasions, when tracking game on foot, hiked all day without tiring. After bagging some of Africa's greatest beasts, elephants and lions and rhinos, he enjoyed celebrating by cooking supper for the entire party over an open fire. And he spent his evenings fulfilling a lifelong ambition, that of reading the complete works of William Shakespeare.

What a blessed relief it is, he wrote Lodge, *to be free of controversy!*

He spoke too soon. In all, he sent two hundred and ninety-six specimens to the Smithsonian, which lacked the facilities and the funds for the display of so large a number. The harassed curators decided to mount fifty, and when Theodore learned that the rest would not be used, he protested vehemently. These specimens, he said, were intended for the edification of the American people, and he demanded that they be mounted and placed on exhibition immediately. The Smithsonian replied it could not accomplish the impossible, and a new quarrel simmered.

But more immediate eruptions were in the making. The hunting party sailed down the White Nile and arrived at Khartoum, in the Egyptian Sudan, on March 14, 1910. One year and ten days had passed since Theodore had left the presidency, Edith and Ethel were waiting for him at Khartoum, and he now considered himself a private citizen, free to come, go and say what he pleased.

Members of the English community in Khartoum were disturbed by the growing national sentiments of both the Egyptians and Sudanese, which conflicted with each other, and a delegation called on Colonel Roosevelt to express the hope that he would help place the situation in its proper perspectives. He obliged on March 16 by delivering a brief, pungent address in which he said that, "English rule in the Sudan is really the rule of civilization. It is incumbent on every decent citizen of the Sudan to uphold the present order of things, to see that there is no relapse, to see that the reign of peace and justice continues."

The Egyptian Nationalists were furiously critical of the outsider's comments, and their rage was exceeded by that of the Sudanese Moslems, who threatened to assassinate the American. Theodore, blithely impervious, dismissed the Moslems as fanatics and proceeded with his family to Cairo. There he discovered that the Egyptian Prime Minister had been murdered by nationalists, and roundly denounced the slaying.

Egypt continued to prey on his mind, and ten weeks later, in London, he shocked the British by reopening the subject when he was elected a Freeman of the City of London. In ceremonies held at the Guildhall he refused to confine himself to the usual polite expressions of thanks, and instead chose to speak "on matters of real concern as to which I happen to possess some firsthand knowledge." Freely acknowledging that he spoke as an outsider, he added, "I advise you only in accordance with the principles on which I have myself acted as American President in dealing with the Philippines.

"In Egypt you are not only the guardians of your own interests, you are also the guardians of the interests of civilization. Now, either you have the right to be in Egypt or you have not; either it is or it is not your duty to establish and to keep order. If you feel that you have not the right to be in Egypt, then, by all means, get out of Egypt. If, as I hope, you feel that your duty to civilized mankind and your fealty to your own great traditions alike bid you to stay, then make the fact and the name agree and show that you are ready to meet in very deed the responsibility which is yours."

No one had ever spoken in such strong terms to Great Britain, the world's foremost power, and the applause at the end of the speech was, as Theodore later said, "restrained." The London press lost its collective temper at the distinguished private citizen from across the sea. The speech, said the *Standard*, was *a social crime not far from a sacrilege*. The *Star*, in a firm lecture, declared, *Mr. Roosevelt should learn that he is not exempt from the customs of civilized nations*.

The *Times* of London retained its objectivity and sense of humor, however. *We have been treated to an unique dressing down, and although we must deplore the manners of a guest who should have paid us the courtesy of waiting until leaving our shores before abusing our hospitality, we are forced to admit that Colonel Roosevelt was correct in all particulars of his unasked advice*.

The most explosive, if unpublicized, incident prior to the Roosevelts' arrival in London took place in Rome. There, Theodore wrote

Lodge, *I had an elegant row with Cardinal Merry del Val, the Papal Secretary of State, who made a proposition that a Tammany Boodle Alderman would have been ashamed to make.*

The furor started after Theodore and Edith met the King and Queen of Italy, and found them "delightful people." Hoping to pay his respects to Pope Pius X as well, Theodore sent word of his desire to the Vatican, through the American Embassy.

Although he did not yet know it, a group of American Methodist missionaries had arrived in Rome a few days earlier, hoping to make converts in the capital of Roman Catholicism. One member of the group, more ignorant and bigoted than his colleagues, had made several speeches in which he had referred to the Pope as "the whore of Babylon," and the Vatican was annoyed.

Rafael Cardinal Merry del Val replied to Theodore's request by saying the Holy Father would be pleased to receive him. But, the Cardinal added, the audience was contingent upon Theodore's pledge not to see the American missionaries.

Theodore's eruption was comparable to one by Mount Vesuvius, which he had seen a few days earlier. Pope Pius, he said, was a "worthy, narrowly limited parish priest, completely under the control of Merry del Val." When he simmered down, he sent the Cardinal a formal reply. *It would be a real pleasure to be presented to the Holy Father,* he said, then plunged into the heart of the matter. *I do not question his right to receive or not to receive whomsoever he chooses, for any reason that seems good to him. For myself, I must decline to make any stipulations which limit my freedom of conduct.*

That might have been the end of the incident, but several Italian newspapers, apparently inspired by Cardinal Merry del Val, indicated that Theodore had created a tempest in a religious teapot. What he well might have done, the Cardinal indicated, would have been to agree secretly that he would not meet the Methodists while simultaneously making a public declaration to the effect that he had rejected such an agreement.

Disgusted by the suggestion, Theodore wrote to Lodge, saying a Tammany politician could not have stooped that low. He was more circumspect in dealing with the world press, which had been alerted by the Italian articles, and confined himself to the statement that he did not intend to see the Pope.

The Methodist missionaries promptly issued a statement of their own, crowing over their "victory." Their joy was short-lived. Theodore said they had made a "scurrilous attack" on the Pope, and refused to receive a delegation they sent to his hotel to congratulate him.

The only satisfaction I had out of the affair, he wrote to Lodge, *was that on the one hand I administered a needed lesson to the Vatican, and on the other hand I made it understood that I feared the most powerful Protestant Church just as little as I feared the Roman Catholics. It is fortunate that I have no further interest in holding public office; this foolish affair would have compromised my usefulness.*

Private citizen and Mrs. Roosevelt continued their special version of an American grand tour of Europe. The French government extended them a welcome as cordial as it was official, and Ambassador to the United States Jusserand returned to Paris for the occasion. Theodore, unawed in the city that liked to think of itself as the cradle of personal liberties, delivered a lecture at the Sorbonne in which he outlined his concepts of the duties of citizenship. Going on to Christiana, he accepted the Nobel Peace Prize he had been awarded four years earlier. In a stirring address the champion of a strong American Navy advocated a limitation of naval armaments, greater reliance by all nations on the Hague Tribunal, and the formation of a World League of Peace. Such a League, he said, would be effective if every major nation contributed men and arms to an international force that would, if necessary, impose peace on nations that threatened war.

The applause of the civilized world still ringing in his ears, Theodore left with Edith for a short visit to Stockholm, and then went on to Berlin. There Kaiser Wilhelm II overwhelmed him with hospitality, giving a dinner for him and staging an all-day military review in his honor. The two men spent the day side by side, on horseback, and official German photographers recorded the occasion. Prints were made with true Prussian efficiency before the day ended, the Kaiser autographed them, and the photos were presented to Theodore, handsomely framed, as mementos.

One of these inscribed photographs inadvertently created a new furor. On the face of a picture showing the pair reviewing goose-stepping German infantry, the Kaiser wrote, *When we two shake hands, we shake the world!*

The German Foreign Office learned too late that the gift had been made, and hurried, emergency consultations were held. It would be beneath the Kaiser's dignity, it was decided, to ask him to request the return of the photo. Also, being practical, the diplomats did not dare to run the risk of arousing the Imperial wrath by going to their monarch. Other tactics, obviously, were needed.

The following morning a delegation from the Foreign Office paid a visit to Colonel Roosevelt. All of the amenities were observed. Theodore offered his guests coffee, and they drank it. Finally, after exchanging polite conversation for the better part of an hour, the diplomats came to the point. Their master had been indiscreet, and while the Foreign Office felt certain it could rely upon Herr President Roosevelt's discretion, someone else might see the inscription and cause embarrassment for the Imperial government by publicizing the Kaiser's bellicose remark.

Theodore enjoyed himself. He waited until his guests finished making their restrained but impassioned pleas for the return of the photographs, then smilingly shook his head. "His Majesty, the Kaiser, gave these photographs to me himself, with his own hand. I propose to keep them."

German embassies and legations in other countries were alerted, and throughout the rest of Theodore's tour he was badgered by Imperial diplomats who coaxed, wheedled and pleaded. He kept the photos, and took them back to Oyster Bay, where they occupied a prominent place in his study.

In Vienna the elderly Emperor Franz Josef, at eighty, the eldest of Europe's reigning monarchs, gave a banquet at Schönbrunn Palace for the private American citizen, and the highest ranking nobles in the Austro-Hungarian Empire attended. The King of the Belgians entertained the Roosevelts in Brussels, and Queen Wilhelmina gave an informal dinner for them in Holland.

Theodore relished his meetings with royalty. *I thoroughly liked and respected almost all the various kings and queens that I met; they struck me as serious people devoted to their people and anxious to justify their own positions by the way they did their duty. Of course, as was to be expected, they were like other human beings in that the average among them was not very high as regards intellect and force. Apparently what is needed is that a king shall be a kind of sublimated American Vice President.*

On May 6, 1910, while the Roosevelts were in Norway, King Edward VII of Great Britain died, and President Taft immediately cabled Theodore, asking him to act as the official United States representative at the funeral. Cutting short their visit to the Continent by a few days, Theodore and Edith immediately proceeded to London. There the arrangements were being made for a state funeral, and Whitelaw Reid, the American Ambassador to the Court of St. James's, briefed Theodore. There would be dinners and lunches, an official wake and, of course, the funeral itself.

That night, in the privacy of their hotel suite, Theodore discussed the situation with Edith. "Did you know that nine kings are going to ride in the funeral procession?" he asked her.

"I'm not surprised." Something, she noted, was agitating him.

"All of them are going to ride geldings, black ones."

She nodded, waiting.

"I've been given a choice. I can either ride a horse or drive in a carriage." His face felt slightly stiff as he tried to grin innocently at her.

"I suppose," she said, her mind leaping ahead, "that you prefer the horse."

"Well, yes. I certainly do!" He realized he sounded a trifle too emphatic, and added lamely, "It may be a long ride, and you know how cramped I feel after I've been sitting in a carriage."

The complaint was new, but she did not indicate surprise.

"There's just one slight difficulty," Theodore said, gnawing at his mustache.

Edith remained silent.

"If I'm to ride a horse, I'll be required to wear a uniform."

"I see," she said, and stiffened.

"Luckily I have my old Rough Riders' uniform in my luggage."

"No, Theodore! You can't wear it!"

"I quite agree," he said hurriedly. "It's out of date now, and except for the greatcoat, it doesn't fit me too well. I've—ah—put on a bit of weight here and there."

Edith wondered if it was safe to relax.

"The tailors here are extraordinary, you know. There are none like them anywhere on earth." Again he grinned. "So I thought I'd have a new uniform made for me tomorrow. A colonel of cavalry's uniform—"

"But you weren't a colonel of cavalry," she protested.

He ignored the interruption. "The most difficult part of the uniform to get quickly will be the boots. A full-dress cavalry colonel's uniform requires patent leather knee-boots."

Edith winced.

"But, as I said, London is unique. Under the circumstances, I'm sure Springy—or Whitey Reid—or someone—could get boots made for me in twenty-four hours or less."

"If you wear a uniform that you shouldn't—and you shouldn't!—I'll have two choices. I can have a fancy dress costume made for myself—"

His attempted hearty laugh rang hollowly.

"—or I can go home by the first ship. There's one sailing tomorrow and another on Thursday."

Theodore blinked behind his glasses. "I see no need for you to do anything drastic."

"That depends." Her smile, sweetly innocent, indicated no awareness of her victory. "A woman who respects her husband doesn't want to see him make himself look foolish. So, when he's determined and won't listen to reason, she plays ostrich and hides her head in sand."

He made a last, blustering effort. "Why would it be so dreadful for me to wear a uniform?"

"Because you're *not* a colonel of cavalry or of anything else. European royalty may hold honorary commissions, or whatever they're called, but you don't. You encourage people to call you Colonel, which is fair enough, since you enjoy it and they can't call you Mr. President. But don't take a courtesy military title so seriously that you'll dress up like—like the tenor in a Franz Lehar operetta."

Theodore was silent for a moment. "When people laugh at me," he said, "I prefer to lead the laughter myself."

At the formal Buckingham Palace dinner held on the evening prior to the funeral, Theodore Roosevelt of the United States was conspicuous in formal civilian attire. He received a cordial greeting from the new British monarch, George V, and soon found himself the center of attention. Kings and Princes who had met him previously were eager to demonstrate their friendship with him, others were anxious to meet him, and he was soon surrounded by a crowd that Ambassador Reid later said "would have resembled a group of eager, freshmen Congressmen if they hadn't been dripping in gold braid and medals."

The first to draw him aside was Prince Ferdinand of Bulgaria, long a storm center of Balkan politics, who, protected by his powerful Russian neighbor, recently had started to call himself the Czar of Bulgaria. "Mr. President," he said, speaking a version of French even more tortured than Theodore's, "I need your help."

"I'm not President of the United States," Theodore replied, and when the bearded Prince looked hurt, he added more diplomatically, "I'm not president of anything, so I don't see how I can help you."

"In all the world you have more influence than any man alive. The Austrians respect you, and it is the Austrians who are applying intolerable pressure to my poor little country—"

"Colonel," someone called in a Prussian-accented German, "don't listen to that rascal!"

Theodore was surprised to see Kaiser Wilhelm bearing down on them.

"That man," Wilhelm declared, pointing a stern finger at Ferdinand, "is entirely unworthy of your acquaintance."

The Bulgarian began to fidget.

Theodore was embarrassed, not knowing whether the Kaiser was serious, and tried to smile at Ferdinand.

"I advise you not to spend any more time talking to him," Wilhelm continued. "He is a poor creature."

An English duke rescued Ferdinand, deftly extricating him and leading him away.

Wilhelm linked his arm through Theodore's. "How are you since we last met, my friend? I wonder if you realize that you are the only civilian and the only commoner for whom the Imperial German Army has ever held a review."

Theodore noted that some of the other royal guests, watching them, were bristling at the Kaiser. "I suppose," he replied, "that's because not many civilian commoners over here are good enough riders to sit a horse all day on a parade ground." He grinned, then added in a voice louder than the Kaiser's, "In the United States we're all commoners, of course, and in our West there are tens of thousands who have a natural talent for riding. Born cavalrymen, every last one of them." His expression remained bland.

Wilhelm was puzzled, and could not decide whether he had been rebuffed.

The sophisticated King Alfonso of Spain came up to help Theodore. "Cousin Wilhelm," he said, "is a lucky fellow to have had you in Berlin. Had you come to Madrid, I was hoping to show you our El Greco and Goya collections."

"I'm sorry there wasn't time for me to visit Spain on this trip, Your Majesty," Theodore said with sincere regret.

Alfonso launched into a spirited discussion of great art works, and the bored Wilhelm drifted away.

At the dinner table Theodore was seated between Prince Henry of Germany and the Duke of Cumberland, with whom he exchanged effortless pleasantries, but other conversations caught his attention, and he did not refrain from giving them the benefit of his advice. "That's precisely what I would have done, Your Majesty!" he boomed at one point, and at another he declared, "If I'd been in your place, Your Majesty, I wouldn't have done that. You were just asking for trouble!"

When the guests adjourned to a drawing room, King George of Greece, whom Theodore later described as "a little bewizened person," came up beside him. "Mr. President," he said, "I beseech your help."

Theodore had grown weary of explaining that he was no longer President. "I'm flattered," he said, "that you think I could do anything for anybody."

"You jest, of course. But I am in earnest. And surely, even in America, you know of the plight of Crete!"

Theodore remembered that the people of the island of Crete had voted for a dissolution of their ties with Turkey and union with Greece, but that the major European nations, trying to maintain a precarious balance of power, had refused to recognize such a realignment. "We know this side of the world chiefly through the immigrants who come to the United States," he said vaguely, "and very few of them have come from Crete."

"When you make an address, sir," King George insisted, "the entire world listens."

"How I wish that were true. I'm delivering a lecture at Oxford University in a few days on 'Biological Analogies in History,' and I can guarantee, Your Majesty, that what I say will be ignored by the world press."

The Greek monarch refused to be put off. "You must make a speech on Crete!" he insisted.

"But I'd have no reason."

Tears came to George's eyes. "You surely know that all of Europe is acting abominably toward Crete!"

"I can't discuss Crete," Theodore replied firmly, "even with you, Your Majesty!"

George looked offended and hurt. "Why not, Mr. President?"

"In the first place, I know nothing about her problems, and contrary to the opinions of some of my good friends, I don't like to talk about things I don't know. In the second place, I have no right to talk about Crete—"

"Surely you sympathize with my people," the Greek monarch persisted.

Theodore saw that others were watching them, some disturbed, others amused. "The American people," he said, speaking slowly and clearly, "and I'm just a private American citizen who has no right to express any views except his own, sympathize with all Europeans. We, or our ancestors, came from your side of the Atlantic, Your Majesty. But our melting pot, as we call it, is something unique. Immigrants go into it as Englishmen and Germans and Greeks—yes, and Turks— and they come out as Americans. That's why we don't take sides in any European quarrels."

Kaiser Wilhelm, although ostensibly otherwise occupied, was listening to every word.

"So you see," Theodore concluded, wanting to end the discussion before it caused still more complications, "there's no way I can oblige you, even if I wanted to."

George of Greece was adamant. "You *must* mention Crete in some of your speeches!"

There was only one way to handle a situation that had become impossible. Breaking the first rule of royal etiquette, Theodore turned his back on the King and walked across the drawing room.

French Minister of Foreign Affairs Stéphen Pichon was pacing up and down the Buckingham Palace courtyard, where the funeral line of march was forming, when Theodore arrived early the next morning. "Ah, Colonel Roosevelt!" he cried, grasping the sleeve of the American's black frock coat. "At last you are here! We must lodge a protest. Two protests! The two greatest republics on earth are being insulted and slighted!"

Theodore, who had stayed up late the previous night telling Edith about the banquet, was too sleepily surprised to reply.

"A Persian prince—a nobody—is being placed in our carriage with us! And look at our coachman, Colonel!"

Theodore glanced at the coachman, and saw nothing out of the ordinary in his appearance.

"The others are wearing scarlet livery! But our driver is in black!"

"I hadn't noticed, but I wouldn't care if he wore green and yellow," Theodore replied.

"Exactly, Colonel, and all the good we accomplished in your seven and a half years in the White House will be undone!"

"Not so fast, Gifford." Theodore made an effort to dwell only on facts. "I suppose you and Ballinger fought fairly often."

"Constantly. He made life so rough for the Reclamation Service that the engineers planned to resign in a body, but I talked them out of it. He prevented us from setting up new ranger stations and . . . The list is endless, but it isn't just Ballinger. Taft himself has had a direct hand in the sabotage. Instead of giving conservation jobs in Interior to professionals when vacancies occurred, Taft left the whole business up to his Postmaster General, Frank Hitchcock, so the Interior Department is being filled with inferior political hacks."

"You make the situation sound grim."

"It's worse than you know. Two of my best people up in Alaska fought Ballinger's water power restoration order—"

"President Taft's order."

"Yes, Colonel. Of course."

"Whether they were right or wrong in their objectives—and they were right—they had no business disobeying a presidential order!"

"I sent a letter to Senator Dolliver of Iowa on the subject, Colonel," Pinchot said, "and he read it from the floor of the Senate. Here's the crux of what I said about my people. *It is clear not only that they acted from a high and unselfish sense of public duty, but that they deliberately chose to risk their official positions rather than permit what they believed to be the wrongful loss of public property.*"

"No member of any President's Administration can criticize the President!" Theodore exclaimed.

Pinchot's smile was strained. "I also said that the issue was conservation versus the spoliation of natural resources."

Theodore tugged at his mustache, then cleared his throat. "I can't blame you for being upset, Gifford. And I can't say that the reversal of my policies—ah—delights me. But if you and Jonathan Dolliver deliberately arranged ahead of time for him to read your letter into the public record—"

"We certainly did!"

"Then you gave the President no choice. Taft had to discharge you!" Theodore's fist crashed on the coffee table, upsetting a small vase.

"That's what Senator Root told the President, or so I've been informed."

"You knew you'd be thrown out. Why did you do it, Gifford?"

"Isn't it obvious, Colonel? I didn't want to be eased out quietly some day. I knew I wouldn't be kept in any event. So I purposely chose an issue I could dramatize."

"Yes," Theodore said heavily. "It's obvious. President Taft was right. I can't stress that enough."

"At the expense of all that you and Jim and I did!"

"I know, Gifford." Theodore put a restraining hand on the younger man's arm. He could not bring himself to admit aloud that he felt a crushing sense of disappointment in William Howard Taft, who, no matter how correct his position as President, was reversing the whole trend of the conservation movement.

Pinchot sensed his pain, and fell silent.

"You'll have dinner with us tonight?"

"I don't want to be in the way, Colonel. You and Mrs. Roosevelt undoubtedly have plans—"

"And they include you, so that settles the matter."

Both men rose, and Pinchot again reached into his pocket, bringing out a bulky sealed envelope. "Senator Lodge asked me to bring you this. He knew I'd reach you faster than the mails."

Theodore laughed as he took the communication, then asked casually, "What's the press response to your discharge from the government?"

Pinchot reddened. "About thirty newspapers want me to run for President in '12, which is ridiculous. I have no political ambitions. And every magazine in the country stands behind me."

"I'm not surprised," Theodore said, shaking hands and arranging a meeting for the evening.

Alone, he opened Lodge's long letter and skimmed through it. Some of the basic facts were already familiar to him. President Taft, soon after taking office, had summoned a special session of Congress for the purpose of passing the revised, liberalized tariff bill that the Roosevelt Administration had demanded. He had accomplished nothing until, acting on Theodore's advice, written from Africa, he had made his peace with Speaker Joe Cannon.

Then the House of Representatives had passed a new tariff bill as progressive as Theodore had wanted. But Senator Aldrich, its sponsor in the Senate, had added almost nine hundred amendments, each of them revising—upward—the duties on various imports. In Theodore's opinion, the Payne-Aldrich Tariff Bill was a bad joke on the American people, and represented a major step backward into the depths of isolationist conservatism.

You'll be very much interested in a press clipping I've enclosed from the Post, Lodge wrote. *The quotation from Taft's speech is accurate.*

Theodore was forced to read the quotation twice before he could believe his eyes. *On the whole,* President Taft had said, *I am bound to say that I think the Payne-Aldrich Bill is the best tariff bill that the Republican party has ever passed.*

"Will Taft," Theodore said aloud, "is turning into a damned fool."

Later that day a messenger arrived from the American Embassy with a letter from the President, sent by diplomatic pouch, which had arrived on the same ship that had brought Pinchot across the Atlantic. Theodore ripped it open.

The Pinchot-Ballinger controversy, Taft wrote, *has given me a great deal of pain and suffering, but I am not going to say a word to you on that subject. You will have to look into that wholly by yourself without influence by the parties if you would seek the truth.*

In spite of his growing list of faults, Taft had not lost his basic integrity, Theodore thought.

But the letter revealed a self-pitying attitude that he found intolerable, no matter how hard he tried to be fair to his successor. *I have had a hard time,* Taft wrote. *I do not know that I have had harder luck than other Presidents, but I do know that thus far I have succeeded far less than have others. I have been conscientiously trying to carry out your policies, but my method of doing so has not worked smoothly. The tariff bill was in my judgment a good bill and a real downward revision, not as radical a change as I favored, but still a change for the better. The revenues from it have been remarkable. But it did not cut low enough the rate on print paper, and so we have had a hostile press, whether Republican or Democratic.*

Theodore read the letter again, slowly, folded it and put it into a coat pocket. Then he walked to the window, where he stood for a long time gazing out at the London street traffic at twilight. Somewhere in the distance a foghorn sounded on the Thames, and as he turned back into the room he shuddered slightly.

Squaring his shoulders, he walked into the adjoining bedroom.

Edith, who had been resting, sat at the dressing table, brushing her hair. She glanced at him, and immediately felt his tension.

"Tomorrow," Theodore said, "we'll have to start packing. I've been away for almost fourteen months, and that's more than enough.

As much as I dread getting back into the boil of American politics, I've got to go home. Now."

In the spring of 1910 Edith Roosevelt wrote to friends that various people, whom she did not identify, were urging her to keep her husband abroad for another year and a half. Someone told Henry Adams, who had recovered his aplomb, and he asked, with a straight face, "Why not for life?"

But Theodore felt compelled to return home, and a huge crowd was on hand to greet the German liner, the *Kaiserin Augusta Victoria*, when she docked on June 18. Not even a heavy rain could dampen the festivities that morning. President Taft had sent his military aide on board the Navy yacht, *Dolphin*, to greet his predecessor at quarantine, fireboats shooting sprays of water high into the air escorted the liner up the Hudson River to her pier, and five bands vied with one another in playing "A Hot Time in the Old Town." The usual contingent of Rough Riders was on hand, and so was the largest press delegation to gather in any one spot since the Taft inaugural.

Theodore, who had written Taft a brief note from his ship, expressing the intention of keeping his mind open and his mouth shut, felt obliged to make a short speech. But, he told the reporters, "the one thing I want now is privacy. I intend to close up like a native oyster. I hope the press won't come to Sagamore Hill, because I have nothing to say."

His request was ignored, and virtually every New York newspaper, as well as many others, assigned a reporter to keep a permanent eye on the colonel. Within a few days the American people learned that a steady procession of progressive Republicans was making its way to Oyster Bay, and that many of the guests had little use for the Old Guard: Senators La Follette and Beveridge, former Secretary of the Interior Garfield, the discharged Chief Forester, Gifford Pinchot. *Is it accidental,* mused the New York *Sun, that most of these gentlemen are of the anti-Taft stripe?*

The President wondered, too, and sent his mentor a belated letter, asking him for a White House visit. Theodore, busily establishing his headquarters at the *Outlook* offices on Fourth Avenue in New York City, declined the invitation in a brief note that the President interpreted as curt.

"I've done nothing to offend him," the hurt Taft said. "At least he could have been polite."

The slight was unintentional, and Theodore decided to make amends by visiting his successor at the Taft summer home in Beverly, Massachusetts. From the start the reunion was ill-fated. The two men spent literally no time alone with each other, thanks to the unexpected arrival of other guests, among them several Old Guard Congressmen who watched the pair carefully for any signs of strain. Those strains were emerging into the open when Theodore returned to Sagamore Hill after a twenty-four-hour stay.

"I'm sure Theodore has no personal political ambitions," Senator Elihu Root said. "But his writing for the *Outlook* and his other work doesn't take up more than a fraction of his time. He's still deeply committed to the principles of his presidency, of course. And on top of everything else he's incapable of retiring from politics. It just isn't his nature."

The breach between Theodore and Taft grew wider. The progressive elements were mentioning La Follette as a possible Republican candidate for President in 1912, and Theodore raised the Wisconsin Senator's hopes by writing an article for *Outlook* that praised him. Gratuitously, in a note, he also informed La Follette that Ted, who was now working in San Francisco, was one of his most enthusiastic supporters.

Root's prediction proved accurate. *Colonel Roosevelt,* the New York *Herald* said, *intends to gain control of the Republican party machinery in both New York and New Jersey in order to elect Governors and Congressmen this fall who are of his persuasion.*

Theodore and Taft met for an hour in New Haven late in September for the purpose of discussing the gubernatorial campaigns, and a new misunderstanding arose. A member of the President's party informed the press that "the Colonel requested this meeting, as he wants President Taft's support."

Theodore's pride was hurt, and he issued an indignant denial. Taft, in turn, thought him ungracious. "It's true," he complained, "that I volunteered to help. But the only reason I did it is because I knew he was going to ask for that help."

A close Roosevelt friend, Henry L. Stimson, won the nomination for Governor of New York, but in New Jersey the Old Guard forced the nomination of its own candidate to oppose Woodrow Wilson of Princeton, who was making his debut in politics. "For a Democrat," Theodore said, "Wilson is a good fellow. He's really a progressive Republican, but doesn't know it."

Meanwhile the attempts to force the return of the former President to the national political arena were gaining momentum. Progressive Republicans in all parts of the country were asking him to make speeches, and were joined, somewhat reluctantly, by party regulars who were growing alarmed by Taft's continuing loss of popularity. Theodore responded to the pressures by making several brief forays into the South, then taking a sixteen-state speaking tour swing through the West.

"How can I keep quiet?" he rhetorically asked no one in particular on board his special train, in the presence of the press. "I see basic American values being subverted and lost. I see the policies and principles I hold dear being destroyed."

In a Denver address he returned, more emphatically than ever before, to an attack on the courts, which protected the "bad" businessman at the expense of the people. He attacked the creation of a neutral ground "which can serve as a place of refuge for the lawless man, and especially for the lawless man of great wealth, who can hire the best legal talent to advise him how to keep his abiding place equally distant from the uncertain frontiers of both state and national power."

President Taft, first and foremost an attorney who felt great respect for the courts, was deeply disturbed.

A few days later, before a huge crowd of farmers and ranchers assembled on the prairie at Osawatomie, Kansas, Theodore delivered the most radical and inflammatory address of his life. The previous night he had explained his underlying philosophy to the correspondents who accompanied him, and to them, as well as to himself, his thinking seemed clear.

There was a marked difference between "good" and "bad" trusts, just as there were sharp differences between "good" and "bad" businessmen of great wealth. What he sought, he said, was equality of opportunity for all Americans within the American economic framework of private property rights and the American political framework of democracy. He seemed anxious that there be no misunderstanding of his own basic concepts.

Then, at Osawatomie, he struck. *Labor is prior to, and independent of, capital,* he declared. *Capital is only the fruit of labor, and could never have existed if labor had not first existed. Labor is the superior of capital, and deserves much the higher consideration.*

The people with worn, tired faces, plainly dressed, applauded him, but there were some in the crowd who looked a trifle uneasy.

"Yes," Theodore said, "that sounded radical. Didn't it? If that observation was original with me, I should be even more strongly denounced as a Communist agitator than I shall be anyhow. It was written by someone else. Not by me. And not by Karl Marx."

He paused for dramatic effect. "It is Abraham Lincoln's. I am only quoting it."

The crowd came alive, and roared its approval. Men laughed aloud, shouted and pounded one another on the back.

Theodore, sharing the joke with them, grinned broadly. Then, suddenly, he sobered as he continued his speech. "The essence of any struggle for liberty has always been, and must always be to take from some one man or class of men the right to enjoy power, or wealth, or position, or immunity, which has not been earned by service to his or their fellows."

The crowd cheered again, and the reporters scribbled furiously.

"The essence of the struggle is to destroy privilege, and give to the life and citizenship of every individual the highest possible value both to himself and to the commonwealth.

"The New Nationalism about which I speak to you today puts the national need before sectional or personal advantage. It is impatient of the utter confusion that results from local legislatures attempting to treat national issues as local issues. It is still more impatient of the impotence which springs from overdivision of governmental powers, the impotence which makes it possible for local selfishness or for legal cunning, hired by wealthy special interests, to bring national activities to a deadlock.

"This New Nationalism regards the executive power as the steward of the public welfare. It demands of the judiciary that it shall be interested primarily in human welfare rather than in property, just as it demands that the representative body shall represent all the people rather than any one class or section of the people."

The correspondents exchanged frequent glances and occasional, urgent whispers as the talk continued. Some thought the colonel was demanding the presidential nomination for himself, so sweeping was his all-inclusive demand for reform. Others, however, were convinced that only because he no longer sought office for himself could he insist that such changes be made.

"I stand for the Square Deal," Theodore declared. "But I mean not merely that I stand for fair play under the present rules of the game, but that I stand for having those rules changed so as to work for a more substantial equality of opportunity and reward."

His specific recommendations devastated the believers in the maintenance of the status quo. It was necessary to regulate corporations, and to achieve this end their political activities had to be curbed. It was necessary to supervise all big business, including the railroads, or the government might be forced to take charge of railroad operations. This alternative would be Socialism, and he deplored the possibility.

He demanded that both "big and little special interests" be deprived of their meddling in the establishment of tariff schedules, and asked for the formation of an expert commission to perform "the vitally needed task." He asked for a graduated income tax, and, more urgently, a drastically graded inheritance tax, which would provide a safeguard against "swollen fortunes."

He renewed his often-repeated plea for an increased conservation of natural resources. In order to achieve a greater honesty in the democratic process, he demanded full publicity for all candidates' campaign expenses. In a society that was turning from rural pursuits to those of the industrial cities, he requested aid for farmers. He made his strongest demand on record for laws to regulate child labor, and to curb abuses in working conditions and hours for women.

In a sweeping conclusion, he told his cheering audience, "We are face to face with new conceptions of the relations of property to human welfare. The man who wrongly holds that every human right is secondary to his profit must now give way to the advocate of human welfare, who rightly maintains that every man holds his property subject to the general right of the community to regulate its use to whatever degree the public welfare may require it."

The West takes it for granted that Roosevelt will be the next Republican candidate for President, the New York *World* said.

Theodore Roosevelt, the Chicago *Tribune* declared, *has written a party platform as well as spoken a personal creed. The Republican party will ignore or reject that platform at its peril.*

The West loves and understands Roosevelt, the Denver *Republican* purred.

The New York *Tribune* went even farther than most newspapers. Recognizing the philosophical nature of the address, it congratulated the Colonel for what it called his *deep and original thought.*

The Old Guard was horrified, and Speaker Cannon said, "This time TR goes too far."

Even Cabot Lodge was careful. "The Colonel and I," he told the inquiring press, "long ago agreed to disagree on many subjects. Nothing could disturb our friendship, which is too old and close to be broken by differences of opinion. But there are some things we do not discuss."

President Taft was too shocked to say anything at all for publication. But he privately lamented the divergence in the paths he and Theodore were taking. "If I only knew what the President wanted," he said, once again referring to his predecessor by the title he now held, "I would do it. But he has held himself so aloof that I am absolutely in the dark. I am deeply wounded, and he gives me no chance to explain my attitude or learn his." The rift was becoming too wide and deep to be healed.

The Democrats swept the Congressional elections of 1910, winning victories in every part of the United States. On the Eastern seaboard, not even the magic of Theodore Roosevelt's active participation saved his candidates. Henry L. Stimson was roundly defeated for Governor of New York by Democrat John A. Dix. And in New Jersey, Woodrow Wilson moved from Princeton University to the Governor's Mansion, in Trenton.

Theodore decided the time had come for him to forget politics and devote himself, with greater energy, to his own writing. With a feeling of relief he returned to Oyster Bay, and spent less time at the *Outlook* offices. "I am almost ashamed of the fact," he said, "that I have been unable to keep myself from being thoroughly happy since election. I think that the American people feel a little tired of me, a feeling with which I cordially sympathize."

In his private conversations he made no secret of his disgust with President Taft. "I cannot abide weakness of any kind in a man who seeks leadership and is elected to a post of responsibility. Taft was elected to the highest position in the country, and has a responsibility to the people at large, which he fulfills only in part, and to his party, which he fulfills not at all.

"The Republicans could have won this election and should have won it. That we did not is due to the absence of energetic, constructive leadership which Taft should have provided. As a President, he is probably better than McKinley, and may be better than Harrison, but he is not a very good President. As a party leader he is a total failure."

Having spoken his mind, Theodore turned to his own writing, and swore he would take no future interest in politics, national or international affairs. There were few who were willing to take him at his word, and among the scoffers was Lodge. "The affairs of the United States are in your bloodstream," he said. "You can no more abandon them than you can stop breathing."

By February of 1911 Theodore forgot his resolves. "The protection which the tariff gives to special interests must be abolished," he said in an address in New York.

President Taft, trying to take his advice to heart, sent a message to Congress on the tariff, and asked for a commercial reciprocity treaty with Canada.

"He's making a terrible mistake," Theodore told friends. "Any tariff reduction should be general. A treaty with Canada alone is premature. It is so narrow in scope that both parties will be injured, neither will benefit and it will end in disaster."

His instincts were right, and he proved to be an almost uncannily accurate prophet. The wheat growers of the West were alarmed because they would be forced to compete on even terms with Canadian farmers. And everyone in the West was outraged because Canadian raw materials would be imported by Eastern industries for less money than their own raw materials could be transported. The Canadians were equally upset, and, as a direct result of the treaty, the government of Sir Wilfrid Laurier fell.

Taft, whose intentions had been good, again seemed revealed as a bumbling failure.

But the President had the stubborn courage of his convictions, and in an attempt to further the cause of peace, proposed to the Senate that the United States sign special treaties of friendship with other nations, in which all disputes would be subject to arbitration by either a joint panel or a third party. As a beginning, he asked for such treaties with Great Britain and France.

Theodore promptly and publicly protested. He approved of a treaty only with Britain, which was a "special case," because her interests and those of the United States had become virtually identical. But he strongly disapproved of similar treaties with any other nation, France included, saying these documents would not be worth the paper on which they were written.

The Senate, already dubious, refused to ratify the treaties. The President was subjected to the humiliation of rejection by his own party as well as the opposition, and was crushed. "I don't understand

Roosevelt," he said. "I don't know what he is driving at except to make my way more difficult. It is very hard to see a devoted friendship going to pieces like a rope of sand."

Taft himself inadvertently struck one of the final blows that destroyed what was left of the relationship. It had become obvious in many quarters that the United States Steel Corporation had benefitted enormously from its acquisition of the Tennessee Coal & Iron Company during the financial panic of 1907, and the President felt compelled to act. He instructed the Justice Department to initiate proceedings, and, early in October 1911, Attorney General George W. Wickersham filed an anti-trust suit against Big Steel.

Theodore was stunned, and his sense of hurt rapidly became transformed into fury. He had been subjected to severe criticism for his dealings with Gary and Frick, and he was able to interpret the White House action in only one way. "Taft knew I made my gentlemen's agreement with Frick and Gary in good faith," he said, "and I'm convinced they were honorable, too. They saved the country from a severe financial collapse, and it isn't fair to penalize them just because it has now developed that they made an unexpectedly good bargain.

"By taking anti-trust action against U. S. Steel, Taft is deliberately impugning my personal honor as well as that of men I have had no reason to doubt or mistrust. This is unpardonable!"

Taft, although slow to anger, was at last exasperated, and struck back. "President Roosevelt knows better than anyone else in the United States that the man who sits behind my desk must put his concept of duty before everything else. I'm sorry he interprets my action as he does, but it can't be helped. I have no choice. I just wish he could see the suit against U. S. Steel as a continuation of his basic policies, which it is."

The particulars of the government suit became known in late October, and the nation was astonished by the Justice Department's contention that Theodore had been fooled by a wily Gary and Frick. The steel executives were portrayed as unprincipled connivers who, at least by implication, had taken advantage of Theodore's innocence and ignorance. No mention was made of Elihu Root's presence at the White House meeting which had determined the future of Tennessee Coal & Iron.

"Taft has given me no choice," Theodore told Cabot Lodge who stopped in New York, en route from Boston to Washington, for a private lunch with him in early November. "He's forced me to call him a liar."

The Senator from Massachusetts had anticipated his reaction, but nevertheless stirred uneasily. "It isn't going to do anyone except the Democrats any good for the most popular living American to abuse his successor as President."

Theodore slashed at his beefsteak with a sharp knife, and his voice rose above the traditional, genteel murmur in the dining room of the Metropolitan Club. "That can't be helped. There's a principle at stake!"

Lodge knew it was useless to argue with him when he began speaking of principles. "What are you going to do, Theodore?"

"It's done. I've written a candid article for the new issue of *Outlook* that exposes Taft as a weathervane who can't stop spinning."

His friend lost interest in his own lunch.

"I've pointed out that he was enthusiastic and emphatic in approving the merger when he was Secretary of War."

Lodge groaned.

"One sentence I wrote sticks in my mind, perhaps because I took special care to say precisely what I meant. *It ill becomes him either by himself or through another afterwards to act as he is now acting.* His real motive is a desire to smear me, not attack the trusts."

"Give him the benefit of sincerity."

"How can I, Cabot? The whole question of the trusts is becoming so complex that we can handle the problem only by new methods. It certainly can't be done by a succession of lawsuits, and Taft is too able a lawyer not to realize it. In my opinion we need a new set of laws, and he ought to be prodding Congress, not chasing the trusts through the courts. I've said that in my article, too."

Lodge nodded glumly.

"What's wrong with your meat? Shall we send it back to the kitchen?"

"No, I'm not hungry today, Theodore."

"I've also said that Taft's approach is practical as it would be for the Army—in a day when firepower is the deciding factor in battle— to return to the flintlocks of Washington's era."

"When does the article appear?"

"It will reach the newsstands on November 18th, Cabot."

"In other words, it's too late right now to stop the printing and substitute another article in *Outlook?*"

"I wouldn't permit it!" Theodore declared.

"Then November 18th will go down in history as the day the Republican party died!"

"Not at all," Theodore replied, his manner becoming reasonable. "The party will become stronger—as will the country—when weak elements are rooted out."

"You think Taft ought to be retired at the end of his term?" Lodge asked carefully.

"I'm tempted to suggest his impeachment and recall right now!"

"You mustn't!"

"I'm being realistic, Cabot. There's precious little chance that Congress would lift a finger."

"I see no grounds for impeachment."

"You don't, eh? It's a good thing for Will Taft that I don't hold a seat in the Senate!"

Lodge, aware that men at nearby tables were avidly listening to every word, tried in vain to indicate, subtly, that he ought to lower his voice.

"A President's goals must be a primary consideration of those who judge him. And as nearly as *I* can judge, Taft's aim is to preserve the bad, ruin the good and make no innovations!"

Long experience had taught Lodge to change the subject when it became apparent that Theodore had lost his perspective. "I suppose you saw the reaction to La Follette's speech in Philadelphia the other evening."

"Yes, the poor fellow floundered so badly that half his audience walked out. He's tired, Cabot. He's been the only real Progressive in the Republican party who has developed a national stature, so he's been swamped with requests to speak, and he's foolishly accepted too many. Only men who have extraordinary vitality can keep their wits about them when they're making anywhere from three to eight speeches every day of the week." Theodore ate the last of his steak and potatoes.

"Try your salad."

Theodore grimaced. "Vegetables are for the young. No, Cabot, I'm afraid La Follette doesn't have the qualities to lead the Progressive wing to a victory of any consequence."

There was a long silence before Lodge, carefully lowering his own voice, asked, "When did you decide to seek the nomination for President next year, Theodore?"

"I've made no such decision!"

"You're holding to your pledge, then. No third term."

Theodore tugged at his mustache, and, finally aware of the interest at other tables, followed his own long-standing advice by speaking softly. "Only the need to step in for the purpose of saving the country from destruction through the preservation of my own policies would persuade me to change my stand."

Lodge showed no surprise. "When will you announce your candidacy?"

"I just told you, I haven't yet made up my mind."

"I see."

"It would be a sacrifice."

Lodge nodded.

"God knows I don't need the glory. I held power long enough, and no longer feel the thrill of command."

"Of course."

"I'd lose my privacy again, and Edith would hate it."

"I'm sure she would," Lodge said sincerely.

"On the other hand, she won't stand in my way."

"You've asked her opinion, then."

"We've been discussing the subject, naturally."

"Naturally."

"I'll let you know as soon as I make the final decision."

"Thank you, Theodore."

"I hope the country would realize I'd be making a great personal sacrifice."

"I'm sure you could make it clear to the voters in every state," Lodge said.

"Do you disapprove, Cabot?"

"I don't think you'd like my advice."

"I'm asking for it."

"Then wait four years. I've detected a strong swing toward the Democrats in every part of the country—"

"Of course you have, and that's one reason I'd consent to run. If I consent. Every day that Taft spends in office loses votes for the Republicans. I believe I could reverse that stampede into the opposition ranks."

"I dare say you could."

"Ah, you admit it, then!" Theodore was triumphant.

"It doesn't take a political genius to know you have the most loyal, active following in the country."

"Then," Theodore demanded, "why should I wait four years?"

"You're forgetting one of the fundamentals of politics. Who controls a political party, particularly the party of the President?"

"I see what you're trying to say. Ordinarily, Cabot, the President controls his party, and nothing can prevent him from winning the nomination for another term—when he's determined to get it."

"Exactly," Lodge said grimly.

"Under the present circumstances, the usual rules don't apply. I'm convinced that party leaders everywhere will desert Taft if I should decide to oppose him."

"And I say you're mistaken. He still controls the party machinery— and the patronage that's the life blood of the party system. We know Taft wants another term. He won't step aside voluntarily. You may destroy the party by opposing him, Theodore."

"We'll put it together again after I beat him."

"But suppose you don't. Suppose you lose. Then what will you do?"

Theodore smiled and shook his head, unable to admit that Taft might defeat him.

In late January 1912 the Republican Governors of seven states sent a formal petition to Colonel Theodore Roosevelt, asking him to emerge from retirement and lead the party to victory in November. An avalanche of mail followed from every state, and Theodore's smiling silence was sufficient asset to prompt a statement from the President.

"I deplore and must oppose," Taft said, "those men who are seeking to pull down the pillars of the temple of freedom and representative government."

Pressures on both sides increased, tempers soared and many Republican leaders throughout the United States, not wanting to be caught in a crossfire, side-stepped commitments. The Democrats smelled the potent, sweet scent of victory in the forthcoming presidential campaign.

The ex-President and the President were careful to avoid direct attacks on each other, but it was inevitable that the strains of self-imposed silence would become unbearable. "He may beat me in an election," Taft told friends, "but I'm going to defeat him at the convention. If he thinks he can take the votes of delegates from the President, his head is getting too big for his shoulders."

The comment was repeated to Theodore, and his reaction sent Elihu Root hurrying to the White House. "I expected an explosion," the junior Senator from New York told the President, "but he didn't say a word. He just listened."

"That means he's very angry," Taft said.

"So angry he'll believe anything about you. I'm afraid your intemperate remarks have exposed you to your enemies—and him to his."

Early in April visitors from Washington reported to Theodore that the President had called him a traitor. It no longer mattered that the authenticity of the alleged statement could not be checked, inasmuch as no one knew to whom the comment had been made.

"My hat has been indirectly in the ring since February," Theodore told the press, after summoning reporters to the *Outlook* office for a conference. "I have tried to keep this entire matter on a high, impersonal level, since I have no personal desire to become President again, and am agreeing to run only because the people will it.

"But I cannot remain silent any longer regarding my personal relationship with the present occupant of the White House. I cannot but feel that he has been disloyal to our past friendship, disloyal to every canon of ordinary decency."

Taft's reply was dignified. "I do not want to fight Theodore Roosevelt," he said, "but he has forced me into battle with him. Therefore I shall fight him. I am a man of peace, but when I fight I want to hit hard."

The President was as good as his word, and messages went from the White House to Republican office-holders everywhere: pledge support to Taft or expect no support in return.

Gifford Pinchot and other Progressives were alarmed when senators and congressmen, governors and mayors, unable to equivocate any longer, publicly announced they would stand behind the President's bid for renomination. But Theodore appeared unconcerned, and, accepting speaking engagements whenever they were offered, repeatedly declared, "I am waging a crusade. We Progressives believe that human rights are supreme, that wealth should be the servant and not the master of the people. We agree with Lincoln that this nation belongs to the people."

Senator Lodge could see no good coming from the struggle. *You are splitting the party,* he wrote to Theodore. *Please behave sensibly and stop believing your own high-sounding words. Surely you know the party regulars cannot support you and will be forced to deny you the nomination.*

The party's nomination, Theodore replied loftily, *means less to me than the principles of my crusade.*

Their friendship survived the strain, however. *I will remain silent at the convention,* Lodge wrote, *because I am incapable of opposing you in the open.*

My dear fellow, Theodore wrote in return, *you could not do anything that would make me lose my warm personal affection for you. I shan't try to justify my viewpoint because it would seem as if I were attacking yours.*

Other Republican office-holders were less tolerant and amiable than Lodge, and scores wrote to Theodore, some attacking him on principle, others launching frontal assaults on his integrity. This opposition had predictable results.

"I have scant patience," he told a huge, cheering audience in New York, "with this talk of the tyranny of the majority. The only tyrannies from which men, women and children are suffering in real life are the tyrannies of minorities." He was thinking, he declared, of those "who have ruled and legislated and decided as if in some way the vested rights of privilege had a first mortgage on the whole United States, while the rights of the people were merely an unsecured debt."

He repeated the theme during his travels in the late spring of 1912, but everywhere he confined himself to his speech-making and made few active efforts to win delegates. To no one, however, would he concede the obvious, that no matter how great his popularity with the voters who were registered members of the Republican party, he could not compete with President Taft for the votes of convention delegates.

The Republican National Committee met in Chicago on June 6 to make final preparations for what promised to be a stirring convention, and the press was on hand in unprecedented numbers. TEDDY DOESN'T STAND A CHANCE, the reporters wired their newspapers, and this information was passed along to the public.

But Theodore blithely ignored what appeared to be inevitable. Arriving in Chicago on June 14 for the convention, he questioned the legality of seating delegates who supported Taft, declared that the convention would be marked by a fight of honesty versus dishonesty, and then issued a rousing, written statement:

What happens to me is not of the slightest consequence. I am to be used, as in a doubtful battle any man is used, to his hurt or not, so long as he is useful and is then cast aside and left to die. It would be far better to fail honorably for the cause we champion than it would be to win by foul methods the foul victory for which our opponents hope. But the victory shall be ours, and it shall be by clean and honest fighting for the loftiest of causes. We fight in honorable fashion for the good of mankind; unheeding of our individual fates; with unflinching hearts and undimmed eyes; we stand at Armageddon, and we battle for the Lord.

The cynical newsmen accorded him the rare honor of applauding after he read them the statement. And the reaction of the general public was equally emphatic. "We stand at Armageddon" became a national byword overnight.

The professional politicians attending the convention were slightly bored, deeply pained, and adamantly stubborn. The Progressives presented their own slates of delegates from virtually every state, and the Credentials Committee met behind closed doors to fight out the issue of whether to seat Taft men or Roosevelt men. At 2:00 A.M. on June 20 the results were announced. No irregularities had been found, and the Taft delegates would be seated.

Theodore's supporters came to his hotel in a group to inform him they would take their fight to the floor of the convention, but he seemingly disagreed. "So far as I am concerned, I am through. If you are voted down in the convention, the real and lawful majority will organize as such. I went before the people in the primaries, and I won," he said, carefully refraining from mentioning that primary elections had not been held in a majority of the states. "Let us find out if the Republican party is the party of the plain people or the party of the bosses and the professional radicals acting in the interests of special privilege."

Many of the politicians realized for the first time that the rumors they had heard might be true. Former President Theodore Roosevelt —himself the titular leader of the Republican party for seven and a half years, and a man who had not bolted when, as a young man, he had opposed the candidacy of James G. Blaine—might be on the verge of forming a third party.

"If he leaves," an unidentified party leader declared, a party leader whose personal description closely fitted that of Uncle Joe Cannon, "he'll be handing the damn election to the damn Democrats on a goddam silver platter."

There was talk of a compromise ticket and a compromise platform, so Theodore called a press conference. "I'll name the compromise candidate," he said. "It'll be me. I'll name the compromise platform. It will be the Progressive platform."

"Are the stories true, Colonel?" a reporter from the New York *World* shouted above the hubbub. "Will you form a new party?"

Theodore grew pale, those who attended the conference later reported, but made no reply.

Several other newsmen repeated the question.

There was a brief silence, and then the former head of the Republican party turned and walked out of the room.

Everyone followed him to his headquarters at the Congress Hotel, but his own suite was barred to the press. All that could be learned was that a strategy meeting was being held behind closed doors, and that Theodore, together with some of his closest associates, was trying to reach a final decision.

California Governor Hiram Johnson emerged from the meeting, and was surrounded by the press. "In my opinion," he said, raising a hand for silence, "the Progressives are foolish to await the inevitable nomination of William H. Taft. The convention is a farce! Look at the California story, gentlemen. Roosevelt won the primary there by more than seventy thousand votes, but the Credentials Committee is seating Taft men, only Taft men. Need I say more?

"We are frittering away our time," he continued, his voice rising to platform level. "We are frittering away our opportunity. Worst of all, we are frittering away Roosevelt."

He ducked back inside, and the newspaper correspondents caught a brief, tantalizing glimpse of twenty-five or thirty men engaged in what appeared to be several separate conversations. Then the door closed again.

The confusion in the living room of the suite was even greater than it appeared. No two men could agree, and when someone became completely frustrated, he left the group with whom he had been talking and drifted to another.

Theodore, gnawing at his mustache, spoke to no one, and the others, by tacit consent, left him alone. His was the ultimate choice, they realized, and he had more to lose than anyone else. Gifford Pinchot's brother, Amos, felt certain that not one man present at the conference harbored false illusions: a third party, everyone was convinced, would be certain to lose the election. Nevertheless, as Theodore had pointed out, there were principles at stake that would influence the United

States for decades to come, perhaps centuries, and everyone believed he was right.

Financier George W. Perkins and Frank A. Munsey, a wealthy magazine publisher, were talking quietly in one corner of the room, and the few who paid any attention to them finally realized that these habitually calm men were excited. Suddenly, with one accord, they made their way to the center of the room and halted Theodore, who was still pacing.

He looked at them, a faint hint of amusement in his eyes.

"Colonel," Munsey said hoarsely, "we'll see you through."

"No matter how much it may cost," Perkins added.

That evening, the night of June 22, Roosevelt supporters by the thousands jammed Orchestra Hall, which Perkins had rented, and there was pandemonium when Theodore walked onto the stage. "Thou Shalt Not Steal," he said in a low tone, and his audience went wild.

The cause for which he stood, and which they were supporting, he said, was bigger than any one individual. It was a cause that would give a new direction to the mainstream of American life, regardless of what might happen in the 1912 election. And, he hinted, he alone had the qualities necessary for leadership in the coming struggle.

Theodore's closing words sparked another near-riot, and his supporters demonstrated for almost an hour when he said, "If you wish me to make the fight, I will make it, even if only one state should support me."

The National Progressive party had come into being. Most of its members came from the liberal wing of the Republican party, while others, drawn in the main by Theodore's magnetism, came from the ranks of independent voters. Thanks to the fund-raising efforts of Perkins, Munsey, and Robert Bacon, ample resources were available for the coming campaign, but the Progressive war chest was still relatively small.

Therefore the delegates who attended the party's convention, which met in Chicago on August 5, paid their own traveling and living expenses. More than ten thousand were on hand for the meeting, and their enthusiasm was unbridled. Senator Beveridge delivered the opening address, a two and one-half hour speech which impelled the New York *Tribune* to remark, *Teddy's Bull Moose Progressives have their hearts in the right places and stand for all that is good and noble, but no one has told them that brevity is the soul of successful politics.*

Certainly Theodore had forgotten that principle. After he was duly nominated for President and Governor Johnson of California was named his running mate, he issued a twenty-five thousand word statement of principles which he called, "A Confession of Faith." It had been his intention to deliver the statement as an address, but it was so long he had to cut it in half.

Perhaps the most disappointing aspect of the Progressive meeting was the absence of professional politicians who could deliver large blocs of votes. *Men who earn their living in politics,* the St. Louis *Post-Dispatch* said, *are required to back winners.* Only three Republican chairmen or deputy chairmen joined the Progressives, and of the seven governors who, a few months earlier, had urged Theodore to run, only two actively campaigned for him.

Editor William Allen White, the "Sage of Emporia," described the Progressive party members as "the successful middle-class country town citizens, the farmer whose barn was painted, the well-paid railroad engineer and the country editor." The women, he declared, "were our own kind, too—women doctors, women lawyers, women teachers, college professors, middle-aged leaders of civic movements, or rich young girls who had gone in for settlement work."

Observers for the two major parties saw no real threat from the Progressives, although the Republicans were gloomy. Colonel Roosevelt, they well realized, would drain away millions of votes that otherwise would have remained within the fold. Equally harmful was the need for President Taft to wage an aggressive campaign, traveling and making hundreds of speeches. In brief, he would be at his worst.

The Democrats were jubilant, but concealed their elation. Their candidate, Governor Woodrow Wilson, was alert, articulate and, above all, a liberal who would prevent defections to the Progressives. The Democratic strategy was simple: they would allow Roosevelt and Taft to knock each other out, and Wilson, they believed, could not lose.

Most newspapermen and professional politicians of every persuasion agreed with them. The single major exception was the man who, only a few years earlier, had been called the most astute politician in the United States. "We're going to win," Theodore repeatedly told cheering crowds, "because we represent pure democracy, the America of tomorrow."

His energy astonished and confounded the critics who had been claiming that he was growing old and tired. Knowing he could win only by appealing to the masses of voters over the heads of their local political leaders, he launched a furious campaign. His special train crisscrossing the country, he preached his humanitarian, moral cause with such insistent fervor that his throat began to bother him, and every day he was forced to receive treatment from a physician.

Then, on the afternoon of October 14, he came to Milwaukee, the "heartland of La Follette Progressivism." Nowhere was his cause more popular, and a mammoth crowd gathered outside the Gilpatrick Hotel to see and cheer him as he left for the hall where he was scheduled to speak to an overflow throng.

Accompanied by several local Progressive leaders, he walked slowly to his waiting automobile, waving and smiling. Suddenly a loud pistol shot sounded, and Theodore fell backward onto the runningboard of his car, clutching the right side of his chest.

The crowd was stunned, but men recovered swiftly, and closed in on the would-be assassin, a short, undistinguished man in shirtsleeves.

With an effort Theodore pulled himself to his feet. "Stand back!" he shouted, waving his left arm. "Don't hurt him!"

Members of his police escort managed to rescue the assailant.

Theodore stared at him, and heard him mumble something about a third term. "The poor creature," he said, and turned back to the crowd. "Give me your pledge you won't hurt him. I'm all right, do you see?" Waving again, he climbed into the car, the local Progressives following.

"Your clothes are bloody, Colonel," one of them said in an urgent voice. "We'll take you to the hospital."

"And disappoint the people who've come to hear me speak?" Theodore coughed, but quickly recovered. "Nonsense. Go to the hall!" he ordered the driver.

His companions protested as the car started off to make the short run.

"Look here," Theodore said. "I'm lucky. That maniac's bullet went through my topcoat, my suit coat, my spectacle case—and the manuscript of my speech. Who says it doesn't pay to be verbose, eh? It spent itself on the manuscript!"

"But the bullet is somewhere inside you, Colonel! And you're bleeding!"

"A little blood never hurt a man."

"But you're pale, sir, and obviously in pain!"

"Oh, I'm having a bit of discomfort, that's all."

"For God's sake, Colonel, let us take you to the hospital!"

"After I've made my speech. Not until then. As long as I can stand on my feet and talk, I will!" Leaning back against the seat, Theodore shook his head. "Garfield was killed by a madman. And McKinley. It's the risk every public figure must take. It's the penalty we pay for the power we seek in a land that isn't yet civilized."

The car pulled to a halt at the stage entrance of the auditorium, and Theodore refused all help as he went inside. Ignoring the remonstrances of his friends, he went to the platform, where he was introduced to the crowd that occupied every seat, stood seven deep at the rear and filled the aisles.

"Friends," he said, as the applause died away, "I shall ask you to be as quiet as possible. I don't know whether you fully understand that I have just been shot."

Women gasped, and there was a stir in the crowd.

Theodore smiled reassuringly. "Don't worry. It takes more than one pistol bullet to kill a Bull Moose."

The audience, reassured, laughed aloud.

"I had my manuscript," Theodore said. "And there is a bullet . . ." A spasm of pain creased his face, and he turned away from the crowd for an instant. "There is where the bullet went through." He pushed the fingers of his left hand through the hole in his suit coat. "And here is the manuscript. It probably saved me from the bullet— going through my heart."

Again the crowd muttered.

The spasm subsided, and Theodore straightened. "The bullet is in me now," he said cheerfully. "And now, friends, I want you to understand that I'm ahead of the game, anyway. No man has had a happier life than I have led."

Several of the men sitting on the platform tried to persuade him to leave and go to the hospital with them.

Theodore silenced them with an imperious wave. "I cannot understand a man fit to be a colonel who can pay any heed to his personal safety. Friends, I'm thinking of the movement. The Progressive movement."

The audience watched in horrified fascination as he took a handkerchief from his pocket, mopped his forehead and wiped his glasses, which he removed for a few moments.

He tried to continue in a conversational tone. "He shot to kill. He shot—the shot, the bullet went in here. I'll show you."

Several men rose from their seats when they saw his bloodstained shirt.

But Theodore waved them to their seats again. "Now, friends, I am not speaking for myself at all. I give you my word, I do not care a rap about being shot. Not a rap."

The group on the stage became more insistent.

"No, no," Theodore said, annoyed. "I am not sick at all. I'm all right."

The audience applauded.

"Now, friends," Theodore declared, "what we Progressives are trying to do is to enroll rich or poor—to stand together for the most elementary rights of good citizenship." He grinned weakly at those behind him on the platform, then at the audience. "My friends are a little more nervous than I am."

A few scattered laughs and giggles were the only response from the crowd.

"Don't you waste any sympathy on me!" Theodore said, suddenly rejuvenated. "I have had an A-1 time in life, and I'm having it now!"

The audience came alive and applauded vigorously.

His wound apparently forgotten, he launched into his prepared speech, and spoke with his accustomed vigor for more than an hour. After he finished and the audience gave him a standing ovation he gripped the sides of the lectern with such force that his knuckles turned white. Then, but not until then, did he allow himself to be taken to the hospital.

The bullet had lodged only a fraction of an inch from Theodore's lung, and only a miracle had saved him from serious injury. The nation breathed a collective sigh of relief, and both President Taft and Governor Wilson suspended their own campaign activities until he recuperated at Sagamore Hill.

Only a few newspapers chastised Theodore, and even they scolded him with affection. *We know Colonel Roosevelt is a courageous man,* the Chicago *Tribune* said. *There was no need for him to jeopardize his life with such a reckless, foolhardy display of courage.*

The Colonel, the Kansas City *Star* declared, taking another approach, *has given the lie to those who claim he is becoming feeble. He is as strong physically as he is strong morally. There is no one in all the world like him!*

Joseph Pulitzer's New York *World* could not resist the temptation to speak with a bluntness that was unusual. *Teddy behaved like an actor strutting across a stage. The only difference is that the blood on his shirt was real. If he wants to strike childish postures, that is his affair, but his misguided friends in the Progressive movement have devoted much time and money to his cause. So he owes it to them to keep himself alive and in one piece until the election.*

Making a gesture to his opponents as shrewd as it was generous, Theodore publicly released them from their promise to stop campaigning until he was completely recovered. "I intend to make only one more speech, from Madison Square Garden on October 30th," he said. "So I want to be fair to them, and urge them to make as many talks between now and election as they may think necessary to win."

A capacity crowd filled Madison Square Garden on October 30, and Theodore immediately revealed his return to his old, fighting form. "It matters little about me," he told the cheering crowd, "but it matters a great deal about the cause we fight for. If one soldier who carries the flag is stricken, another will take it from his hands and carry it on. If I go down, another will take my place. For always, the army is true. Always the cause is there."

More than rhetoric was needed, however, and on November 5 Woodrow Wilson was elected President of the United States. His electoral victory was a landslide, and although Theodore took Michigan, California, and Pennsylvania, as well as several smaller states, Wilson beat him by 435 electoral votes to 88, with Taft obtaining only 8. The popular vote was a better indication of the candidates' true strengths. Wilson won with 6,293,454; Theodore was supported by 4,119,538; Taft had 3,484,980. Other elements were at work in the country, too, and voters who veered to the left gave Socialist party candidate Eugene V. Debs more than 900,600 votes. Even the Prohibition party candidate, Eugene W. Chafin, polled almost a quarter of a million.

Theodore promptly congratulated President-elect Wilson, ignored President Taft and issued a statement to console his followers. "I accept the result with entire good humor," he declared. "As for the Progressive cause, I can only repeat: the cause in itself must triumph, for this triumph is essential to the well-being of the American people."

He soon made it clear to his friends and supporters, however, that he had no intention of trying to build a permanent third party force in American politics. *You need not fear the disruptions caused by the Progressives,* he wrote Lodge soon after the election. *I hope I am a sound enough politician to know that nothing can be accomplished*

without the party machinery that only office-holders can create.
Therefore I intend, at the appropriate moment and without fanfare,
to return to the Republican party. Once my failing energies are re-
stored, I will work, within the Republican party, for the Progressive
principles I hold so dear.

"My day is past," Theodore said, and soon after the election he
started writing his *Autobiography*. Fleetingly, in its pages, he relived
his victories and defeats, but he suffered from unrelieved depression,
and one theme was predominant in his conversations with his many
friends, as it was in his voluminous correspondence.

"I'm finished," he said. "I've been put out to pasture. It had to happen some day, and I shouldn't mind. But I do hate the taste of dry
grass that we old horses must eat."

Those who knew him best could not feel sorry for him, however.
"The volcano will erupt again," Henry Adams said. "When smoke
starts to pour from his nostrils and he belches flames, everyone will
know he's been eating something more substantial than dry grass."

Occasional spurts of smoke and fire indicated that Adams was right.
When floods overran the Mississippi Valley in the spring of 1913, Theodore issued a new, urgent call for more stringent conservation measures to be undertaken by the Federal government and the states. As
president of the American Historical Association he delivered a "state
of the Union" message in which he demanded greater humanitarian-
ism, coupled with greater morality. In his spare time he filed a libel
suit against a Michigan editor who had slandered him, and won the
suit. And when Ethel was married to Richard Derby, neither William
Howard Taft nor Elihu Root was invited to the wedding.

Speaking invitations from organizations in Brazil and Argentina
aroused him from what he believed to be a lethargic state, and he became wildly excited when he heard of an unexplored river that flowed
through the jungles from the Brazilian lowlands to the Amazon. Even
the name of the stream, the River of Doubt, was intriguing.

"I want to explore that river!" he declared, and immediately began a furious correspondence with the Brazilian Foreign Ministry.
The Brazilians, although flattered by his interest and awed by his
name, were aware of the hardships and dangers that might be encountered, and were reluctant to assume responsibility for the safety
of a distinguished guest who was in his fifty-sixth year.

But Theodore persisted, and won his skirmish. It was agreed that the Brazilians would sponsor an expedition of exploration, headed by Theodore, who would be accompanied by his son, Kermit, and twenty-one other persons, most of them scientists. Edith protested in vain, as did Theodore's friends, who thought it mad that a man of his age, almost totally blind in one eye, would even dream of conducting such a venture.

"I'll consider your objections," Theodore said, and went off to South America. On February 27, 1914, the expedition set out across the great plateau of southwestern Brazil from the Paraguay River.

From the outset the party encountered difficulties that would have sent even the most intrepid back to civilization. The heat was almost unendurable, and the party was under constant attack from mosquitoes, flies and other insects. Several boats were swept from their moorings one night, when the River of Doubt rose unexpectedly high.

Native Indians of the Brazilian interior, who were believed to be cannibals and had driven out other explorers, captured and ate two of the party's pet dogs. A boat was smashed on the rocks of rapids, and a native boatman, trying to salvage supplies, was drowned.

Theodore suffered an attack of his "Cuban fever," and, to his disgust, had to spend several hours each day as a passenger in one of the boats. But the thought of turning back did not enter his mind. *We are having a bully time,* he wrote in his journal.

And so he was, in spite of all the difficulties and his physical ailment. He helped the botanists and zoologists collect specimens, he learned the basic principles of cartography and drew maps that later were praised for their accuracy, and he wrote long, detailed descriptions of the tropical jungles through which the party traveled.

Gradually, inexorably, the tragedies and near-catastrophes became worse. Kermit barely saved himself from being swept over rapids. Another boat was lost, and the terrain became so rough that it was necessary to abandon large quantities of equipment. Food supplies ran very low, and Theodore, insisting that he could eat little because of his fever, ordered the others to share his rations. He was indignant when they refused.

One of the native boatmen lost his senses one night, and, running amok, killed a scientist and threatened several others. Theodore came to the rescue of his companions and shot at the man, but missed, and the insane native disappeared into the jungle, never to emerge.

Then, one day, Theodore slipped in the water and slashed his leg on a rock while trying to prevent the loss of a boat in rapids. The wound would not heal in the tropical heat, his temperature rose above 105 degrees, and he became delirious. Kermit later revealed he recited poetry, discussed politics and, above all, demanded that the party go on without him. At dawn he recovered his wits, but still insisted that the others leave him behind.

No one would consider the idea, of course, and he was carried in a litter by Kermit and George Cherrie, a field naturalist. He suffered intensely for several days, and some members of the party despaired of his life. But they were unaware of his remarkable recuperative powers, and were astonished when, in spite of intermittent high fever and his injury, he reassumed command after a convalescence of seventy-two hours.

On April 30 the expedition reached the town of Manáos, on the Amazon River, a short distance above its junction with the River of Doubt. Fifteen hundred miles of unexplored territory had been mapped, thousands of specimens were being taken back to civilization, and the heart of a continent had been opened. The Brazilian government promptly called the river the Roosevelt, and conferred a decoration on the head of the party.

Theodore had lost sixty pounds on the journey, walked with a slight limp and had been debilitated by malaria. But he was ecstatic over his triumph, and for the first time revealed that, in his spare time, he had written the better part of a book, *Through the Brazilian Wilderness*.

I THANK YOU FROM MY HEART, he telegraphed the Ministry of Foreign Affairs in Rio de Janeiro, FOR THE CHANCE TO TAKE PART IN THIS GREAT WORK OF EXPLORATION.

Two days later the name of Colonel Theodore Roosevelt reappeared in newspaper headlines throughout the world. Armchair adventurers marveled, and men in many lands applauded. "Think of what might have happened," Henry Adams said, "if certain people it isn't necessary to name had been with him when he was delirious, begging to be left in the jungle to die. The imagination cannot encompass such a scene."

Returning to the United States after his greatest adventure, Theodore discovered that a treaty had been concluded with Colombia during his absence. This document, which gave Colombia $25,000,000 in indemnity for "any losses that may have been suffered in the past," also ambiguously offered the "sincere regrets of the United States that anything may have caused a disturbance in the amicable relations of our two nations."

Theodore's fury was uncontained. The payment to Colombia, combined with the apology, tarnished his own reputation and cast a heavy, permanent shadow on his acquisition of the Panama Canal Zone, he believed. And he hastened to counterattack.

Secretary of State William Jennings Bryan, he said, was "an amiable, special prize idiot. This is not news to the millions who three times refused him the highest office in the land."

But the real villain was President Woodrow Wilson. In a series of intemperate statements, Theodore lashed out at the President, calling him "insincere and ridiculous," a "nincompoop," a "two-faced charlatan unworthy of the presidency," and "a misplaced college professor who is trying to ruin us."

The White House refused to reply, but Wilson's friends let it be known that the assault was not unexpected. The President, supported by a Democratic-controlled Senate, had done what he believed right and just, even though he knew he would earn the undying enmity of Theodore Roosevelt.

Neither then nor at any later time did Theodore's rage over the matter subside. His attitude was best summed up by his statement to Democratic Senate Majority Leader William J. Stone of Missouri in an apoplectic letter: *I regard the treaty as a crime against the United States, an attack upon the honor of the United States, and a serious menace to the future well-being of our people. Either there is warrant for paying this enormous sum and for making the apology, or there is not.*

It is my firm belief there is not.

Since the events relating to this treaty took place during my Administration, I am in possession of all the facts, and I categorically assure you that my associates and I were in the right. Every action we took was in accordance with the highest principles of private and public morality.

The outbreak of World War I in mid-summer, 1914, temporarily stilled Theodore's thunder against the Wilson Administration. The assassination of Archduke Francis Ferdinand, heir to the Austrian throne, sent the Emperor Franz Josef's troops into Serbia to smash a rebellion, and within a few days virtually all of Europe was at war. Belgium was occupied, her neutrality violated by the armies of Kaiser Wilhelm, and the Germans were goose-stepping down the highways of France toward Paris, a march that was halted by French infantry rushed to the front in every available type of motor vehicle, including the buses and taxicabs of Paris.

Although diplomats and soldiers in many lands had been preparing for war, public opinion in the United States was almost totally unprepared for the outbreak of hostilities. Virtually the entire nation approved the proclamation issued by President Wilson that announced the strict neutrality of the United States.

No one quite knew where Theodore Roosevelt stood. Some newspapers reported that he welcomed the intervention, on August 4, of Great Britain on the side of the Allies, and quoted him to the effect that Britain could not, for her own safety, permit Germany to gain control of Europe.

Other newspapers cited his personal friendship with the Kaiser, and quoted him to the effect that the defeat of Germany would destroy the balance of power in Europe and would lead to even worse tragedies, among them a probable second great war.

Theodore protested that no one had quoted him correctly. Asked by the New York *Times* to clarify his position, he said, "I feel certain the people of the United States will support the President—any President—who sees to it that the United States comes through this crisis unscathed."

A few days later he seemed to veer strongly toward the Allies when the First Secretary of the German Embassy in Washington came to New York for the express purpose of seeing him and delivering a message to him.

Clicking his heels and bowing, the diplomat said, "His Imperial Majesty has instructed me to inform President Roosevelt of the great pleasure he has felt after having the opportunity to receive and entertain the *Herr* President at Potsdam."

Theodore raised an eyebrow, but said nothing.

"His Imperial Majesty believes he can rely upon the sympathy and understanding of the *Herr* President Roosevelt in the present situation."

"I see," Theodore said.

The German diplomat was nonplused by the vagueness of his reply. "What word shall I send to Berlin, sir?"

"Be good enough to thank his Imperial Majesty for his very courteous message to me." Theodore spoke coolly, without emotion. "Assure him I well remember the honor done me in Germany, and always will be deeply conscious of it."

The diplomat relaxed a trifle, and smiled.

"Tell him I shall never forget the way in which he received me in Berlin!"

"Gladly, *Herr* President." The First Secretary's smile grew broader.

"Tell him," Theodore continued in the same tone, "that I shall also remember the cordiality and friendship with which King Albert of the Belgians received me in Brussels."

In spite of his feelings of strong personal sympathy for the Belgians and for Great Britain's need to protect her own interests by entering the war, Theodore refused to support the Allied cause. Progressives and liberals were anti-German and looked to him for leadership, but an article he wrote in the August 22 issue of *Outlook* was a sharp disappointment to them.

In it he reaffirmed his support of the neutral stand taken by the Wilson Administration, and promised his future support, on the condition that he continued to approve of its conduct. He wrote: *I am not now taking sides one way or the other as concerns the violation or disregard of treaties. When giants are engaged in a death wrestle, as they reel to and fro they are certain to trample on whomever gets in the way of either of the huge, straining combatants.*

In the following month's issue of *Outlook* he expanded these thoughts. *We can maintain our neutrality,* he wrote, *only by refusal to do anything to aid unoffending weak powers which are dragged into the gulf of bloodshed and misery through no fault of their own. Of course it would be folly to jump into the gulf ourselves to no good purpose; and very probably nothing that we could have done would have helped Belgium. We have not the slightest responsibility for what has befallen her, and I am sure the sympathy of this country for Belgium is very real.*

Nevertheless, this sympathy is compatible with full knowledge of the unwisdom of uttering a single word of official protest unless we are prepared to make that protest effective; and only the clearest and most urgent National duty would ever justify us in deviating from our rule of neutrality and non-interference.

By November Theodore's firm attitude was undergoing equally firm revision. He felt what he called "natural sympathy" for the Belgians and for the British, "with whom we have a special affinity, a special relationship." Other factors were influencing him, too. His sons were clamoring for action, and wanted to volunteer in the Canadian or British armies. And some of his principal Progressive party supporters, among them Gifford Pinchot, Hiram Johnson, and Bainbridge Colby, were running for office and felt entitled to his support in their campaigns.

It seemed only "natural" for him to step up the pace of his attacks on President Wilson, whom he continued to despise because of the Colombian treaty. Wilson was already a "weasel-wording politician, utterly cold-blooded, without a single scruple." It was easy to add another epithet: pacifist.

Wilson could not ignore the attacks, which were made with the increasing vigor that marked any effort Theodore made. In his annual message to Congress, written in December 1914, the President refused to change the nation's neutral posture. *We shall not alter our attitude,* he wrote, *because some amongst us are nervous or excited.*

Theodore retaliated swiftly in a book of essays, *America and the World War,* which he published early in 1915. In it he declared: *President Wilson has been much applauded by all the professional pacifists because he has announced that our desire for peace must make us secure it by a neutrality so strict as to forbid our even whispering a protest against wrong-doing, lest such whispers might cause disturbance to our ease and well-being. We pay the penalty of this—supine inaction on behalf of peace, for ourselves, by forfeiting our right to do anything on behalf of peace for the Belgians.*

It is a grim comment on the professional pacifist theories as hitherto developed that, according to their view, our duty to preserve peace for ourselves necessarily means the abandonment of all effective effort to secure peace for other unoffending nations which through no fault of their own are trampled down by war.

"We must remove our blinders," Theodore told Cabot Lodge when the Senator from Massachusetts paid a visit to Sagamore Hill. "Wilson's splendid isolation can't last forever."

"I'm hoping it won't be necessary forever."

Theodore gestured sharply. "Don't fool yourself, Cabot. The war has bogged down in the trenches. German artillery isn't strong enough—strong as it is—to blast the British and French out. And none of the new weapons, airplanes or armored cars or the like, can bring the fighting to a halt."

"You're a pessimist. That's a new attitude."

"I'm a realist. The two sides are evenly matched. Russia and the Austro-Hungarians will knock each other out. The situation at the eastern end of the Mediterranean is confused, and won't influence the basic outcome. What I mean is that the Turks and Greeks and all the rest may kill each other off by the thousands, but the war will be decided in the main confrontation between the British and French on one side and the Germans on the other."

"I dare say you're right."

"I know I'm right," Theodore said irritably. "And just look at the war developments." He reached out to tap a pile of newspapers with the walking stick he used to ease the pressure on the leg he had injured in the jungles of Brazil. "Call it what you will—and the people who are thinking of themselves as military experts are calling it many things— there's a stalemate. Military experts! They make me ill!"

Lodge knew he was on delicate ground. "Which of them are wrong, Theodore?"

"Every last one! I've had several offers to go over as a correspondent, and I'm tempted to accept one of them!"

"In your physical condition—"

"There's nothing wrong with my physical condition! You sound like Edith. I'm as hearty and strong as I've ever been in all my life! I may not box or do jiujitsu any more, but I still ride—and walk—and only last week I promised to take Kermit and his bride on a camping trip."

Rather than reply in words, the Senator from Massachusetts reached out and touched the gnarled-handled walking stick.

"Oh, that," Theodore said. "I use it as a convenience when my leg aches a bit."

Lodge merely smiled.

"We've been friends for almost forty years, Cabot, but when I see that smug expression you sometimes put on, I wonder how I've been able to tolerate you."

"I'm just wondering how you'd manage as a correspondent when your leg bothers you."

"One of your troubles is that you never listen! I said I use the cane strictly as a convenience. I *never* actually *need* it!"

"I'm not so young myself," Lodge said, "and I'm old enough to admit it."

"As a matter of fact," Theodore said, "I've been mulling the idea of forming a volunteer division of troops. Some of my Rough Riders and other outdoorsmen—"

"All of you are too old!"

"My Rough Riders would be the senior officers and noncommissioned officers, naturally. We'd form a full division of cavalry, the first of its kind since the Napoleonic Wars—"

"You're an incurable romantic, Theodore."

"I'd offer our services to the British or the French."

"Would they take you?"

"So fast that Woodrow Wilson's head would spin on its pointed end —like a top. Think of the propaganda value to the Allies. The former President of the United States is granted a commission as a major general, and—"

"Theodore, I sometimes despair of your wisdom. Men would be killed or wounded. You'd be in personal danger—"

"Naturally. I do know something about war, Cabot!"

"—and you might be captured. Think of the hash you'd make of Wilson's strict neutrality."

Theodore's high-pitched laughter was prolonged.

"And think of what Kaiser Bill would do to his old friend if he captured you after you'd been serving with his enemies. If the stories I've been reading are just partly true, the Germans are not treating prisoners with much consideration."

"I'm not afraid of anyone or anything on earth. You know that, Cabot!"

"I know that you're unpredictable," Lodge said.

"I'm inclined to favor the French."

"I thought you were more partial to the British."

"Oh, I am, but they'd be less inclined to grant me a commission and pay for the costs of supporting my division in the field."

Lodge stared at him. "You speak as though you have some positive knowledge of their reactions."

"Oh, I do. I asked Spring-Rice to make informal inquiries for me at the War Office. There are all sorts of possible complications. You know British law."

"I also know you."

"But the French are far more inclined to waive the law. And it would be a grand gesture of the sort they'd appreciate. I'd announce that I was returning the favor the Marquis de Lafayette made to General Washington in our Revolution. It would be a great boon to French morale, which is rather low these days. Not that I can blame them, with those terrible casualties they've been suffering."

"It would also commit the American people to the war. You're not just another former military man, Theodore."

"I'm well aware of it. That's why Georges Clemenceau would welcome my division of cavalry. With open arms."

Lodge made no attempt to hide his consternation. "Have you been
in touch with the Premier?"

"Not directly." Theodore was vague.

"You have no right to do that! You'll embarrass the President when
he's making every effort to preserve a real neutrality."

"It's my privilege to disagree with the President," Theodore said
severely.

Lodge knew better than to remind him he hadn't felt that way when
he had been in the White House. "I wonder if it has occurred to you
that the President might forbid you to form such a division."

"I'm a free American citizen, and every man in my command would
be a free American citizen, too. Wilson is too much of a coward to
stand up to me, and if he tried—by issuing an emergency decree of
some sort—I'd fight him to a standstill in the courts. He couldn't stop
me from leading my men to France."

"I've often said that nothing you do surprises me, Theodore, but
I'm wrong. I'm stunned. You sound as though you've made up your
mind to do this foolish thing."

"It isn't foolish. And you are wrong, Cabot. I simply haven't made
up my mind yet. I've made one mistake, and I don't want to make another."

"What was the mistake?"

"Supporting Wilson's neutral stand for several months. You see, I
assumed he was speaking the truth. That he'd examined the facts, and
was right when he said we had no responsibility for what happened to
Belgium. Then I went over the Hague Convention myself. Have you
read it lately?"

Lodge shook his head.

"You should," Theodore said. "Action on our part is mandatory when
a nation that signed the Convention is attacked without due cause."

The point was being debated, endlessly, by authorities in international law of many nations, but Lodge knew the futility of opposing
Theodore after he had made up his mind on an issue.

"I tried to stand by the President. But I believe it's my patriotic duty
right now to oppose the President!" Theodore's jaw jutted forward.

"You're going to be asked your reasons," Lodge said, speaking
mildly.

"They should be obvious."

"To you and me, perhaps, but not to millions of Americans who'll want guidance, Theodore."

"Our neutrality is incomplete and ineffective. We've placed no embargo on travel by American citizens to and from Europe, nor on the transportation of goods across the Atlantic. Nor, for that matter, have we restricted American carriers to American ports. So our citizens still sail the high seas, our ships still go from one nation to another, trading our products for those of belligerents. If the Kaiser hopes to win the war—and he's a keen student of history, I can tell you—he'll have to try Napoleon's master plan. He'll have to cut off Great Britain by isolating her from the world."

"I suppose he will." Lodge was still impressed by his incisive thinking in matters of fundamental strategy.

"He must! That means, sooner or later, that Germany will launch a major campaign to halt British shipping everywhere."

"Not even your superefficient Germans can immobilize the world's most powerful fleet and the largest merchant marine on earth!" Lodge scoffed.

"They're not my Germans, Cabot, but make no mistake about it. Terror can be one of the most potent weapons in war. If you'll remember the anaesthetizing effect of Greek fire in the sixth and seventh centuries, and right down through the Middle Ages—"

"You seem to forget," Lodge interrupted dryly, "that I taught you much of what you know about history."

"So you did." Theodore grinned, unabashed. "Very well, you grasp my point, I'm sure. Look at the way the German invasion of Belgium literally numbed England and France. They could have stopped the Kaiser if they had acted fast enough, but they dillied and dallied, and the German armies pushed into France before their enemies recovered."

"What's the connection—"

"Just this. The damage that a few German surface raiders can do is enormous. And it remains to be seen what the new German underseas craft can accomplish, but I'd like to venture a prediction. This war will be remembered because it introduced submarines on a large scale."

"When I taught history, Theodore, I didn't ramble aimlessly. I wish you had paid closer attention to my lectures."

"If I told you that you put me to sleep, Cabot, you'd have a right to call me rude."

"As well as a liar."

"All right. Let me spell it all out for you. There are accidents in every war. There will be accidents in this one. Innocent bystanders are often hurt, be it in war or peace. We're bystanders, but our innocence is somewhat questionable."

"You don't think our neutrality is sincere?"

"Hardly," Theodore said. "Even our citizens of German descent feel sorry for the Belgians. Everyone else is pro-Allies. Including those who come from the nations tied to Germany. The Austro-Hungarians hate their Hapsburg oppressors. The Poles are the most violent patriots in the world, and will support anyone who promises them a free, united Poland. Our Russians have no use for Russia, but they love the personal freedoms of England and France. And so on. Add the Belgian issue, and you'll find we're almost unanimously anti-German right this minute."

For decades Lodge had wondered whether Theodore's feelings had coincided with those of the majority, or whether some sixth sense enabled him to grasp the essence of popular sentiment before anyone else was aware of it. Whatever his complicated mental and emotional processes, he was rarely mistaken.

"Right now, of course, our people are confused. It wasn't so long ago that they became accustomed to accepting positive leadership from the White House." Theodore paused, brooding. "They still look there, even though that spineless, craven coward can't lead anyone anywhere, except to disgrace and ruin. So it's small wonder we're a confused nation."

"You're confusing me."

"I'm not joking, Cabot. Our instincts put us in the camp of the Allies. Our tradition requires us to seek leadership from the White House, so we try—even though in vain—to accept Wilson's insistence that we stay neutral. There's a national tragedy in the offing."

Lodge, groping, began to agree, even though he himself had been an advocate of neutrality.

"One of these days," Theodore said, "American lives and American property will be lost. One of these days there will be accidents that will hurt us, wound our pride as well as do damage to us. Then—watch out!"

"You think we'll go into the war?"

"It's inevitable!"

"That's strong language, Theodore."

"Look back through history for precedents, Cabot. Not only are we already leaning heavily toward the Allies, but our commitment to them will be complete when Americans are killed and our ships are sent to the bottom. We'll demand that we go to war ourselves."

"You're neglecting one factor."

"If you mean the economic and political involvement, they're present, too. The bulk of our trade is with the Allies. And it will better serve our interests to take the side of nations that already have their colonies and aren't interested in further expansion. It would be dangerous to join the Germans. Anybody who ties his kite to an aggressor's is risking a landing on rough territory."

"Assuming that everything you've said is right," Lodge declared, "I still don't see why we're in particular danger."

"Wilson is being so blasted neutral he won't let our weapons plants build munitions. He won't build up stockpiles of grains and other food. We'll be caught short when we're forced into the war. We'll be totally unprepared, and more lives than I care to estimate will be lost because we aren't ready to fight."

"That can't be allowed to happen."

"I won't let it happen!" Theodore exclaimed, raising his voice. "The only thing that prevents me from organizing a division of cavalry for the French is the knowledge that I'm needed right here at home. I'm needed more badly than ever before, and I'm going to live up to the call of duty. I'm launching what may be my last crusade. I'm going to prepare the American people for war!"

Ignoring the bouts of fever that sapped his strength, his failing eyesight and the infection in his leg that debilitated him anew, Theodore threw himself into his self-appointed struggle. Writing constantly for many publications, making speeches wherever he was asked, he carried on his one-man crusade to prepare the United States for entry into the war.

President Wilson and members of his Administration fought back, pleading for the maintenance of neutrality, but, as Lodge said, "They lack Theodore's genius for simplifying issues."

"I'm grateful to God," Wilson told his Cabinet, "that no major incident has pushed us closer to the war. I dread to think what Roosevelt would do and say if American blood should be spilled."

Forced to assume a more virulent public stance, the President openly ridiculed the stand taken by Colonel Roosevelt, and Theodore's ire was aroused to a higher pitch. *Upon my word,* he wrote to Lodge,

Wilson and Bryan are the very worst men we have ever had in their positions.

His fears of an Allied defeat grew stronger, and he reverted to the nightmare of his own Administration, the possibility that Japan would menace American power in the Pacific. "If Germany should win in Europe," he told Elihu Root, with whom his relations were becoming friendlier, "I think it almost certain that she'd make an alliance with the Japanese. And it would then be only a matter of time—and not much time at that—before they made a joint attack on us. Sooner or later we'll be forced to fight Germany, you know, and our chances of success will be far less if we wait than they'll be if we join forces, right now, with the powers already fighting her."

Aware that the American people were as yet emotionally unprepared for a declaration of war, however, he stopped short, in his public statements, of urging an open declaration of war.

On the night of May 7, 1915, Theodore was in Syracuse, New York, where he was appearing as a principal in a libel suit. As he prepared for bed after spending the better part of the day in court, the telephone in his hotel suite rang, somewhat to his surprise, as the hotel had been instructed to screen his calls.

The speaker at the other end of the line was a newspaperman, calling from New York City. "Colonel," he asked, "have you heard the news?"

"What news?"

"About the British passenger liner, the *Lusitania*. She was sunk today off the Irish coast by a torpedo from a German submarine. According to our advices, she was sent to the bottom without warning."

Theodore was too shocked to reply. Although he had predicted just such a catastrophe, the sinking of smaller vessels, among them the British steamer, *Falaba,* and an American oil tanker, the *Gulflight,* had convinced him there would be no attack on a major vessel. The huge Cunard liner *Lusitania* was one of the largest ships afloat, and he could scarcely imagine a vessel of her size being sunk.

"Are you on the line, Colonel?"

"Yes, I'm here. What were the damages?"

"More than eleven hundred men, women, and children were drowned. Twenty-eight of them were Americans."

"My God!" Theodore's voice was low. "That's murder!"

"May we quote you to that effect, Colonel?"

"Of course! What justification do the Germans offer?"

"They say she was carrying munitions."

"Is the charge true?"

"I don't know, sir. There's been no corroboration or denial by the British."

"It doesn't matter in the least," Theodore replied without hesitation. "Murder is murder. There were innocent civilians on board, weren't there?"

"Yes, sir."

"Was the *Lusitania* armed?"

"No, Colonel."

"That proves it, then. Murder!"

"Would you care to make a fuller statement, sir? That's why we're calling you."

"Of course!"

"If you'd like, I can phone you again in an hour or so, if you want time to—"

"That won't be necessary," Theodore said. "If you're ready, I'll start dictating right now."

"Ready, Colonel." The newsman was surprised by Theodore's readiness to issue a statement without preparation.

"Here you are," Theodore said. "This represents not merely piracy, but piracy on a vaster scale of murder than old-time pirates ever practiced. It is warfare against innocent men, women and children traveling on the ocean, and our own fellow countrymen and countrywomen, who are among the sufferers. It seems inconceivable that we can refrain from taking action in this matter, for we owe it not only to humanity, but to our own national self-respect."

Resentment of the sinking ran high throughout the United States. *It is a deed*, the *New York Nation* declared, *for which a Hun would blush, a Turk be ashamed and a Barbary pirate apologize. The torpedo that sank the* Lusitania *also sank Germany in the opinion of mankind.*

President Wilson reacted by ordering the State Department to send a series of diplomatic notes of protest to Germany, in which the United States demanded that such lawless practices cease, that assurances be given to bar their recurrence and that reparations be paid. Secretary Bryan thought these communications brought the United States too close to active participation in the war, and resigned, to be replaced by the State Department's counselor, Robert Lansing.

Theodore considered the measures woefully inadequate, however. "Wilson sends so many notes they ought to be given serial numbers, like dollar bills," he said. "I do believe that Woodrow Wilson is our very worst President since Buchanan. He is an abject creature."

The preservation of American rights became Theodore's new battle cry, and he renewed his call for preparedness in order to protect those rights. He scheduled so many speaking engagements that the newspapers wondered aloud whether he wanted the Republican nomination for President in 1916, he wrote so many articles that he was accused, falsely, of hiring writers to help him, and he held press conferences several times each week.

"Where does he get all that energy?" William Howard Taft asked. "At least I'm glad it is being directed against Wilson these days, and not against me!"

Theodore bombarded Congress, directly and indirectly, with requests to increase the size of the Regular Army and to create a new force of Reserves which he called the Continental Army in honor of George Washington's troops. He proved impossible to resist, and in spite of President Wilson's reluctance, the Regular Army was expanded to 200,000 men and the National Guard, which was inefficient and flabby, was reorganized and strengthened.

No one knew where the phrase originated, but the newspapers began to call Theodore "the Bugle That Woke America." And a new spelling was suggested for his name: P-r-e-p-a-r-e-d-n-e-s-s. When he began to campaign for a stronger Navy, even Wilson made no attempt to fight him, and bills vastly increasing the size of the Navy had easy sailing through Congress.

"I'm too busy for politics," Theodore said when the Progressives suggested that he become their candidate for President in 1916.

"Are you standing aside because you know we'll lose?" George Perkins asked him.

"Well, let's say it's unlikely we'll win. Unless our candidate gets the Republican nomination, too."

"From what my Wall Street friends tell me," the financier replied, "that's unlikely."

"Unless the candidate were someone like Cabot Lodge."

Perkins was startled. "You must be joking, Colonel!"

"Senator Lodge is my oldest and dearest friend," Theodore said stiffly.

"I know. But you can't seriously suggest that the Progressives support him. He doesn't stand for one of our principles, not one."

"I was afraid you'd feel that way."

Perkins wondered whether the attacks of malaria that he suffered might be affecting his mind. It was inconceivable that the Progressives could offer Lodge any support, even re-election to the Senate.

"Of course," Theodore said, "Cabot doesn't want to be President."

Perkins silently sighed in relief. "I've heard, as I'm sure you have, that Hughes is the strongest of the Republican candidates."

"As long as I'm associated with the Progressive party, I refuse to back Charlie Hughes," Theodore snapped. "I'd campaign for him against Wilson, but I'd campaign for the devil himself against that nincompoop."

"If the Progressive party hopes to remain in existence," Perkins said, "we've got to put up a candidate for President."

"Provided that our man won't split the Republican vote again—and re-elect Wilson. That would be a tragedy, the worst of our century!"

Perkins was stubborn. "You're our best bet, Colonel—"

"I can't and won't run again. Too many members of the Old Guard haven't forgiven me for 1912."

"We don't want or need them."

"Ah, but we do," Theodore said. "Look at the results of the last election, George. Nothing counts but results, and our national danger is too great for mere moral victories. We must either win the election, or bow ourselves out of existence."

"But all the things we stand for—"

"Must be put aside until the national emergency is ended. The safety of the country in a world at war must be our only serious consideration. When the war is won, our domestic problems will become paramount again. Until then, they must be shelved."

Perkins realized it was impossible to penetrate his armor. Obviously Theodore could think only of preparedness, and the issues for which he had fought in the past had faded into at least temporary insignificance.

"There's one man who might win for us. He's been doing grand work with me waking up the country."

Perkins looked at him apprehensively.

"I mean Leonard Wood, of course."

The financier winced. "General Wood is a patriot. No one would deny that."

"No one could!"

"He's never been associated with the Progressives," Perkins said carefully. "I'm not suggesting that we nominate Governor Johnson, who doesn't have national stature, or Gifford Pinchot. But we need someone who will be recognized as a bona fide Progressive."

"If we select Leonard Wood, I'll go on platforms with him—in whatever time I have available, that is—and I'll see to it that the people associate his name with the Progressive cause!"

It was true, the financier reflected, that the colonel's vanity was expanding, and it was difficult to blame his foes for criticizing him, although they went too far when they said he had become an egomaniac.

"Do you find any other flaws in Wood?"

"I certainly do. General Wood is a military man, and we'd be accused of dragging the country into a war. Or trying to." Perkins took a deep breath. "You're already committed to our entry into the war, Colonel, although you haven't said as much in public yet. Why haven't you? Because the people aren't ready for the final step. The Progressives aren't ready. And the party would be committing suicide if we nominated a prominent military man who has had no experience as a civilian except his term in Manila."

Theodore returned to earth with a thud. "I suppose you're right," he said reluctantly. "So I'm afraid we'll just have to disband the Progressive party. Or suspend our operations until the war has been fought —and won. You might say that we're a war casualty, a major one."

"He kept us out of war," the Democrats said, and all through the campaign Congress was in session, strengthening the Army, authorizing new battleships and organizing the new Council of National Defense.

"The Democrats," Theodore said, "are trying to have it both ways. Charles Evans Hughes may be a cold, selfish, and difficult man, but I've got to stump for him. The Republicans offer us democracy, while Wilson offers only hypocrisy."

Traveling around the country in a manner reminiscent of his own campaigns, Theodore frequently forgot that he was advocating the candidacy of Hughes. Instead he urged universal military service, claiming that a strong, war-ready United States would not be required to fight. Everywhere he was greeted with an enthusiasm that made the Democrats happy. "I'm glad," Wilson is alleged to have said, "that Hughes is the candidate, not the Colonel."

In Detroit a throng estimated at more than a half-million people cheered Theodore's motorcade. In Kansas City he spoke before an explosively demonstrative crowd of fifty thousand. Even more came to hear him in Chicago, and at least fifty thousand were turned away in St. Louis.

His fury rising higher with each speech, Theodore mercilessly excoriated Woodrow Wilson. And in his final address of the campaign, in New York City, on November 3, 1916, he launched his most withering assault. Wilson was spending the last pre-election days at his summer home, Shadow Lawn, and Theodore could not resist the urge to utilize that name.

Throwing aside his prepared speech, he said in an emotion-racked voice, "There should be shadows now at Shadow Lawn; the shadows of the men, women and children who have risen from the ooze of the ocean bottom and from graves in foreign lands; the shadows of the helpless whom Mr. Wilson did not dare protect, lest he might have to face danger; the shadows of babies gasping pitifully as they sank under the waves; the shadows of women outraged and slain by bandits. Those are the shadows proper for Shadow Lawn; the shadows of deeds that were never done; the shadows of lofty words that were followed by no action; the shadows of the tortured dead."

Is Hughes his own candidate? the New York *World* asked caustically. *Or is he another of Roosevelt's puppets? We sometimes wonder how often Theodore Roosevelt intends to run for President, either in his own right or as a master puppeteer for someone else. If Hughes wins, it will be a victory for Roosevelt. But if the President wins, alas!—the world will know that Mr. Wilson is the winner, but Roosevelt will disclaim full responsibility for the loss, and the blame will be pinned exclusively on Hughes.*

The issues were clouded by the presence of large numbers of United States troops in Mexico, which somewhat dimmed the luster of the Democrats claim that Wilson had kept the country out of war. The results of the election reflected the uncertainties, and the balloting was so close that the outcome was not known until November 10, three days after the election.

Woodrow Wilson won re-election by the narrowest of margins, obtaining 277 electoral votes to 254 for Hughes. The popular vote, 9,128,-837 to 8,536,380, showed how closely the race had been contested.

"Hughes lost," Theodore said, "because he didn't stress Progressive themes. And Wilson won because the people haven't grasped the need to be prepared for a war that's inevitable."

On the last day of January 1917, the German Ambassador, Count Johann von Bernstorff, delivered a note to the State Department announcing the resumption of submarine warfare against neutral as well as belligerent shipping. Almost apologetically, the Kaiser's representative explained that American supplies, which were crossing the Atlantic in large quantities, were so helpful to the Allies that Imperial Germany had no choice. But he tried to soften the blow by granting an exception: one American ship would be permitted to sail each week to England, provided it complied with a number of strict regulations.

In effect the United States was being forbidden freedom of navigation on the high seas, a restriction that no major power could accept. Forty-eight hours after President Wilson received the communication he severed diplomatic relations with Imperial Germany, informing the Senate, "I think you will agree with me that this Government has no alternative consistent with the dignity and honor of the United States."

Theodore was outraged by what he considered the President's cowardice. "I don't think Wilson is capable of understanding the emotion of patriotism, or the emotion of real pride in one's country. Whether we will really go to war or not, Heaven only knows, and certainly Mr. Wilson doesn't."

In mid-February Ambassador von Bernsdorff sailed for home on a Danish ship, accompanied by one hundred and fifty members of the embassy and consulate staffs.

A new sensation jarred the American people when the so-called Zimmerman Note was made public. This document was purportedly a proposal made by Germany to Mexico, suggesting that the latter recover her "lost provinces," California, Texas, New Mexico, and Arizona. Many Americans were amused, but Theodore was among those who were infuriated.

"My God," he said, "why doesn't Wilson do something? His refusal to take positive action is utterly beyond me."

By March 20 he felt he could no longer maintain even a façade of public silence. On that day he spoke at the Union League Club in New York before conservatives who, in 1912, had damned him so bitterly. "Let us at long last face the issues of the day squarely," he declared. "Let us no longer hide behind the protective armor of a Great Britain fighting for her own existence. Let us stop burying our heads, ostrich-like, in the sands of so-called neutrality.

"Let us dare to look the truth in the face.

"Let us dare to use our own strength in our own defense and strike hard for our national interest and honor.

"There is no question about 'going to war.' Germany is already at war with us. The only question for us to decide is whether we shall make war nobly or ignobly."

By an ironic coincidence, President Wilson and his Cabinet held a secret meeting that same day in order to settle the very question that Theodore had raised. Secretary of State Robert Lansing, strongly supported by Secretary of War Newton D. Baker, presented the same argument that Theodore had used. For all practical purposes, they said, Germany was already in a state of war with the United States, which, by clinging to a non-existent neutrality, was shackling herself. Therefore, they declared, the nation should go to war at once. The President took the matter under advisement.

Finally, on the evening of April 2, Woodrow Wilson took the fateful step, and sent a message to Congress. He asked for a joint declaration of war "for democracy, for the right of those who submit to have a voice in their own governments, for the rights and liberties of small nations, for a universal dominion of right by such a concert of free peoples as shall bring peace and safety to all nations and make the world itself at last free."

Theodore promptly issued a public statement, which he subsequently incorporated in an article in the *Metropolitan Magazine*. "The President's great message of April 2nd is literally unanswerable. Of course, when war is on, all minor considerations, including all partisan considerations, vanish at once. All good Americans will back the President with single-minded loyalty in every movement he makes to uphold American honor, defend American rights, and strike hard and effectively in return for the brutal wrong-doing of the German government."

All four of the Roosevelt sons entered military service, Ted as a field-grade officer, Kermit in the tank corps, Archie in the infantry, and Quentin in the most glamorous of military occupations, that of an aviator. The records they soon achieved in combat were impressive. Ted, who was twice wounded, became commander of the 1st Battalion of the 1st Division's 26th Regiment. Kermit won the British Military Cross, and Archie, who was also wounded, was awarded France's highest decoration, the Croix de Guerre.

Theodore himself had no intention of being left on the sidelines now that the time for action had come. He immediately sent a letter to Secretary of War Baker, offering to raise a division, or even a corps, of "volunteer outdoorsmen," and he promised to have his troops in the field, ready for action, within a very short time.

I am a retired Commander-in-Chief of the United States Army, he wrote, *and eligible to any position of command over American troops to which I may be appointed.*

The regiment, First United States Volunteer Cavalry, in which I first served as Lieutenant-Colonel, and which I then commanded as Colonel, was raised, armed, equipped, drilled, mounted, dismounted, kept for two weeks on a transport, and then put through two victorious aggressive fights, in which we lost a third of the officers, and a fifth of the enlisted men, all within a little over fifty days.

Secretary Baker sent him a noncommittal letter of appreciation, thanking him for his "patriotic spirit." Theodore brooded quietly, and then, far less quietly, found his own way of demanding immediate action. The first that Baker learned of the new development came in a telephone call from Assistant Secretary of the Navy Franklin D. Roosevelt, who asked if he could come across the street to the War Department for a brief chat.

Baker greeted the tall young man who bore such a strong resemblance to his distinguished relative, and shook his hand cordially. "You sounded a trifle upset on the phone just now, Frank," he said.

"I've been calmer, Mr. Secretary." Franklin Roosevelt's laugh was similar to Theodore's. "There's a visitor sitting in my office at this moment. He wants to see you."

Baker raised a patrician eyebrow.

"The colonel."

The Secretary of War had reseated himself behind his desk, but jumped to his feet again.

"He didn't want to drop in on you unannounced. In view of the attacks he's made on the Administration, he didn't want to risk a chilly reception."

"I'll be delighted to receive him, Frank!"

"I'm not so sure of that, Mr. Secretary." Franklin Roosevelt's grin creased his whole face. "I'm sure you must know what he wants."

"That blasted special corps of volunteers?"

"I'm afraid so. He wants to see the President, today, now, and hopes you'll go along to the White House. From the way he's been talking, he wants to get the whole matter settled this morning."

"Has he spoken to the President, Frank?"

"No, Mr. Secretary. He assumed that you—"

"Of course." Baker reached for his telephone. "I'll make the arrangements with Mr. Wilson while you escort the colonel over here." He laughed wryly. "To tell you the truth, I'd rather spend the next few hours being shelled by a battery of German Big Berthas."

Theodore exerted his charms to the utmost, and Wilson was enchanted. The President and ex-President chatted for more than an hour in the office that was so familiar to Theodore, and, on the surface, their past hostilities to each other were forgotten. They exchanged anecdotes of the presidency, expressed mutual sympathies for the problems that Congress caused any occupant of the White House and, with the self-assurance of men in the public eye long accustomed to leadership, displayed mutual respect and cordiality.

Secretary Baker, sitting silently in a corner, was virtually forgotten. He entered the conversation briefly when Theodore casually mentioned the purpose of his visit, but was spared any substantial comment when both of the principals smoothly moved on to another topic.

"The Colonel," Wilson later said, "is a great big boy. I was charmed by his personality. There's a sweetness about him that's very compelling. You just can't resist the man."

Theodore's reaction was somewhat more restrained when he told the Longworths, with whom he was staying, about the visit. "Wilson," he said, "received me pleasantly, very pleasantly. I complimented him on his war message and told him it would rank with the world's greatest state papers if it were made good. I also told him I wanted a chance to help him make it good. I found there was a confusion in his mind about what I wanted to do. So I explained everything to him. Carefully, in full detail. He seemed to take it well, but—remember—I was talking to Woodrow Wilson."

Not trusting the President's sentiments, Theodore used every form of political pressure at his command. Senators and members of the House called on the President to urge the Roosevelt appointment. Governors, among them several of Wilson's fellow Democrats, wrote him letters making the same request. Members of the Supreme Court, friends and academicians, even a number of **high**-ranking foreign diplomats discreetly added a word.

French Premier Georges Clemenceau openly pressed for the appointment, as did the French and British press. American newspapers inevitably joined in, some favoring and others opposing the novel idea. Meanwhile Theodore himself was swamped with applications, and tens of thousands more poured in at the War Department.

General John J. Pershing, the American commander of the expedition being sent to Europe, was less than enthusiastic. He informed Secretary Baker that the granting of Theodore's request would open the door to many others like it, and would not only harm the Army's attempt to raise troops systematically, but might drain off some of the best officer material badly needed in units the War Department was forming.

Pershing also objected on other grounds, which he worded delicately in a memorandum to the Secretary of War. *It is necessary,* he wrote, *that officers, especially those in high command, should be thoroughly trained and disciplined.*

Discipline was the sticking point. Secretary Baker well knew, as did President Wilson when they sat down together to discuss the problem, that Theodore might be disinclined, at any time, to obey orders given him by Pershing or by British or French overcommanders to whom his unit might be assigned. Having known the supreme commandership of United States armed forces himself, and considering himself a military expert as well, it was possible—all too possible—to imagine him defying a direct order from the President.

"This," Baker said, "would transform strictly military matters into political disputes, and would harm the entire national effort to win the war."

"Colonel Roosevelt," President Wilson said, "is a splendid man and a patriotic citizen, but he is not a military leader. His experience in military life has been extremely short. He and many of the men he wants to take with him are too old to render effective service. Also, he has shown an intolerance of discipline."

Theodore's request was politely and gently turned down.

His reaction was bitter, but no worse than the Administration expected, and Wilson was prepared for a renewal of the assaults that had been launched on him since he had concluded the treaty with Colombia.

He did not have long to wait. "I've been blackballed," Theodore said. "This is a very exclusive war."

But the winning of the war was more important to him than his personal hatred, and he made the first of an extended series of tours of the country, his sole aim being that of rallying public opinion behind the war effort. He also concluded an agreement with the Kansas City *Star* to write a series of editorial columns on subjects of his own choice, and many other newspapers clamored for the columns. In them he renewed his attacks on the Administration, criticizing much that the President was doing.

"Theodore," said Henry Adams, "is the only man on earth who can walk in opposite directions, simultaneously, with a sure, firm step. In one breath he exhorts the people to fight, and in the next he criticizes everything the government does! It would be an understatement to call him extraordinary."

Then, on July 17, 1918, the war came home to Theodore and Edith Roosevelt. Secretary Baker informed them that Lieutenant Quentin Roosevelt—aged twenty-one—had died in combat, gallantly, and that his aircraft had crashed behind German lines. He was buried where he fell.

Theodore wrote a tribute to his fallen son: *Only those are fit to live who do not fear to die; and none are fit to die who have shrunk from the joy of life. Both life and death are parts of the same Great Adventure. Never yet was worthy adventure worthily carried through by the man who put his personal safety first. Pride is the portion only of those who know bitter sorrow or the foreboding of bitter sorrow. But all of us who give service, and stand ready for sacrifice, are the torch-bearers. We run with the torches until we fall, content if we can then pass them to the hands of the other runners. The torches whose flame is brightest are borne by the gallant men at the front, by the gallant women whose husbands and lovers, whose sons and brothers are at the front. These men are high of soul, as they face their fate on the shell-shattered earth, or in the skies above or in the waters beneath; and no less high of soul are the women with torn hearts and shining eyes; the girls whose boy-lovers have been struck down in their golden morning, and the mothers and wives to whom word has been brought that henceforth they must walk in the shadow.*

These are the torch-bearers; these are they who have dared the Great Adventure.

Nothing was the same, yet everything continued as before. Theodore wrote and lectured, talked and traveled, held press conferences and watched every move the government made in its attempts to win the war. His energy seemed to spring from an unlimited source, but even Edith, who knew he was tiring, did not try to slow his pace.

Then, in February 1918, he was taken ill. Treated at the Roosevelt Hospital in New York City for abscesses in his ears and another on his leg, he returned home to Oyster Bay after a month, almost totally deaf in one ear. But in the spring he made a speaking tour, and in the autumn he went out on another.

The whole country took it for granted that he would become the Republican candidate for President in 1920, and the unanimity of all factions of the party seemed to please him. "If the people want me, I'll run," he said, and only members of his immediate family knew that Quentin's death had made him indifferent.

His greatest joys now were his grandchildren, his sons' wives and Flora Payne Whitney, the girl to whom Quentin had become betrothed before going overseas to die. On them he lavished his undiminished affection and zest for life.

On November 11, 1918, the day the fighting in the First World War was ended by an armistice, Theodore returned to the hospital with what was diagnosed as inflammatory rheumatism, complicated by the malaria from which he had suffered for so many years. He returned to Sagamore Hill in time for Christmas, and there, from his convalescent's bed, he dictated scores of letters, wrote his columns for the Kansas City *Star*, received his grandchildren and told them the endless stories that seem to spring without effort from an untiring imagination.

On Sunday, January 5, 1919, he wrote letters, corrected proofs of an article he had written for the *Metropolitan* and then spent a long time staring out of the windows. "I wonder if you'll ever know," he said to Edith, "how much I love this place."

That night he went to bed shortly after 11:00 P.M., and said to his valet, "Please turn out the light."

Early the next morning Theodore Roosevelt, 26th President of the United States, historian and author, explorer and hunter, naturalist and conservationist, husband and father extraordinary, gave up the life he loved. He died in his sleep, without pain.

He was buried on the side of a knoll at Sagamore Hill, with about five hundred persons in attendance. Among them were the children he had loved, the captains and the kings. They buried him without music or eulogy, as he had wanted.

Long after everyone else had left the graveside, William Howard Taft stood alone over the mound of earth, his cheeks wet.

BIBLIOGRAPHY

Abbott, Lawrence F., *Impressions of Theodore Roosevelt*, New York, 1919.
——, *The Letters of Archie Butt*, New York, 1924.
Adams, Henry, *Letters*, (3 vol.), New York, 1922.
——, *The Education of Henry Adams*, New York, 1918.
Albany *Evening Journal*
Allen, Frederick Lewis, *Since Yesterday*, New York, 1940.
——, *The Great Pierpont Morgan*, New York, 1949.
Amer, James E., *Theodore Roosevelt, Hero to His Valet*, New York, 1927.
Bailey, Thomas A., *Theodore Roosevelt and the Japanese-American Crises*, Stanford, 1934.
Baker, Ray Stannard, *An American Chronicle*, New York, 1945.
Balles, Blair, *Tyrant from Illinois, Uncle Joe Cannon's Experiment with Personal Power*, New York, 1951.
Beale, Howard K., *Theodore Roosevelt and the Rise of America to World Power*, New York, 1956.
Beard, Charles A. and Mary, *The Rise of American Civilization*, (2 vol.), New York, 1930.
Beer, Thomas, *Hanna*, New York, 1929.
Bishop, Joseph Bucklin, *Theodore Roosevelt and His Times*, New York, 1923.
Boston *Advertiser*
Boston *Transcript*
Bowers, Claude G., *Beveridge and the Progressive Era*, New York, 1932.
Brooklyn *Eagle*
Bryan, William Jennings and Mary Baird, *The Memoirs of William Jennings Bryan*, Philadelphia, 1925.
Buffalo *Express*
Bunau-Varilla, Philippe, *Panama*, London, 1913.
Butt, Archibald W., *Taft and Roosevelt*, (2 vol.), Garden City, New York, 1930.
Charnwood, Lord, *Theodore Roosevelt*, Boston, 1923.
Chessman, G. Wallace, *Governor Theodore Roosevelt*, Cambridge, 1965.
Chicago *Inter-Ocean*
Chicago *News*
Chicago *Tribune*
Churchill, Allen, *The Roosevelts, American Aristocrats*, New York, 1965.
Cincinnati *Times Star*
Cleveland *Plain Dealer*
Cobb, William T., *The Strenuous Life: The Oyster Bay Roosevelts*, New York, 1946.

Collier's Weekly

Cutright, Paul R., *Theodore Roosevelt the Naturalist*, New York, 1956.

Dana, Samuel Trask, *Forest and Range Policy*, New York, 1956.

Davis, Oscar K., *Released for Publication*, New York, 1925.

Dean, Arthur H., *William Nelson Cromwell*, New York, 1957.

De Chambrun, Clara, *The Making of Nicholas Longworth*, New York, 1933.

Dennett, Tyler, *John Hay*, New York, 1933.

————, *Roosevelt and the Russo-Japanese War*, New York, 1925.

Denver *Post*

Denver *Republican*

Depew, Chauncey M., *My Memories of Fifty Years*, New York, 1922.

Donovan, Robert, *The Assassins*, New York, 1955.

Duffy, Herbert S., *William Howard Taft*, New York, 1930.

Dunn, Arthur W., *Gridiron Nights*, New York, 1915.

Dunne, Finley Peter, *Mr. Dooley at His Best*, New York, 1938.

Ellis, Elmer, *Mr. Dooley's America*, New York, 1941.

Everybody's Magazine

Faulks, William Dudley, *Roosevelt and the Spoilsmen*, New York, 1925.

Fay, Bernard, *Roosevelt and His America*, Boston, 1933.

Ford, Worthington C. ed., *Letters of Henry Adams 1892–1918*, Boston, 1938.

Franklin, John Hope, *From Slavery to Freedom*, New York, 1947.

Garraty, John A., *Right-Hand Man, The Life of George W. Perkins*, New York, 1960.

Gompers, Samuel, *Seventy Years of Life and Labor* (2 vol.), New York, 1925.

Griswold, Alfred W., *The Far Eastern Policy of the United States*, New York, 1938.

Gwynn, Stephen, ed., *Letters and Friendships of Sir Cecil Spring-Rice*, Boston, 1929.

Hagedorn, Hermann, *The Bugle that Woke America, The Saga of Theodore Roosevelt's Last Battle for His Country*, New York, 1940.

————, *Roosevelt in the Badlands*, Boston, 1921.

————, *The Basic Life of Theodore Roosevelt*, 1918.

————, *The Roosevelt Family of Sagamore Hill*, New York, 1954.

————, *The Roosevelt Treasury*, New York, 1957.

————, ed., *Works of Theodore Roosevelt* (20 vol.), New York, 1926.

Harbaugh, William Henry, *The Life and Times of Theodore Roosevelt*, New York, 1961.

Harper's Weekly

Harrison, Carter H., *Stormy Years*, New York, 1935.

Hart, Albert Bushnell and Fergeler, Herbert Ronald, ed., *Theodore Roosevelt Cyclopedia*, New York, 1941.

Hay, John, *Letters and Extracts from the Diary*, Henry Adams, ed., (3 vol.), Washington, D.C., 1908.

Hays, Samuel P., *Conservation and the Gospel of Efficiency*, Cambridge, 1959.

Hechler, Kenneth W., *Insurgency, Personalities and Politics of the Taft Era,* New York, 1940.

Hibbard, Benjamin Horace, *A History of the Public Land Policies,* New York, 1939.

Hill, Howard C., *Roosevelt and the Caribbean,* Chicago, 1927.

Hofstadter, Richard, *The Age of Reform,* New York, 1955.

Hoover, Irwin Hood, *Forty-two Years in the White House,* Boston, 1934.

Hoyt, Edwin P., *Teddy Roosevelt in Africa,* New York, 1966.

Jessup, Philip C., *Elihu Root,* (2 vol.), New York, 1938.

Johnson, Gerald, *American Heroes and Hero Worship,* New York, 1943.

Kansas City *Star*

Kennan, George F., *American Diplomacy, 1900–1950,* Chicago, 1951.

Kohlsaat, H. H., *From McKinley to Harding,* New York, 1923.

La Follette, Robert M., *Autobiography,* Madison, 1913.

Lang, Lincoln A., *Ranching with Roosevelt,* Philadelphia, 1926.

Leary, John J., *Talks with T. R.,* Boston, 1920.

Leech, Margaret, *In the Days of McKinley,* New York, 1959.

Letters from Theodore Roosevelt to Anna Roosevelt Cowles, New York, 1924.

Link, Arthur S., *Wilson,* New York, 1947.

——, *Woodrow Wilson and the Progressive Era,* New York, 1954.

Lodge, Henry Cabot, ed., *Selections from the Correspondence of Theodore Roosevelt and Henry Cabot Lodge,* (2 vol.), New York, 1925.

——, *The Senate of the United States,* New York, 1921.

London *Standard*

London *Star*

London *Times*

Longworth, Alice Roosevelt, *Crowded Hours,* New York, 1940 edition.

Looker, Earle, *The White House Gang,* New York, 1929.

Lorant, Stefan, *The Life and Times of Theodore Roosevelt,* New York, 1959.

Los Angeles *Times*

McCaleb, Walter F., *Theodore Roosevelt,* New York, 1931.

McGeary, M. Nelson, *Gifford Pinchot: Forester-Politician,* Princeton, 1960.

Mawry, George E., *The Era of Theodore Roosevelt,* New York, 1958.

——, *The Era of Theodore Roosevelt: 1900–1912,* New York, 1958.

Memphis *Scimitar*

Milwaukee *Sentinel*

Miner, Dwight C., *The Fight for the Panama Route,* New York, 1940.

Moore, J. Hampton, *Roosevelt and the Old Guard,* Philadelphia, 1925.

Morison, E. and Blum, John M., ed., *Letters of Theodore Roosevelt,* (8 vol.), Cambridge, Mass., 1951–54.

Nevins, Allan, ed., *Letters of Grover Cleveland,* Boston, 1933.

New Orleans *Times-Democrat*

New Orleans *Times-Picayune*

New York *Herald*

New York *Journal*

New York *Post*
New York *Sun*
New York *Times*
New York *Tribune*
New York *World*
North American Review
Outlook
Papers of John L. Pershing, Library of Congress.
Papers of Theodore Roosevelt, Library of Congress.
Papers of Elihu Root, Library of Congress.
Papers of Woodrow Wilson, Library of Congress.
Platt, Thomas C., *Autobiography*, New York, 1910.
Pinchot, Gifford, *Breaking New Ground*, New York, 1947.
Pratt, Julius W., *A History of United States Foreign Policy*, New York, 1955.
———, *America's Colonial Experiment*, New York, 1950.
Pringle, Henry F., *The Life and Times of William Howard Taft*, New York, 1938.
———, *Theodore Roosevelt*, New York, 1931.
Pusey, Merlo J., *Charles Evans Hughes* (2 *vol.*), New York, 1951.
Putnam, Carleton, *Theodore Roosevelt: the Formative Years*, New York, 1958.
Reisner, Christian F., *Roosevelt's Religion*, New York, 1922.
Riis, Jacob, *Theodore Roosevelt the Citizen*, New York, 1904.
Robbins, Ray M., *Our Landed Heritage, The Public Domain*, Princeton, 1942.
Robinson, Corinne Roosevelt, *My Brother, Theodore Roosevelt*, New York, 1923.
Rochester *Union and Advertiser*
Rocky Mountain News
Roosevelt, Kermit, *The Happy Hunting Grounds*, New York, 1920.
Roosevelt, Theodore, *African and European Addresses*, New York, 1910.
———, *African Game Trails*, New York, 1910.
———, *America and the World War*, New York, 1915.
———, *American Ideals*, New York, 1897.
———, *Autobiography*, New York, 1913.
———, *Book-lover's Holidays in the Open*, New York, 1916.
———, *Essays on Practical Politics*, New York, 1888.
———, *Fear God and Take Your Own Part*, New York, 1916.
———, *Foes of Our Own Household*, New York, 1917.
———, *Gouverneur Morris*, New York, 1888.
———, *Hero Tales From American History* (with Henry Cabot Lodge, New York, 1895).
———, *History As Literature*, New York, 1913.
———, *Hunting Trips of a Ranchman*, New York, 1885.
———, *Letters to his Children*, New York, 1919.
———, *Life Histories of African Game Animals* (with Edmund Heller), 2 *vol.*, New York, 1914.
———, *New Nationalism*, New York, 1910.

————, *Oliver Cromwell,* New York, 1900.

————, *Progressive Principles,* New York, 1913.

————, *Ranch Life and the Hunting Trail,* New York, 1888.

————, *Realizable Ideals,* New York, 1912.

————, *The Great Adventure,* New York, 1918.

————, *The Naval War of 1812,* New York, 1882.

————, *The Rough Riders,* New York, 1889.

————, *The Strenuous Life,* New York, 1900.

————, *The Winning of the West, (4 vol.),* New York, 1889–96.

————, *Through the Brazilian Jungle,* New York, 1914.

————, *Wilderness Hunter,* New York, 1893.

————, Collection, Harvard College Library, Cambridge, Mass.

Roosevelt, Theodore, Jr., *All in the Family,* New York, 1929.

Roosevelt, Mrs. Theodore, Jr., *Day Before Yesterday,* Garden City, Long Island, 1958.

Schriftgiesser, Karl, *The Amazing Roosevelt Family,* New York, 1942.

Scribner's Magazine

Sewall, William W., *Bill Sewall's Story of TR,* New York, 1919.

Spencer, Samuel R., Jr., *Booker T. Washington and the Negro's Place in American Life,* Boston, 1955.

Steffens, Lincoln, *The Autobiography of Lincoln Steffens, (2 vol.),* New York, 1931.

Stephenson, Nathaniel W., *Nelson W. Aldrich,* New York, 1930.

Stout, Ralph, ed., *Roosevelt in the Kansas City Star,* Boston, 1921.

Street, Julian, *The Most Interesting American,* New York, 1915.

Sullivan, Mark, *Our Times, 1900–1925, (2 vol.),* New York, 1926.

Taft, Helen H., *Recollections of Full Years,* New York, 1914.

Thayer, William Roscoe, *Theodore Roosevelt, an Intimate Biography,* New York, 1919.

Thompson, Charles Willis, *Presidents I Have Known,* Indianapolis, 1929.

Wagenknecht, Edward, *The Seven Worlds of Theodore Roosevelt,* New York, 1958.

Wall Street Journal

Walters, Everett, *Joseph Benson Foraker,* Columbus, Ohio, 1948.

Ware, Louise, *Jacob A. Riis,* New York, 1938.

Washburn, Charles G., *Theodore Roosevelt; the Logic of His Career,* New York, 1916.

Washington *Post*

White, William Allen, *A Puritan in Babylon,* New York, 1938.

————, *Masks in a Pageant,* New York, 1928.

Williams, William Appleman, *The Tragedy of American Diplomacy,* Cleveland, 1959.

Wister, Owen, *Roosevelt: The Story of a Friendship,* New York, 1930.

Wood, Frederick S., ed., *Roosevelt as We Knew Him,* Philadelphia, 1927.